Probabilistic Safety Assessment and Risk Management PSA '87

Volume II

Verlag TÜV Rheinland GmbH, Köln

P S A ' 8 7

INTERNATIONAL TOPICAL CONFERENCE ON PROBABILISTIC SAFETY ASSESSMENT & RISK MANAGEMENT
Swiss Federal Institute of Technology (ETH), Zürich, August 30 – September 4, 1987

S P O N S O R S

Swiss Nuclear Society (SNS)
European Nuclear Society (ENS)
in collaboaration with the
American Nuclear Society (ANS)

C O - S P O N S O R S

Commission of the European Communities,
OECD Nuclear Energy Agency, Canadian
Nuclear Society, Atomic Energy Society
of Japan, Society for Risk Analysis and
in cooperation with the International
Atomic Energy Agency (IAEA)

O R G A N I Z I N G   C O M M I T T E E

Representatives of SNS

Pellaud B. (Chairman)
Tiberini A. (Co-Chairman)

Representatives of ENS

Couture J.
Feuz P.

Ex-Officio Member

Yadigaroglu G.

Conference Secretary

Hunter A. (ENS)

MEMBERS OF THE TPC WHO ATTENDED THE
PAPER SELECTION COMMITTEE MEETING,
HELD IN ZURICH, 28-29 JANUARY 1987:

Barents M. S.
Bayer A.
Cullingford M.
Devooght J.
Fabian H.
Fray R. R.
Fuchs H.
Herttrich P. M.
Hubert P.
Hörtner H.
Joksimovich V.
Lanore J.-M.
Liwaang B. T. F.
Mancini G.
Mercier O.
Rutgers E.
Squarer D.
Stadie K.B.
Versteeg M. F.
Villadoniga J. I.
Villemeur A.
Vinck W.
Wall I. B.

G E N E R A L   C H A I R M E N

Professor Norman C. Rasmussen
Dr. F. R. Farmer

T P C   M E M B E R S H I P

Yadigaroglu G. (Chairman)
Torri A. (Co-Chairman)
Chakraborty S. (Co-Chairman)
Aldrich D.C. SA Int. (USA)
Apostolakis G.E. UCLA (USA)
Arrieta L. CNEN (BRA)
Barents M. S. Electrowatt (GBR)
Bayer A. KfK (FRG)
Bonaca M. V. NEA SC (USA)
Budnitz R. FRA (USA)
Camarinopoulos L. TU Berlin (FRG)
Carlson D. D. Sandia (USA)
Carnino A. EDF (FRA)
Comptdaer Y. Westinghouse Int. (BEL)
Cullingford M. IAEA
Cummings Garth LLNL (USA)
De A.K. Govt. of India (IND)
Devooght J. Université Libre (BEL)
Fabian H. KWU (FRG)
Fray R.R. PG&E (USA)
Fuchs H. Motor Columbus (SUI)
Gittus J.H. UKAEA (GBR)
Hayns M. R. UKAEA (GBR)
Herttrich P. M. BMI (FRG)
Heuser F.W. GRS (FRG)
Holtzclaw K. W. GE (USA)
Hörtner H. GRS (FRG)
Hosemann J.P. EIR (SUI)
Hubert P. CEPN (FRA)
Joksimovich V. NUS (USA)
King F. Ontario Hydro (CAN)
Lambert H. E. (USA)
Lanore J.-M. CEA (FRA)
Liparulo N. Westinghouse (USA)
Liwaang B. T. F. SKI (SWE)
Mancini G. CEC
Mercier O. EIR (SUI)
Osmachkin V. Kurchatov (URS)
Rasmussen J. Riso (DEN)
Rutgers E. NOK (SUI)
Sato K. JAERI (JPN)
Snell V. G. AECL (CAN)
Speis T. P. US NRC (USA)
Squarer D. Westinghouse (USA)
Stadie K. OECD/NEA
Stamatelatos M. GA Tech. (USA)
Valeri A. ENEA (ITA)
Versteeg M. F. MHPPE (HOL)
Villadoniga J. I. CSN (ESP)
Villemeur A. EDF (FRA)
Vinck W. CEC
Volta G. CEC
Vourinen A. P. FCRNS (FIN)
Wall I. B. EPRI (USA)
Wechsler L. Kurchatov (URS)
Zaffiro C. ENEA (ITA)

CIP-Kurztitelaufnahme der Deutschen Bibliothek

Probabilistic safety assessment and risk management / PSA '87. Ed.: Europ.
Nuclear Soc. and Swiss Nuclear Soc. — Köln: Verlag TÜV Rheinland —
    (Risk and safety)
    ISBN 3-88585-417-1
NE: PSA <1987, Zürich>; European Nuclear Society
Vol. 2 (1987)

ISBN 3-88585-417-1
© by Verlag TÜV Rheinland GmbH, Köln 1987
Gesamtherstellung: Verlag TÜV Rheinland GmbH, Köln 1987
Printed in Germany 1987

Table of Contents

Session D1 : Consequence analysis

Thursday September 4, 09.00-12.30 hrs (oral session)

LIST OF AUTHORS/PAPERS FOR REFERENCE:

Abe K.	D1.3/107
Ahlstrand R.	C5.6/80
Albert R.N.	A8.9/206
Altieri D.	B4.9/36
Amendola A.M	A1.2/89 A7.1/59 A1.1/253
Amico P.J.	A6.3/147 C2.5/136
Amos C.N.	B2.3/128
Ancelin C.	A7.4/156
Anderson D.G.R.	B3.2/54
Aoi S.	B4.10/27
Apostolakis G.	A4.6/137 A4.4/159
Armas Garçia A.	A8.2/9
Ashton P.	C7.3/172
Atefi B.	C2.5/136
Babic P.	B1.6/222
Balestri S.	A7.12/87
Balfanz H.-P.	C2.1/272
Barbas Th.	A7.11/78
Barents M.S.	B1.3/259
Bars G.	C5.2/37
Barsell A.W.	B4.1/251
Batt D.L.	C2.4/130
Benda B.J.	A6.8/72
Bengtz M.	A1.5/33 B4.13/52
Benjamin A.S.	B2.3/128
Berenblut B.J.	E1.3/109
Berger J.P.	B1.1/151
Besi A.	A7.12/87
Bickel J.H.	A4.3/230 A5.8/229
Bier V.M.	A8.10/103 A4.6/137
Bloch M.	B4.6/164
Boardman J.	D1.5/177
Boehm F.	A5.6/45
Bohn M.P.	A6.8/72
Borysiewicz M.	B1.8/170
Bouissou M.	A5.1/225
Bourgade E.	A2.6/224
Boyd G.J. Lewis S.R.	B2.3/128
Bozoki G.	D2.3/124
Brearley I.R.	D1.5/177
Breeding R.J.	C4.6/144
Breiling G.	C1.5/155
Broyd T.W.	D2.6/127
Budnitz R.J.	A6.1/247 A6.7/135
Buhl A.R.	C6.7/122
Burns N.L.	B2.7/264
Bykov A.A.	C7.8/271 C3.3/274
Cacciabue P.C.	A1.2/89
Caisley J.	C3.1/180 A1.4/192
Calvo J.I.	C1.3/31
Camarinopoulos I.	A1.4/192
Campbell D.J.	D2.2/133 A8.10/103
Cantarella J.	A5.2/85
Capobianchi S.	A7.11/78
Carlesso S.	A7.12/87 A7.11/78
Carlsson L.	B1.4/51
Carlyle S.G.	C7.1/163
Caron J.L.	A3.5/38
Cathey N.G.	A8.13/131
Cattaneo F.	A7.13/161
Cave L.	C6.3/196 E1.3/109
Cavicchia V.	A2.7/202 C2.2/238 B4.14/218
Chan E.M.	B3.2/54

Chan P.S.W.	F1.2/245
Chelliah E.	C4.8/123
Cheng S.-K.	B3.4/8
Chexal B.	F1.2/245
Chicken J.C.	E2.7/34
Chow P.C.	B3.2/54
Chu B.B.	C4.1/255 C4.6/144
Chu T.-L.	B3.3/70 B3.6/71
Cipriani F.	B4.4/90
Clarotti C.A.	A4.2/258
Colombo A.G.	A7.12/87
Contini S.	B4.11/86
Cooper P.J.	D1.5/177
Copp R.	C6.7/122
Crane G.R.	C3.5/213 A3.7/220
Crellin G.L.	A8.6/97
Cummings G.E.	A6.3/147 A6.2/240
Cunningham M.A.	C2.8/134 B2.3/128
da Silva Pagetti P.	A5.5/23
Dach K.	B1.5/227
Dahms C.F.	B4.1/251
Dastur A.R.	F1.2/245
Davis P.R.	C6.5/16
De Sanctis S.	A7.13/161
de Souza Borges W.	A5.5/23 C2.7/60
de St Quentin S.	A7.4/156
Demin V.F.	C7.8/271 C3.3/274
Deremer R.K.	B3.5/99 C3.6/98
Desaedeleer G.	D2.12/58
Devooght J.	A5.2/85
Dinnie K.S.	B3.2/54
Dinsmore S.C.	A1.5/33 A4.1/32
Dobrosavljevic N.	B4.7/5
Doerre P.	A5.7/205 A2.5/211
Dombek F.S.	A3.6/219
Doskocil W.	C3.6/98
Dressler E.	C4.5/228
Drouin M.T.	B2.6/121
Dubreuil-Chambardel A.	A5.1/225
Ducamp F.	C5.4/39
Dumolo R.N.	B1.3/259
Dusek J.	B1.5/227 B1.5/227
Dussarte D.	B4.6/164
Egan M.J.	D1.5/177
Ellia-Hervy A.	A3.5/38 C5.4/39
Eltawila F.	C1.1/233
Evans K.G.	C6.8/280
Evans M.G.K.	B4.8/201 B3.4/8
Fabian H.	E1.7/208 C3.7/203 C6.6/209
Farmer F.R.	P4.1/277
Farruk A.A.	C3.4/102
Feigel A.	C3.7/203 E1.7/208 D2.5/210
Fenstermacher T.E.	D1.6/150
Ferrell W.L.	B2.6/121
Fickeissen K.O.E.	C4.6/144
Fischer F.	D1.2/167
Fisher J.E.	C5.3/30
Fitzpatrick R.	B3.6/71
Fleming K.N.	B3.5/99 A2.2/244 A2.3/101 C3.6/98
Fontana M.H.	C6.7/122
Francia González L.	A8.5/63
Frederick L.G.	C3.5/213
Fuchs H.	C5.1/246
Fuoto J.	C6.5/16
Gaertner J.P.	C5.5/169 E1.6/197 B4.12/193

Kajimoto M.	D1.3/107
Kalfsbeek H.W.	A7.14/88
Kane P.	D2.8/183 D2.1/184
Kang S.-K.	C1.4/142
Kaplan S.	A2.3/101
Kastenberg W.E.	C5.7/40 C6.3/196
Kelly G.B.	C2.5/136
Kelly N.	E2.2/44
Khanin L.G.	C3.3/274
King F.K.	B3.2/54
Kiper K.L.	C3.6/98
Knochenhauer M.	B4.13/52
Kobayashi M.	A5.3/13
Koeberlein K.	E2.4/198
Kohut P.	D2.3/124
Kolaczkowski A.M.	B2.6/121
Koletsos A.	A7.11/78
Komarov E.I.	C3.3/274
Komsi M.	C5.6/80
Koren J.M.	B4.12/193
Kosonen M.	B1.7/178
Koyama K.	B4.10/27
Kröger W.	A1.4/192 C6.1/239
Kulig M.	B1.8/170
Kunsman D.M.	B2.3/128
Kuz'min I.I.	A5.4/270
L'Henoret J.	A3.5/38
LaChance J.L.	B2.6/121
Lainoff S.M.	C4.6/144
Lambert H.E.	A6.7/135
Lambright J.A.	A6.8/72
Lancet R.T.	C6.4/28
Lange F.	E2.2/44
Lanore J.M.	A3.5/38
Larm T.	C5.6/80
Le P.	A7.4/156
Leach L.P.	F1.4/250
Leaver D.E.	C6.5/16
Ledermann L.	A1.3/25 A1.7/273
Leicht R.	C7.5/212
Lewis E.E.	A5.6/45
Lewis J.	D1.6/150
Liew S.K.	D2.6/127
Lin W.H.	A8.1/12
Liparulo N.	B2.7/264
Locchi G.	B4.4/90
Lukic Y.D.	B4.14/218
Lutz R.J.Jr.	D2.12/58
Malaro J.A.	C2.8/134
Mancini G.	A1.1/253 A7.11/78
Mankamo T.	B1.7/178 C4.3/207
Martin J.A.	C4.7/232
Massin H.L.	C3.5/213
Matsuoka T.	A5.3/13
Mattei J.M.	C5.2/37
Mattson R.J.	C6.5/16
McCandless R.J.	B2.5/265
Mertens J.	C6.1/239
Meslin T.	A2.6/224 B1.1/151
Mills J.C.	C6.4/28
Minarick J.W.	A8.11/55 B3.7/56
Minarini C.	B4.9/36
Minton L.A.	E1.6/197
Mira McWilliams J.	A8.5/63
Mohsen B.	C5.6/80

FRENCH PWR NUCLEAR POWER PLANTS : PROBABILISTIC STUDIES OF ACCIDENT SEQUENCES AND RELATED FINDINGS :

A. VILLEMEUR (1), J.M. MORONI (1), J.P. BERGER (2), T. MESLIN (3)

(1) (Electricité de France   (2) (Electricité de France
Direction des Etudes et Recherches   SEPTEN
1, avenue du Général de Gaulle   12-14, avenue DUTRIEVOZ
92141 CLAMART CEDEX - France)   69628 VILLEURBANNE CEDEX
                                                France)

(3) (Electricité de France
Service de la Production Thermique
3, rue de Messine
75384 PARIS CEDEX 08 - France)

Abstract :

This paper presents the major studies performed in France by EDF in the framework of probabilistic studies. It describes the part played by these studies especially as regards :
- the assessment of the allowed outage time in the event of a safety component unavailability,
- the risk assessment in the event of a total loss of system (heat sink, electric power supplies....)
The specific features of the French "living" PSA, now still in progress, are also presented.

From the very beginning of the French nuclear power plant program (in 1975) EDF, the French utility, undertook to develop probabilistic methods to study the reliability of safety related systems in nuclear power plants.
Initially, these studies were part of a research and development effort and were not used for regulatory purposes. Thus a first program (1976-78) aimed at studying the reliability of all safety related systems was performed at the Fessenheim power plant, the first 900 MWe PWR nuclear power plant, which was commisioned in 1977. Analysis techniques, such as the FMEA, fault trees and Markov graphs as well as the corresponding computer programs were used and developed to that end.

Some improvements of safety related systems were thus derived and introduced in nuclear power plants of the 900 MWe PWR type belonging to the CP1 and CP2 standardized series (some thirty nuclear power plants). As agreed with the Safety Authorities, EDF perfomed from 1981 to 1983 detailed studies of the reliability of all the safety related systems (fifteen) for the Paluel PWR power plant, the first of the 1300 MWe standardized series including some twenty nuclear power plants. These studies were incorporated in the regulatory process and were examined by the Safety Authorities before the power plant start-up.

Concerning the new standardized series of 1400 MWe power plants (N4 project), the first plant of which has been ordered and should be started in 1992 approximately, EDF, in agreement with the Safety Authorities, has undertaken probabilistic studies of accident sequences related to the loss of some safety related systems. These studies, their teachings and the methods used are explained in this paper.

In parallel, as agreed with the Safety Authorities, probabilistic methods are used since 1980, as a support for defining technical specifications in the event of partial unavailabilities of safety-related systems. We deal with this approach in the paper.
Since 1986, EDF is carrying out a "living" Probabilistic Safety Assessment for the Paluel power plant. The main features of that PSA are also described here.

2. Probabilistic safety studies related to "beyond-design basis" situations

Over the last years, to further improve the safety of its PWR reactors, EDF has studied for all of them, the potential consequences of some major situations such as the total losses of frequently or permanently used redundant systems.
To face such "beyond-design basis" situations, now called in France "complementary design basis situations", additionnal means were defined and then implemented.
Moreover, operating procedures were developed to specify when and how these additionnal means should be used :
- Procedure H1 : Total loss of the heat sink or of the systems used to remove residual heat
- Procedure H2 : Total loss of feedwater to the steam generators
- Procedure H3 : Total loss of the electric power supplies
- Procedure H4 : Long-term loss of the low pressure safety injection system or of containment spray system during post-LOCA recirculation .

At the beginning of 1983, EDF decided to carry out four probabilistic studies for the future 1400 MWe N4 standardized PWR units, in order to evaluate the risk resulting from the loss of the above-mentioned systems and the benefit drawn from the additional means provided and the related operating procedures.
It was agreed upon with the Safety Authorities that :
- the probability of accident sequences initiated by such accidents and resulting in a core melt should not exceed a target level of 10^{-7} reactor x year x situation;
- for each situation, the use of the appropriate additional means should not result in a core melt frequency reduction greater than a target value of 100.

Otherwise, the design of N4 plants would have to be improved in order to meet these two objectives.

Some distinctive features of these four probabilistic studies should be underlined. In all of them :
- Detailed human reliability analyses, uncertainties calculations and numerous sensitivity studies were performed
- Common cause failures were taken into account ;
- Equipment and systems repairs were also taken into account except for failures of components located inside the reactor building.

In the first three of them (H1, H2 and H3 studies) every possible initial state of the reactor was taken into account, from full power to shutdown for refuelling.
In the fourth one, the accident sequences were quantified assuming a total duration of 1 year for these sequences.
Many results and teachings of these studies have already been presented at international meetings (1-3). The main ones are briefly described here-after.

In all cases, it was demonstrated that the French target of 10^{-7} /reactor x year x situation was reached. Moreover, the additional means and procedures used to face these beyond-design basis situations were deemed satisfactory :the benefit drawn from them was substantial but not too high (core melt frequency reduction beetwen 10 and 200). For instance, during a one year post-LOCA recirculation phase the core melt probability was calculated to be approximately 1,1 10^{-7} provided the appropriate additional means were used (connections between LHSI pumps and containment spray pumps and use of "PUI" pump and heat-exchanger). Had these additionnal means not been used, the core melt probability would have been approximately 2 10^{-6}.

These studies have pointed to the importance of human factors, common cause failures and repairs. Moreover, they have shown that the risk of core melt during reactor shutdown states is not negligible. Finally they have been used to help in formulating and improving Technical Specifications.

3. Probabilistic Safety Studies and Technical Specifications

The Technical Specifications give, among others, the Allowed Outage Time (AOT) for every safety-related equipment whose availability is required during normal operation. These AOTs are fixed using a deterministic approach and probabilistic calculations for PWRs and Fast Breeder Reactors (5).

3.1 Inadvertent unavailabilities
A ground rule telling the operator whether or not he is allowed to continue operating the plant at its nominal power is available to him as soon as such an unavailability is detected. The rule gives the operator the AOT, and the operator has to assess the repair time of the unavailable equipment. Then the operator has to compare the assessed repair time with the AOT :
- if the repair time is below the AOT, the operator may continue to operate the plant at full power,
- if the repair time exceeds the AOT, the operator must place the plant in a safe shutdown condition.
The inadvertent unavaibility of a safety-related equipment results in a risk increase which is a function of its duration. Thus, for each of these components, an AOT is calculated assuming a risk increase target of 10^{-7}/unavailability.

3.2 Scheduled unavailabilities
For some important safety-related equipment, scheduled unavailabilities are allowed during normal operation. For calculating the corresponding AOT a rule similar to the above-mentioned one is used. The risk increase due to such unavailabilities should be limited to a target value of 10^{-7}/equipment x year.

3.3 Examples of AOTs
The use of probabilistic studies to help in calculating AOTs has resulted in many AOT updatings. For instance :
- diesel generator : AOT = 1 week (1300 MWe) ;
- auxiliary transformer : AOT = 36 hours (1300 MWe),
- LHSI pump AOT = 3 days (1300 MWe)

4. PSA

The French PSA is performed on unit 3 of the Paluel nuclear power plant which belongs to the 1300 MW-P4 series. Three EDF Directions and FRAMATOME work on the study. It began in January 1986 ; it will be completed approximately by the end of 1988. It consists of three main phases :
- the preliminary analysis which is now in its final phase,
- the provisory analysis which will take into account updated reliability data, additional initiating events and specific thermohydraulic studies.
- the final phase in which the remarks of our external review will be considered. This review is carried out by the technical support of the French Safety Authorities : the IPSN-DAS/CEA

4.1 The aims
One of the first aims of the French study is to make sure that our specific approach to safety both at the design and operation level contributes to significantly reduce the probability of a core melt. It will be very interesting to take all the "French particularities" into account (procedures and additional means, human redundancy..) and to compare the results with other studies.

Another aim is a balanced and homogeneous safety study. We will be able to compare the probabilities of the different sequences leading to the core-melt. That comparison will reveal the possible weak points in our approach. A big effort has been devoted to " some initiators"; it will be very interesting to know whether some sequences have been neglected while some others were "overstudied".

The PSA is a good tool for comparing sequences when similar methods and data are used.
The French technical specifications have long been determined using, among others, probabilistic methods (ref. above). At the conclusion of the studies performed the AOTs in case of unavailability of safety components will be reevaluated, and we can hope that the values will be higher.

As a PRA is a big and important study, EDF wants to use it in the future, in order to help the designer and the operating branch. A PRA should have the following two characteristics :
- the "transparency" : people who did not work on the study will have to use it : every assumption has to be clearly written.
- easy performance of sensivity studies; this led us to plan a "living PSA"

4.2. Main Characteristics of the PSA
The PSA is a level one study. Levels two and three are considered to contain too many uncertainties, and already, procedures can be used on French PWRs in order to protect the environment in case of a core melt (for example : depressurization, if necessary, of the containment through sand bed filters so as to avoid overpressurization and failure of the containment). The study will not take into account the external hazards such as aircraft crashes, flooding ... : most of them have been studied using probabilistic methods at the plant design stage, and it will be easy to compare the risks in question with the results of the PSA.
Thus, that level one PSA will be a very detailed analysis taking all the reactor states into account, including the shutdown states.
The concept of a "living" PSA, i.e. a study that can be updated to allow for

changes in data and knowledge, led EDF to make an important effort on codes.
The LESSEPS software is now being developped for the calculation of all the accident sequence probabilities and of the core melt probability; of course, it
will include codes for fault tree evaluation (minimal cut sets), event tree evaluation and states graph evaluation (Markovian and semi-markovian processes)
(9). In the framework of the automation and computerization of reliability studies, expert systems are used. One of them, EXPRESS (8) will help the analyst
to build fault trees for the study of safety system reliability. Most of the
failures and failure combinations are automatically generated and the specialist can devote more time to the tricky problems.

4.3 Initiating events
All the initiating events are classified into seven major families : primary
breaks, secondary breaks, steam generator tube ruptures, ATWS, loss of electrical sources, primary side transients (inadvertent dilution, spurious safety injection ...), secondary side transients.

4.4 Data
One of the major sources of data on component reliability is the SRDF. In this
reliability data bank, all the failures of some 1000 components (for each pair
of units) are recorded and analysed; the whole operating expertise amounts now
to approximately 200 reactors x years. Moreover, many specific investigations
have been made in order to determine some data precisely and to assess the reliability parameters of other components. At the present time all the common
cause failures occuring in the French PWRs have been analysed and data are ela-
borated (10).
Moreover a probabilistic analysis of incidents in 900 and 1300 MWe PWRs is un-
dergone. It will lead, among others, to the identification of additional initiating events.
As regards human factors, the PSA will use the knowledge acquired on operators
behaviour on simulators (6-7) ; error probabilities will be extracted from the
CONFUCIUS data bank, which mainly contains the results of tests on simulators.

5 Conclusion

Probabilistic assessments are increasingly used for both design and operation
of nuclear power plants. Thus, the "living" PSA in progress can be easily updated to take changes in data and knowledge into account.

REFERENCES

/1/ N. SCHEKTMAN, A. VILLEMEUR, JP BERGER, J. BOISSEAU ,
     A. DUBREUIL-CHAMBARDEL , F. MOSNERON-DUPIN
     Design of nuclear power plants : use of probabilistic methods and
     implementation to the situation of complete loss of electrical supply
     - ANS/ENS Topical meeting on Probabilistic Safety Methods and
     Applications ; February, 24-28, 1985
     San Francisco, California, USA

/2/ JM MORONI, E. BOURGADE, A. DUBREUIL-CHAMBARDEL,
F. MOSNERON-DUPIN, A. VILLEMEUR, JP. BERGER
Probabilistic Safety assessment : total loss of the heat sink in a
PWR - International Meeting on Thermal Reactor Safety - February 2 -
6, 1986, San Diego, California, USA

/3/ N. SCHEKTMAN, JP. BERGER, A. VILLEMEUR, J. BOISSEAU, T. MESLIN,
A. ELLIA-HERVY
Accidents hors dimensionnement : modifications et validation
probabiliste - Séminaire international sur la modification
d'installations nucléaires aux fin de la sûreté - Munich - RFA -11/15
novembre 1985

/4/ JP. BERGER, A. VILLEMEUR, A. DUBREUIL-CHAMBARDEL
Apport des études probabilistes à la conception des centrales nucléaires françaises - International Atomic Energy Agency Seminar on Implications of Probabilistic Risk Assessment -Blackpool, United Kingdom,
March 18-22 1985 -

/5/ B. MAGNON, A. VILLEMEUR, C. ANCELIN
Residual heat removal in the Creys Malville power plant : from
reliability analyses of systems to allowable operating times
International ANS/ENS Topical meeting on Probabilistic Safety
Methods and applications February 24-28 1985, San Francisco, Califor-
nia, USA

/6/ A. VILLEMEUR, F. MOSNERON-DUPIN, M. BOUISSOU
A Human Factors Data Bank for French Nuclear Power Plants International Topical Meeting on Advances in Human Factors in Nuclear Power Systems - April 21-24, 1986 - Knoxville, Tennessee, USA

/7/ M. LLORY, P. LEMAITRE, M. GRIFFON-FOPUCO, T. MESLIN
Analysis of operator's behaviour under accidental transients -Antici-
pated and Abnormal Transients in Nuclear Power Plants - Atlanta - USA,
12-15 avril 1987

/8/ C. ANCELIN, P. LE, S. de SAINT QUENTIN
Express : an expert system to perform system safety study International Topical Conference on Probabilistic Safety Assessment and Risk Management - Zurich -Switzerland, August 31 -
September 4, 1987

/9/ A. VILLEMEUR, M. BOUISSOU, A. DUBREUIL-CHAMLBARDEL
Accident sequences : methods to compute probabilities
International Topical Conference on Probabilistic Safety Assessment
and Risk Management - Zurich - Switzerland, August 31 -
September 4, 1987

/10/ MESLIN T. (EDF SPT, PARIS), BOURGADE E. (EDF DER, Clamart)
Common cause failure analysis and quantification on the basis of operating experience
International Topical Conference on Probabilistic Safety Assessment
and Risk Management - Zurich - Switzerland August 31, September 4,
1987

LESSONS LEARNED FROM 21 NUCLEAR PLANT PRAs

B. John Garrick
[Pickard, Lowe and Garrick, Inc., Newport Beach, California, USA]

Introduction

In 1982, an attempt was made to highlight the lessons learned from some 10 probabilistic risk assessments (PRA) performed by the Pickard, Lowe and Garrick, Inc. (PLG) PRA team (Reference 1). That number has grown to 21, and it is the purpose of this paper to reexamine this experience base in terms of what we are learning about nuclear plant risk.

The approach is to sample the 21 PRAs for key information rather than attempt to address each plant individually. The plants are not identified, except by a code letter and number, to get around the problem of sensitive comparisons. In general, the letters "P" and "B" denote pressurized water reactors (PWR) and boiling water reactors (BWR), respectively. The numbers following the letters (e.g., P1, P2, etc.) distinguish among specific plants.

The discussions center around the scenario-based definition of risk (Reference 2), which basically asks the following three questions:

- What can go wrong?

- What is the likelihood?

- What is the consequence?

A top-down format is adopted for discussing results and making comparisons. In particular, the top-down topics are:

- Public Risk (the offsite health consequences)

- Owner/Operator Risk (plant damage that does not result in significant public risk)

- Risk Initiators (the first of a chain of events)

- Risk Scenarios (the accident sequences important to risk)

- Underlying Contributors (equipment failures and causes, operator actions, maintenance, etc.)

The foundation from which top-down results are produced is the PRA methodology. Advances in methodology will be introduced to demonstrate the relationship among these top-down topics.

This analysis relies on PLG's experience involving 14 PWR plants and 7 BWR plants. Unfortunately, the scopes of the PRAs vary considerably, thus complicating the discussions and, especially, any one-to-one comparisons. Throughout the discussions, an attempt will be made to make observations and comparisons with similarly scoped studies. Table 1 highlights the scopes of the

various analyses performed. In the language of the U.S. Nuclear Regulatory
Commission (USNRC) PRA Procedures Guide (Reference 3), there are three levels of
PRA, each of which addresses the scenario-based definition of risk. Level 1
terminates with core melt, Level 2 with release categorization, and Level 3 with
offsite health effects.

Plant	Scope	External Events	Plant	Scope	External Events
PWRs			BWRs		
P1	Phased, Level 1	Yes	B1	Phase I, Level 1	No
P2	Phased, Level 3	Yes	B2	Phase I, Level 1	No
P3	Phased, Level 3	Yes	B3	Phased, Level 2	No
P4	Phased, Level 3	Yes	B4	Phased, Level 1	No
P5	Phased, Level 3	Yes	B5	Phase I, Level 1	No
P6	Phase I, Level 1	No	B6	Phased, Level 3	Yes
P7	Phased, Level 1	Yes	B7	Phase I, Level 1	No
P8	Phased, Level 1	No			
P9	Phase I, Level 1	Limited			
P10	Phased, Level 3	Yes			
P11	Phased, Level 1	Yes			
P12	Phased, Level 3	Yes			
P13	Phased, Level 1	Yes			
P14	Phase I, Level 1	No			

NOTES:

1. Phased implies that it was a full-scope PRA within a particular "level"
   category.
2. Phase I implies a limited-scope PRA.
3. In the language of the USNRC PRA Procedures Guide, there are three
   levels of PRAs. Level 1 terminates with core melt, Level 2 with
   releases, and Level 3 with offsite health effects.

Table 1: PRA Scopes for 21 Nuclear Plants Analyzed by PLG

Public Risk

Of the 21 PRAs in the data base, only 8 have been full-scope (i.e., phased),
Level 3 studies. Many of these were early studies, and some were included in
Reference 1. With less interest in Level 3 PRAs, there are fewer lessons
learned about public risk than there might have been.

One reason the interest in Level 3 PRAs has subsided is that these early studies
were quite convincing that the public health risk is small. In particular,
without exception, the public risk was well within the safety goals proposed by
the USNRC. Since the same result was not as obvious with respect to the issue
of core damage, attention was shifted to core melt studies (Level 1) and,
following Chernobyl, some limited interest in Level 2 investigations. It is
expected that interest in Level 3 PRAs will return as quantitative risk
management practices mature. It is believed that Level 3 PRAs are necessary for
cost-effective and high confidence management of the owner/operator risk and
public risk.

The few Level 3 PRAs that have been performed since the Reference 1 review
continue to verify the conclusion that the public health risk is indeed small.
For plants that have large, dry containments, only a small fraction of the
analyzed core melts would result in exceeding the capacity of the containments.
That is, in the majority of core melt cases, the containment will remain
intact. In other cases, the releases occur only after many hours or even days
have passed since the beginning of the accident and the opportunity exists for

extensive emergency response. The result is that, at least for this class of containments (i.e., large, dry), the risk to the public is extremely small and more recent studies continue to verify this conclusion.

For other containment types, the results are not quite as conclusive. These include the ice condenser containments for a few pressurized water plants and the pressure suppression systems employed by the boiling water reactors. It is expected that PRA-based capacity assessments of these containments will soon match the comprehensiveness of the analyses performed on several large, dry containment systems. Meanwhile, these containments and their plant-specific responses during accidents are a source of uncertainty in the estimates of risk to the public.

To illustrate the effectiveness of several large, dry containments for six representative PWR plants, consider Figure 1. It can be observed that the containment remains intact for 30% to more than 90% of the possible core melt scenarios associated with these plants. Figure 1 also points up the reason for the extremely low occurrence frequency of any early fatalities. In particular, the percentage of core melt scenarios that result in early releases (i.e., releases responsible for almost all the early fatalities) is small, varying from around 1% to approximately 15%. Another important finding from the studies relates to the location of the early fatalities with respect to the plant. In general, almost all of the early fatalities occur within a short distance from the plant. Depending on the plant, 90% to 95% of the fatalities occur within 2 miles of the plant.

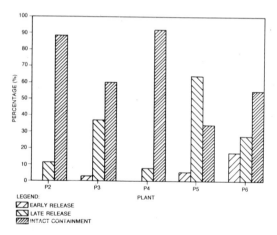

Figure 1:   Radioactivity Release Classification for Large, Dry Containments

Owner/Operator Risk

Whereas the full-scope PRAs have greatly increased the confidence of the nuclear safety communities in the very low risk to the public, there is less confidence about the matter of the risk to the owner/operator of the plants. In particular, a nuclear utility's financial condition can be greatly threatened and maybe even destroyed by an event involving severe core damage although the public may not be threatened at all.

Before discussing specific core damage results, it is important to provide some
background on the context of the results. As previously indicated, discussions
and comparisons of PRA results are complicated by the variety of scopes that are
practiced. Beside the Levels 1, 2, and 3 breakdowns, other factors that affect
scope include: the data base (e.g., generic versus plant-specific data), the
initiating event scope (e.g., internal events or external events or both), and,
finally, whether to comprehensively treat such issues as dependent failures and
uncertainties.

A further scoping practice by the PLG team that has proven to be very efficient
and cost effective is the concept of the phased PRA. Table 2 highlights the
approach. The phased approach is based on the old notion of "the method of
successive approximation." In addition to serving the need to get results
early, it has also been very effective in controlling closure of the risk
model. As soon as Phase I is complete, the options for completing the PRA
become clear and much more manageable.

```
• Full-Breadth, Limited-Depth Scope for Phase I
  - Emphasis on Plant Model
  - Coarse Set of Initiating Events
  - Limited Treatment of External Events
  - Inferences about Offsite Health Effects
• Refinement of Risk Model in Follow-On Phases
  - Refinement of Initiating Event Set
  - Detailed Treatment of Important External Events
  - Detailed Treatment of Offsite Public Risk (if desired)
  - Structured for Quantitative Risk Management
```

Table 2: Phased Probabilistic Risk Assessments

With respect to core melt, a typical evolution of a phased PRA is illustrated in
Figure 2. The Phase I (computed) implies a result that comes out of the
computer but does not reflect all known information at this point of the
analysis. Thus, to truly reflect the state of knowledge for Phase I, it is
necessary to impact the results with well-documented judgment. Such factors as
operator recovery and recent plant changes are often involved. Of course,
Phase II is building refinements and verifiable updated information into the
computer model, along with refinement in expert judgment.

To illustrate the results from actual phased PRAs, consider Figure 3. These six
PRAs are all full scope, including the use of plant-specific data and a full
treatment of external events. Furthermore, these PRAs reasonably represent the
range of all the similarly scoped PRAs performed by the PLG team. For a
Phase I, there is a variation between the 5th and 95th percentiles by a factor
of 28 to 4,000. The corresponding range for Phase II is 5 to 42. The
difference in the two phases is a much improved state of knowledge. This point
would have been more clearly made had the scopes within the two phases been
identical, which they were not. Meanwhile, in going from Phase I to Phase II,
the central tendency parameters, the median and the mean, generally shifted to
lower values. There is no guarantee this will always be the case although this
reflects the fact that, in a Phase I study, conservative assumptions are often
substituted for the lack of detailed analyses.

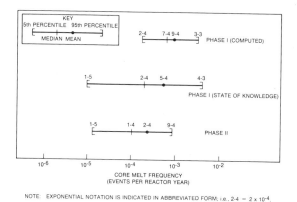

Figure 2:   Core Melt Results from a Phased PRA

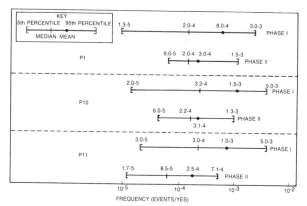

Figure 3a: Comparison of Core Melt Distributions for Phase I and Phase II Studies

For similarly scoped studies, it is interesting to observe where the median and mean core melt frequencies lie. For full-scope studies, Figure 4 is representative of the range of values for the median and mean core melt frequencies. Although the uncertainties vary considerably, the means and medians are reasonably bunched together. In particular, the means vary from 1.4×10^{-4} to 3.1×10^{-4} and the medians from 8.5×10^{-5} to 2.2×10^{-4}. That they would be bunched together is clearly explainable. In all cases, the PRAs were used to make changes in the plants; i.e., to manage the risk. The result is a natural convergence to reasonably achievable risk levels.

Figure 5 presents a cross section of core melt results for boiling water reactors. Unlike the PWR results discussed above, all of these results derive from limited-scope PRAs. The limitations in scope are primarily related to a coarse set of initiators, limited data analysis in some cases, limited treatment of operator actions, and no treatment of external events. Some of the effects of these would be offset should the scopes be expanded. For example, experience indicates that a more detailed treatment of data and initiators reduces the uncertainty and, usually, the risk, while consideration of external events will increase the risk.

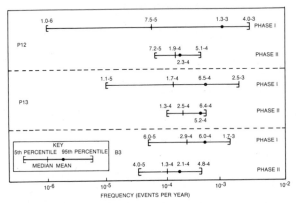

NOTE: EXPONENTIAL NOTATION IS INDICATED IN ABBREVIATED FORM; i.e., 1.0-6 = 1.0 x 10⁻⁶.

Figure 3b: Comparison of Core Melt Distributions for Phase I and Phase II Studies

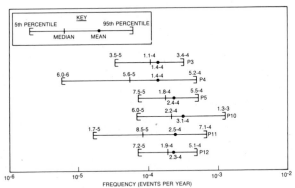

NOTE: EXPONENTIAL NOTATION IS SHOWN IN ABBREVIATED FORM; i.e., 3.5-5 = 3.5 x 10⁻⁵.

Figure 4: Core Melt Frequencies for Full-Scope Studies

Reviewing Figure 5 indicates that the median and mean core melt frequencies for this set of BWRs vary from 7.6×10^{-5} to 4.9×10^{-4} and 5.5×10^{-4} to 1×10^{-3}, respectively. A variation in mean core melt frequency by a factor of 1.8 for the set of six plants is small compared to the average variation between the 5th and 95th percentiles of 50. These results illustrate the importance of uncertainty analysis in putting risk information into its proper perspective. Factors of 2 in core melt frequency are of little significance to a parameter that may vary by a factor of 10 to a 100.

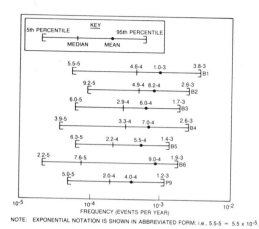

NOTE: EXPONENTIAL NOTATION IS SHOWN IN ABBREVIATED FORM; i.e., 5.5-5 = 5.5 x 10⁻⁵.

Figure 5: Core Melt Frequencies for Limited-Scope Studies (No External Events)

Perhaps, the most important observation about the owner/operator risk is that the PRAs have demonstrated the ability to control the risk. Keeping visible what the risk is and what is contributing to it makes possible the implementation of actions to achieve positive control.

Risk Initiators

Fundamental to the scenario-based approach to risk analysis is the identification and quantification of what are called initiating events. An initiating event is generally taken to be any initial event that causes a plant to depart from its otherwise normal state of operation. An initiating event is usually the first of a chain of events leading to a variety of end states, including restabilizing the plant, or various levels of plant damage, such as severe core damage. The class of initiating events of greatest interest are those most important to core melt, releases of radioactive material, and offsite health effects to the public.

Initiating events are the starting point for structuring the scenarios that are the basis for the risk model. The initiating events are grouped into categories to ensure completeness, while keeping the number of such categories to a manageable level. Initiating events tend to fall into three major groups: transients, loss of coolant accidents, and such common cause events as fires and earthquakes. Whereas a full-scope PRA may involve 20 to 80 initiating event categories, a Phase I PRA further collapses them into 4 to 9 categories.

A review of the 21 PRAs was performed to identify trends in initiating events important to risk. The trends, if they exist at all, are certainly not obvious--again making the point that the risk of a nuclear power plant is very plant specific. However, there are some observations that can be made.

For the full-scope (equivalent to a two-phased study) PRAs performed on PWRs (eight were reviewed), the initiating events most frequently appearing in core melt scenarios were small LOCAs, loss of offsite power, the external event initiators of fires and earthquakes, and the failure of critical area ventilation systems. Other initiators that were important in some PWR plants were loss of main feedwater, loss of component cooling water, and, to a lesser extent, steam generator tube rupture. The loss of area ventilation initiators were much more visible in newer plants in which critical equipment was housed in closed rooms and was thus more dependent on room cooling to prevent overheating. On the other hand, the older plants were generally more susceptible to such external events as fires and earthquakes. Perhaps, the most important observation is that the rank order of the initiators was different for each plant and that no single initiator was a major contributor to risk in all the plants.

Those full-scope PRAs that were Level 3 studies, five of the above eight, also provided some interesting insights into initiators. In particular, these studies demonstrated that different initiators are important for different damage states. For example, the above initiators, while important for core melt, were generally not important contributors to offsite health effects. The principal reason for this difference is rooted in the effectiveness of the containment systems in these plants. An important initiator for offsite health effects is the interfacing LOCA, yet its importance to core melt is very small since its frequency is extremely small.

For the BWR group, the situation is a little different. The core melt scenario initiating events are dominated by transients. The most visible transients are related to loss of feedwater, excessive feedwater, pressurization transients (e.g., closure of main steam isolation valves), and loss of offsite power. In those cases for which external events were considered, as before, fires and earthquakes were the most visible. Except for the fact that transients as a major group were important core melt contributors, there was wide variation among plants, as before, in the detailed nature and ranking of the initiators.

A somewhat global look at internal versus external contributors for six PWRs is given in Figure 6. It is clear that external events are important considerations in the quantification of risk. In some cases, they are the largest contributor to risk.

Figure 7 provides some indication of how the external event risk is distributed. Again, there is considerable plant-to-plant variability.

Excluding external events, it is possible to group the BWR initiating events into three very broad categories; general transient, LOCAs, and loss of offsite power. Figure 8 illustrates the relative contribution of these broad categories to core melt for six BWRs. This somewhat dramatically illustrates the observation made above on the dominance of transients as a group.

Risk Scenarios

One of the key results from a PRA is a list of those sequences of events most important to risk. Such information puts the risk contributors in context with how things go wrong and in what sequence. Figure 9 is a ranking of abbreviated scenarios important to risk for PWR plant P7. Contextualizing the contributors to risk is essential to controlling the risk. Figure 9 is an impressive example of why it is important to quantify the risk from external events; the first internal event to appear on the list (loss of offsite power) is ranked number 8 and contributes only 4% to the core melt frequency.

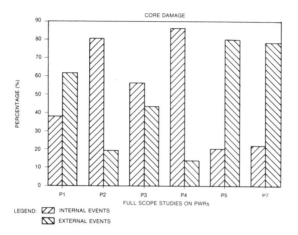

Figure 6: Internal versus External Contributors to Core Damage

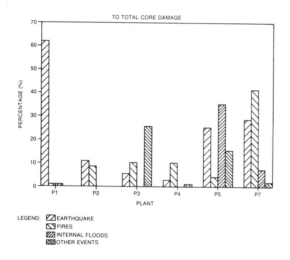

Figure 7: Contribution of External Events

Figure 10 presents the top-ranked risk scenario for 11 plants. The BWRs do not include external events in their risk models. It is interesting to observe the wide variability in the importance of the top-ranked accident sequence (from 6% to 59%).

Earlier, the point was made that the ranking of contributors is damage index dependent. Figure 11 illustrates this point for a particular PWR plant. For example, the scenario involving the interfacing system LOCA is number 1 for the damage index of early deaths and number 15 for core melt frequency.

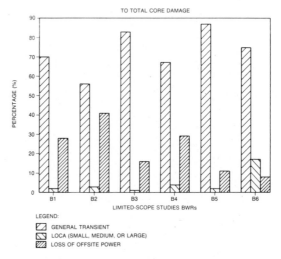

Figure 8: Contribution of Internal Events

INITIATING EVENT (RANK)	CORE MELT SCENARIO	PERCENT OF CORE MELT
FIRE (1)	REACTOR TRIP, LOSS OF ALL FEEDWATER, NO BLEED AND FEED COOLING, RCP SEAL LOCA	14
SEISMIC (2)	STATION BLACKOUT, REACTOR TRIP, LOSS OF ALL FEEDWATER, NO FEED AND BLEED COOLING, RCP SEAL LOCA	7
SEISMIC (3)	REACTOR TRIP, LOSS OF ALL FEEDWATER, NO FEED AND BLEED COOLING, RCH ON MINIMUM SPEED, NO PUMP SEAL LOCA	6
LOSS OF OFFSITE POWER (8)	REACTOR TRIP, NO STEAM GENERATOR COOLING, FEED AND BLEED COOLING, FAILURE OF RECIRCULATION COOLING	4

Figure 9: PWR 7 - Contributors to Core Melt

Underlying Contributors

Looking beyond scenarios, there are system failures important to risk, such causes of system failures as human error or hardware failures, and there is a whole spectrum of contributors in the category of dependent failures.

Considering the older PWRs first, it is clear that hardware associated with electric power, recirculation cooling, and containment heat removal are very important. The reliability of these systems is very dependent on operator actions. An important reason that operator actions play a major part in controlling the risk of the older plants relates to the heavy dependency of those plants on manual actions. Generally, the dependence on operator actions for short-term response to abnormal conditions is coupled with a relatively short time available to diagnose and take corrective action.

PLANT	SCENARIO	FREQUENCY (PER YEAR)	PERCENT OF CORE MELT
P2	SEISMIC, LOSS OF AC POWER	5.6×10^{-6}	11
P3	WIND, LOSS OF AC POWER	3.6×10^{-5}	27
P4	SMALL LOCA	8.2×10^{-5}	59
P9	LOSS OF CHILLED WATER AND FAILURE TO RECOVER	N/A*	N/A*
P10	LOSS OF COMPONENT COOLING WATER	3.8×10^{-5}	12
P11	SMALL LOCA WITH FAILURE OF SUMP RECIRCULATION VALVES	1.4×10^{-5}	6
P13	LOSS OF CONTROL BUILDING VENTILATION	1.6×10^{-4}	30

*NOT AVAILABLE

Figure 10a: Leading Contributor to Core Melt for Various PWR Plants

PLANT	SCENARIO	FREQUENCY (PER YEAR)	PERCENT OF CORE MELT
B1	GENERAL TRANSIENT, FAILURE OF PUMPS IN BOTH PLANT SERVICE WATER DIVISIONS	2.3×10^{-4}	23
B3	LOSS OF FEEDWATER WITH FAILURE OF OPERATORS TO ENSURE LONG-TERM DECAY HEAT OR POOL COOLING	7.5×10^{-5}	8
B5	LOSS OF ALL FEEDWATER AND FAILURE OF REACTOR TO SCRAM	3.2×10^{-4}	58
B6	FULL PRESSURIZATION, ELECTRIC POWER AVAILABLE FROM OFFSITE, FAILURE TO SCRAM	3.43×10^{-5}	38

Figure 10b: Leading Contributor to Core Melt for Various BWR Plants (Internal Events Only)

SCENARIO	RANK WITH RESPECT TO CORE MELT FREQUENCY	MEAN ANNUAL FREQUENCY (CONTRIBUTION TO CORE MELT)	RELATIVE RANK WITH RESPECT TO LATENT EFFECTS RELEASE FREQUENCY	MEAN ANNUAL FREQUENCY OF LATENT EFFECTS RELEASE	RELATIVE RANK WITH RESPECT TO EARLY DEATHS RELEASE FREQUENCY	MEAN ANNUAL FREQUENCY OF EARLY DEATHS RELEASE
SMALL LOCA; FAILURE OF HIGH PRESSURE RECIRCULATION COOLING	1	8.2-5	7	8.2-9	2	8.2-9
LARGE LOCA; FAILURE OF LOW PRESSURE RECIRCULATION COOLING	2	1.1-5	8	1.1-9	4	1.1-9
MEDIUM LOCA; FAILURE OF LOW PRESSURE RECIRCULATION COOLING	3	1.1-5	9	1.1-9	5	1.1-9
FIRE; OTHER FIRE AREAS SUCH AS THE CABLE SPREADING ROOM, AUXILIARY FEEDWATER PUMP ROOM, ETC.	4	6.7-6	10	6.7-10	7	6.7-10
LARGE LOCA; FAILURE OF SAFETY INJECTION	5	6.4-6	11	6.4-10	8	6.4-10
FIRE; SPECIFIC FIRES IN SWITCHGEAR ROOM AND CABLE SPREADING ROOM CAUSING RCP SEAL LOCA AND FAILURE OF POWER CABLES TO THE SAFETY INJECTION PUMPS, THE CONTAINMENT SPRAY PUMPS, AND FAN COOLERS	6	5.7-6	1	5.7-6	3	1.1-9
SEISMIC; LOSS OF CONTROL OR AC POWER	7	4.7-6	2	4.7-6	6	9.4-10
INTERFACING SYSTEM LOCA	15	5.7-7	5	5.7-7	1	5.7-7

NOTE: EXPONENTIAL NOTATION IS INDICATED IN ABBREVIATED FORM; i.e., 8.2-5 = 8.2-5 = 8.2×10^{-5}.

Figure 11: Comparison of Core Melt and Release Frequency Contributions of Major Scenarios for Plant P4

For the newer PWRs, the picture is a little different. Although there is a little less dependence on manual actions by operators, there is greater dependence on other systems, such as area ventilation systems. The reason for this is the trend toward more compartmentalizing of equipment into rooms where systems operation is dependent on room cooling to avoid thermal degradation of equipment. Other equipment visibly important to risk includes electric power systems, auxiliary feedwater, component cooling water, the reliability of safety and relief valves, recirculation systems, coolant safety injection systems, and the main feedwater system.

For BWRs, the reactor scram system has always been an important contributor to risk, although in varying degrees among the seven plants reviewed. Other systems of significance to risk include diesel generators (including electric power in general), relief valve performance, main steam isolation valves, service water systems (especially pumps), automatic depressurization systems, and hardware failures in residual heat removal systems. Figure 12 illustrates the contribution of broad system categories to core damage for plant B5.

RANKING	SYSTEM FUNCTION	FREQUENCY (EVENTS PER CALENDAR YEAR)	PERCENT
1	REACTOR SCRAM	4.1×10^{-4}	52
2	DIESEL GENERATORS	3.2×10^{-4}	40
3	SAFETY VALVES CLOSE	8.2×10^{-5}	10
4	RELIEF VALVES CLOSE	6.8×10^{-5}	8
5	MANUAL PRESSURE RELIEF	4.2×10^{-5}	5
6	LIQUID POISON INJECTION	3.6×10^{-5}	4
7	RELIEF VALVES OPEN	2.5×10^{-5}	3
8	CORE SPRAY INJECTION	1.7×10^{-5}	2
9	CONTAINMENT SPRAY	1.0×10^{-5}	1
10	EMERGENCY CONDENSER OPERATION	5.6×10^{-6}	<1

Figure 12: BWR B5 - Plant Systems Contributing to Core Damage

Methodology

The major advances in PRA methodology have come in two areas: the structuring of the risk model to facilitate timely risk management and the improvements in the modeling of specific risk contributors, which experience indicates are important.

To use a risk model to support timely decisions about plant operations, it is necessary to evaluate plant changes quickly in terms of their effect(s) on risk. This capability has been achieved by structuring the risk model to allow easy assembly and decomposition of results with respect to the elements (as specific initiating events) contributing to risk. The scenario-based approach to risk analysis has been a powerful aid to this process.

Of the many areas for which the modeling has been improved, there are three that should be noted: the treatment of dependent events, human actions, and selected external events (especially earthquakes).

Although all of the PLG PRAs have given considerable emphasis to the treatment of dependent events, each succeeding study has involved specific improvements. For example, the modeling of functional and shared equipment intersystem dependencies in the event sequence and systems models have been improved by the use of segmented, or modularized, event trees. Plant walkdowns have become more thorough, as experience reveals where the attention should be focused. Location dependence is built into the risk model to address spatially dependent physical interactions. There have also been considerable refinements made in the beta factor method to handle different levels of common cause failure impact in systems with three or more components. Finally, there has been the development of a common cause event data base for estimating design specific common cause failure parameters.

Recent PRAs have concentrated much more on improving the treatment of operator actions in terms of their effect on risk. Since most of the plants involve extensive manual operations, especially the older ones, and since it is the objective of PRA models to be as realistic as possible, it is necessary to incorporate the operator into the models. For many scenarios, incorporating operator actions results in substantial improvements in safety. Risk models now incorporate the likelihood of operators successfully restoring failed systems or initiating a system when automatic initiation has failed. Operator failures are also modeled; for example, many core damage scenarios include operator failures to take a procedural action; e.g., to switch over from injection to recirculation following a LOCA, to provide high pressure injection pump minimum flow recirculation when throttling high pressure injection (HPI), and to initiate HPI cooling.

Another technique that has improved the treatment of operator actions involves the use of the simulator. Training simulators have been used to provide operations personnel with a realistic simulation of scenarios important to risk for their specific plant. The results have been fed back into the risk models to better represent operator response to accident situations.

With respect to the modeling of selected external events, earthquakes have been found to be more important to risk than initially believed. While it has always been assumed that earthquakes were important for California plants, the PRAs have revealed that they may be an important contributor to risk for plants at other U.S. locations, including the east coast and the southeast.

There have been several improvements in the modeling of earthquakes in the PRAs. The fundamental plant risk model is now constructed with earthquakes and other external events. As a result, the earthquake becomes somewhat of an initiating event that can be propogated through the basic risk model without the need for constructing a separate model. In particular, the basic risk model now contains those components that may be affected by an earthquake, such as structures and cable trays.

Another improvement in earthquake analysis relates to the treatment of relay chatter analysis. For earlier studies, it was assumed that relay chatter from seismic events was always recoverable; i.e., if chatter resulted in circuit breaker trips leading to valve openings or closures or to motor disconnects, it was assumed that the breakers would routinely be repositioned. The fragility analyst in the past assumed all relays have similar chatter fragilities. Recent studies are showing that there is a range of fragilities applicable to relays, depending not only on their location in buildings and cabinets but on the type of design (pendulum, solid state, rotary, etc.) and manufacturer.

More importantly, it has been found that a significant number of circuits can be "locked out" after breaker trip and that the operator cannot reset all the breakers from the control room. Therefore, to accomplish a sound seismic risk analysis, all the relays serving important equipment in the PRA should be identified along with their type, manufacturer, location in buildings, and location within the cabinet. After determining which relay can chatter and cause breaker trips not automatically recoverable, the various relay chatter fragilities need to be individually determined, then introduced into the basic risk model. Following an early round of quantification, it can then be determined if individual recovery actions and simultaneous recovery actions need to be modeled and introduced into the basic risk model.

Conclusion

There is little doubt that the application of the PRA thought process to nuclear power plants has contributed enormously to the understanding of nuclear plant safety. Its greatest value has been in providing perspective and context to what is important to safety. The ability to have insight on how to allocate resources to ensure continued safety is a major step forward in the risk management of nuclear power plants. Figure 13 illustrates the power of the process. Each iteration of the risk model reveals the most important contributors to risk. Fixes or corrective actions can be implemented and the risk model can guide the effort toward a balanced design.

SYSTEM(s) OR OPERATOR ACTION	PERCENT REDUCTION IN CORE DAMAGE FREQUENCY IF THE INDIVIDUAL SYSTEM (OR OPERATOR ACTION) FAILURE FREQUENCY COULD BE REDUCED TO ZERO			
	FIRST ITERATION	SECOND ITERATION	THIRD ITERATION	FOURTH ITERATION
1. ELECTRIC POWER	11	65	43	52
2. AUXILIARY FEEDWATER	9	11	11	31
3. TWO TRAINS OF ELECTRIC POWER RECOVERED				21
4. LOW PRESSURE INJECTION/DECAY HEAT REMOVAL	4	3	8	19
5. FAILURE TO RECLOSE PORV/PSVs		5	20	17
6. ESFAS/ECCAS			14	15
7. HIGH PRESSURE INJECTION SYSTEMS	3	9	15	14
8. OPERATOR RECOVERY OF ELECTRIC POWER DURING STATION BLACKOUT		50	14	14
9. SUMP RECIRCULATION WATER SOURCE				11
10. COMPONENT COOLING WATER			3	8
11. THROTTLE HPI FLOW (OPERATOR ACTION)			1	4
12. FAILURE OF MAIN STEAM SAFETY VALVE TO RECLOSE			1	4
13. SERVICE WATER	32	<1	10	4
14. SAFEGUARDS CHILLED WATER	20	8	13	1
15. BWST SUCTION VALVE				1
16. CONTAINMENT ISOLATION			1	
17. STEAM GENERATOR TUBE RUPTURE	7	<1		
18. HIGH PRESSURE RECIRCULATION (OPERATOR ACTION)	5	2	11	
19. MAIN FEEDWATER		4	1	
20. FAST TRANSFER OF ELECTRIC BUS			7	
21. OTHER	4	6	6	< <1
RELATIVE CORE MELT FREQUENCY	1.00	0.30	0.10	0.06

Figure 13: Contributors to Core Damage for Four Phases of Risk Management

In the case of the PLG PRAs, the greatest contribution has come from the full-scope risk models. Quantitative risk management requires the fine structure of the risk contributors so that the options for controlling risk can be clearly seen and for assurance that the risk from all causes is being considered. In this regard, there is some concern about the current trend toward "quickie" PRAs. It is important that the industry not slip into a totally risk compliance mode and simply do what the authorities require for regulatory purposes. The PRA provides the owners of nuclear plants a powerful tool to expose the real contributors to risk of specific, not generic, plants and to greatly increase public confidence in the safety of nuclear power. The small investment in high confidence risk models is well worth the enormous benefits for us all.

Acknowledgments

The author wishes to acknowledge the invaluable assistance of the PLG staff in developing source material for this paper. I especially want to thank Brian A. Fagan for his assistance in extracting key results.

References

1. Garrick, B. J., "Lessons Learned from First Generation Nuclear Plant Probabilistic Risk Assessments," Society for Risk Analysis Workshop on Low-Probability/High-Consequence Risk Analysis, Arlington, Virginia, June 15-17, 1982.

2. Kaplan, S., and B. J. Garrick, "On the Quantitative Definition of Risk," RISK ANALYSIS, Vol. 1, pp. 11-27, March 1981.

3. American Nuclear Society, and Institute of Electrical and Electronics Engineers, "PRA Procedures Guide - A Guide to the Performance of Probabilistic Risk Assessments for Nuclear Power Plants," U.S. Nuclear Regulatory Commission, NUREG/CR-2300, April 1983.

LEIBSTADT NUCLEAR POWER STATION PROBABILISTIC ANALYSIS
OF INTERNAL FAULTS LEADING TO BEYOND DESIGN BASIS EVENTS

R.N. Dumolo and M.S. Barents

Electrowatt Engineering Services (UK) Ltd, Grandford House,
16, Carfax, Horsham, West Sussex. RH12 1UP

ABSTRACT

This paper reviews the work undertaken to quantify the probability of
internal faults leading to beyond design basis events for Leibstadt
Nuclear Power Station and to highlight the differences between these
results and those which have been published for similar reactor types.
These differences are related to the difference in Leibstadt system
design, particularly including the benefit to be gained from the
Special Emergency Heat Removal (SEHR) system in relation to decay heat
removal. The paper summarises the predicted dominant fault sequences,
and assesses the effectiveness of the Leibstadt specific design changes
to prevent or mitigate their occurrence.

1. INTRODUCTION

This paper discusses the work undertaken and the results of a Level-1
Probabilistic Risk Assessment (PRA) for Leibstadt Nuclear Power Station
which is a BWR/6 with a Mark III containment located on the River Rhine
in the north of Switzerland. Various PRA related studies have been
carried out by Electrowatt Engineering Services (UK) Ltd since 1980 and
are still continuing. The early studies concerned a detailed
reliability analysis of the emergency core cooling systems. Extension
of these studies to include other safety and non-safety related systems
culminated in a Level-1 PRA, a determination of the core damage
frequency due to internal initiating events.

2. SYSTEMS RELIABILITY ANALYSIS

Detailed analysis of selected Emergency Core Cooling Systems was
undertaken principally to determine the contribution to system failure
probability due to failures in the control logic. Concern over the
reliability of the control logic was raised because the particular
solid state control system installed at Leibstadt, which had been used
in various conventional power stations, had not previously been
qualified for use in a nuclear power plant. Analysis of the systems
was undertaken using fault tree analysis techniques. Results from the
analysis revealed that the initiation and control logic contributed
typically between 10 to 20% of the overall system failure probability
(Table 1). The dominant failure modes identified in the control logic
were associated with the Functional Control Unit which sends signals to
all equipment on a system demand e.g. valve and motor drive control
units. The relatively low contribution of control logic failures in
the case of SEHR system arises because it is a totally redundant
system.

System	Total System Failure Probability	Failure Probability (Perfect Logic)	Contribution of Control Logic to Total Failure Probability
High Pressure Core Spray	1.44E-2	1.12E-2	22%
Low Pressure Core Injection (A Train)	1.29E-2	1.12E-2	13%
Special Emergency Heat Removal	2.40E-3	2.21E-3	8%

TABLE 1: Contribution of Control Logic Failures To Total System Failure Probability

3. LEVEL-1 PROBABILISTIC RISK ASSESSMENT

This Level-1 PRA drew on information from the Reactor Safety Study Methodology Applications Program analysis which was undertaken for Grand Gulf (Ref. 1), since Grand Gulf is the reference plant for Leibstadt. In addition information and data was also taken from the PRA of Limerick (Ref. 2).

One of the tasks of this study was to identify all major systems differences between Leibstadt and Grand Gulf, concentrating on those systems which influence the achievement of safe shutdown conditions post fault. The principal differences identified were:-

i)	Vapor Suppression System	—	Leibstadt has no containment spray system
ii)	Automatic Depressurisation System	—	Leibstadt ADS valves have dual activation
iii)	Low Pressure Core Injection System	—	Minor differences in crossover lines and heat exchangers
iv)	Power Conversion System	—	Grand Gulf feedwater pumps are steam driven; Leibstadt feedwater pumps motor driven
v)	Special Emergency and Heat Removal System	—	Leibstadt specific system – no equivalent at Grand Gulf
vi)	Containment	—	Leibstadt containment differs from Grand Gulf in some minor aspects.

LOCA and transient initiator event trees used in this study were the same as those used in the Grand Gulf study. The decision was made because the functional response of Leibstadt was assumed to be identical to Grand Gulf. Functional level fault trees representing failure of the appropriate success criteria and involving systems and there interactions were analysed using appropriate computer codes.

Overall the analysis lead to a calculated core melt frequency for
Leibstadt of 5.91E-6 per reactor year. Transient initiators accounted
for over ten of the dominant sequences leading to a core damage
scenario. The overall contribution of the LOCA and transient
initiators to the total core melt frequency are given in Table 2 below.

	Core damage frequency	%
LOCA events	1.45E-7	2.5
Transient events	5.76E-6	97.5
Total	5.91E-6	100.0

TABLE 2: Contribution of LOCA and Transient Events to Core
Damage Frequency

Further analysis of these results reveal that failure to achieve
reactor subcriticality accounts for about 70% of the total core melt
frequency.   The other dominant functional failure is failure of
emergency coolant injection. The breakdown of dominant sequences into
functional failures is given in Table 3.

Function Failure	Core Damage Frequency For Each Initiator Group		Total Core Damage Frequency	Fraction of Total Core Damage Frequency
	LOCA	Transient		
Reactor Subcriticality	7.25E-8	4.03E-6	4.10E-6	69.4%
Emergency Coolant Injection	2.63E-8	1.60E-6	1.63E-6	27.5%
Decay Heat Removal	4.62E-8	1.26E-7	1.72E-7	2.9%

TABLE 3: Core Damage Frequency Related to Function Failures

4.   COMPARISON WITH SIMILAR PLANTS

The reference plant for Leibstadt is Grand Gulf Nuclear Station,
operated by the Mississippi Power and Light Co. in the United States of
America. Grand Gulf has been analysed both as part of the Reactor
Safety Methodology Applications Program (RSSMAP) (Ref. 1) and more
recently as part of the Accident Sequence Evaluation Program (ASEP) and
the Severe Accident Risk Reduction Program (SARRP). The results of
these latter studies are summarised in Ref. 3.

The overall core damage frequency for Leibstadt of 5.9E-6 per year compares with the mean value of 2.9E-5 per year for Grand Gulf quoted in Ref. 3. Whilst these values are similar, the various contributors are quite different.

The results for Grand Gulf indicate that all of the important accident sequences leading to core damage involve station blackout. All other sequences, including ATWS, individually contribute less than 1 per cent to the core damage frequency. This conclusion is markedly different to that for Leibstadt, where ATWS sequences are calculated to contribute nearly 70% of the core damage frequency.

The two most dominant accident sequences for Grand Gulf resulting from the station blackout scenario are:

a)   Inability to operate the low pressure decay heat removal systems followed by failure of the HPCS and RCIC systems due to extreme temperature conditions in the containment (81% of core damage frequency).

b)   Inability to operate the low pressure decay heat removal systems followed by failure of the HPCS and RCIC due to loss of all DC power (13% of core damage frequency).

For Leibstadt, the SEHR system has a low pressure decay heat removal capability, and would be able to provide coolant make-up for both the dominant core damage scenarios identified for Grand Gulf. It should be noted that the SEHR system has its own dedicated diesel generators and these should not be subject to common mode or common cause faults due to their different layout and design compared with the other diesel generators on the site. Analysis of the decay heat removal systems for Leibstadt has been undertaken in detail and has been presented in Ref. 4. Consequently it can be seen that even a modest reliability claim for the SEHR system (say E-1 to E-2 failure probability per demand) will give a significant reduction in the frequency of core damage resulting from blackout situations. Indeed, if Grand Gulf were fitted with such a system then station blackout would not be seen to be a dominant accident scenario. It therefore has to be concluded that even for stations whose designs are quite similar, conclusions with regard to dominant contributions to core damage and to overall risk, are strongly dependent upon specific design differences.

REFERENCES

1.   Reactor Safety Study Methodology Applications Program: Grand Gulf #1 BWR Power Plant. NUREG/CR-1659, October, 1981.

2.   Probabilistic Risk Assessment - Limerick Generating Station - Philadelphia Electric Company. March, 1981 - Docket Nos. 50-352 and 50-353.

3.   Reactor Risk Reference Document, NUREG-1150, February, 1987.

4.   Reliability Analysis of a BWR Decay Heat Removal System, R.N. Dumolo and Dr. A. Tiberini. International Meeting on Thermal Reactor Safety. Chicago, 1982.

QUALITATIVE REVIEW OF
PROBABILISTIC SAFETY ASSESSMENT CHARACTERISTICS

Lennart Carlsson   (Swedish Nuclear Power Inspectorate, Stockholm,
                    Sweden)
Stefan Hirschberg   (AB ASEA-ATOM, Västerås, Sweden)
Gunnar Johanson   (Systecon AB, Stockholm, Sweden)

Keywords: Swedish, PSA, Comparison, Qualitative, Decision making

1   The Swedish Reliability Evaluation Program

Plant specific Probabilistic Safety Assessments (PSAs) constitute a
major part of the present Swedish periodic safety review. The results of the analyses are to be reported to the Swedish government
in a document given the acronym ASAR (As operated Safety Analysis
Report). The basic studies are limited to the core damage level
(level 1 PRA); although plant-specific studies on core melt and containment behaviour are being carried out, these studies will not be
included in the present phase of the ASAR program. Level 1 plant-
specific PSAs for all Swedish plants will be completed during the
period 1982-90. The utilities are responsible for carrying out the
analyses, and the Swedish Nuclear Power Inspectorate (SKI) carries
out the review of the studies. Until now the following studies have
been completed, mainly as a part of the ASAR program.

Plant	PSA	ASAR
o Ringhals 1	1984	1986
o Ringhals 2	1984	1985
o Barsebäck 1&2	1985	1986
o Forsmark 3	1985	(1993)
o Oskarshamn 3	1986	(1993)
o Oskarshamn 1	1986	1984
o Oskarshamn 2	1987	(1988)

In addition, PSAs for the Forsmark 1&2 plants, are presently being
performed. By the end of 1987 PSAs for 10 out of 12 Swedish plants
will be available. The remaining plants, Ringhals 3 & 4, are planned
to be analyzed and reported by 1990.

2   The SUPER-ASAR Project

As shown above the Swedish PSAs have been generated in a relatively
short period of time. The reviews of the studies, carried out by
SKI, clearly indicate significant differences in scope, degree of
detail, coverage etc. Application of a broad spectrum of methods and
assumptions has given a major impact on the results of PSAs, which
complicates a proper comparison. Having this as a background SKI
initiated in 1986 the SUPER-ASAR project.

The main objectives of this project are as follows:

o   To survey and compare the results of Swedish PSAs with due con-
     cern of differences in assumptions, modeling and completeness
     aspects

o   To facilitate use of completed studies in the process of deci-
     sion making

o   To supply background for establishment of priorities for re-
     search projects within the area of probabilistic safety analysis

The project has been divided into two phases, figure 1. During the
first phase, which is the subject of this paper, the qualitative
features of the studies have been reviewed. The results obtained,
will constitute the basis for in-depth sensitivity studies, which
are to be performed within the second phase to facilitate the use of
PSAs in decision making.

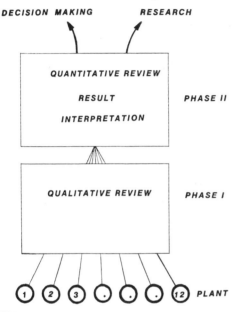

PLANT SPECIFIC LEVEL 1 PSAs

Figure 1: SUPER-ASAR subtasks

The SUPER-ASAR project is coordinated in such a way that results of
several other activities in the PSA-field, being carried out in
Sweden, can be utilized within this integrated project. Comparative
studies need a general frame-work in order to be useful for decision
making.

3   Scope and Limitations of Swedish PSAs

As a first step in the review it was necessary to survey scope and
limitations of each PSA performed within the Swedish program.

The PSAs examined are limited in scope to level 1 analysis. Only
internal initiating events are considered in the first step. Presently, external event analyses are being planned or are in progress.

The scope for each study is shown by categories of initiating events in table 1.

Type of event	Barsebäck 1&2	Forsmark 3	Oskarshamn 1	Oskarshamn 3	Ringhals 1	Ringhals 2
Internal LOCAs	yes	yes	yes	yes	yes	yes
External pipe breaks	yes	yes	yes	yes	yes	yes
Transients, power operation	yes	yes	yes	yes	yes	yes
Transients, cold stand-by	no	no	no	no	no	yes
Transients, overhaul period	no	no	no	no	no	yes
Transient type of common cause initiators	partly covered 1)	yes	partly covered 1)	partly covered 1)	yes	partly covered 1)
Fire	in progress	no	yes (not complete)	no	in progress	in progess
Flooding	no	no	no	no	yes	no
Earthquake	in progress	no	no	no	in progress	no
Cold over-pressurization	not applicable (n.a)	n.a	n.a	n.a	n.a	no

1) no dedicated analysis

Table 1: Scope of Swedish PSAs

4   Initiating Events

An important part in reviewing PSAs is the definition of initiating events (IE). The IEs are generally divided into transients and LOCAs. Frequencies for IEs are different due to several reasons. It would certainly be easier for the user if the same definitions had been used. Differences in operating experience influence the frequency of transients; grouping of events and transfers from other events or accident sequences are examples of important factors in this context. The differences found are not many. However, even small discrepancies in classification and grouping of initiating events may dramatically mislead the user of the PSA results.

PSA results can be presented in many different ways depending on IE-definitions. For example, when bringing back all transfers to the IEs from which they origin, the black bars (S2, Q1) in the histogram summarizing results of one of the Swedish PSAs, figure 2, will be removed and instead the crossed section of the bars for Tm+Ts, Tt and Te will appear. Another example of inconsistency is loss of off-site power (LOSP). In Sweden LOSP can contain loss of 400 kV net, loss of 130/70 kV net and failure of in-house turbine operation. All possible combinations of losses of these functions have been used as definition of the initiating event; therefore the boundaries for operation experience interpretation and for estimation of IE frequency, differ substantially from one analysis to another.

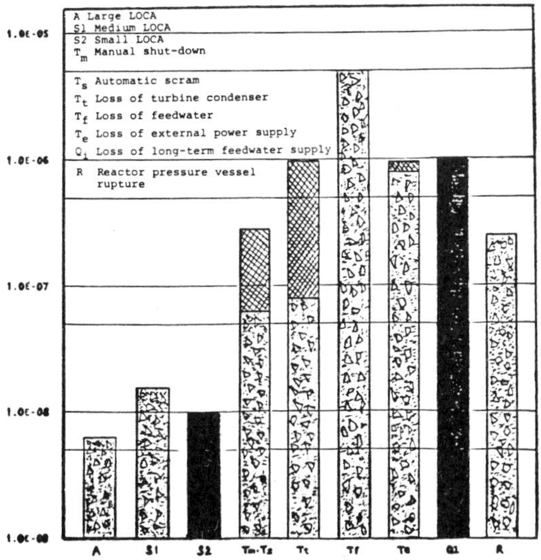

Figure 2: PSA result histogram

An important phenomenon in the context of LOCAs is "leak before break". This has motivated in-depth studies of possible failure combinations which may lead to major pipe breaks. Relevant factors in this context are probabilities of pipe failure (e.g. cracks), no detection of such a failure, no detection of leakage in time and probability that an undetected failure will lead to a break.

The resulting conclusion is that a proper comparison of PSA results requires a standarized initiating event definition. This means that new formats for presentation of results will be used when interpreting and comparing the studies.

5 Modeling of Accident Sequences

The qualitative review of accident sequence modeling is performed through a careful survey of systems credited and corresponding success criteria. The survey includes development of functional sequence diagrams for all plants and all initiating events. These diagrams were found to be very useful when comparing the plant specific accident sequence models. The evaluation identified major discrepancies in models and assumptions used in analysis of all safety functions such as reactor shut-down, pressure relief, feedwater supply and decay heat removal. Also different treatment of containment dependencies has been observed. The nature of the discrepancies includes such issues as core melt definitions, functional dependencies, system crediting and success criteria.

6 Systems Analysis

The systems analysis review includes a survey of system and component fault trees with the objective to establish base case component and train level fault trees representing model pattern and level of detail in the analysis. Failure modes represented in the analyses

are studied in detail in order to identify modeling assumptions from
basic event and system operation point of view. The model pattern
and system analysis assumptions are thereafter evaluated and compared,leading to identification of issues to be addressed in the sensitivity studies.

The results from the qualitative system analysis review show that
discrepancies related to system failure modes exist. Dependencies,
human interactions, success criteria and component failure data are
subjects of a parallel reviw and therefore many sources of discrepancies are excluded from the systems analysis review.

7   Reliability Data

Qualitative aspects of reliability data are more a question of how
data were collected, identified and used. In Sweden a realiability
databook has been produced and new editions are released every third
year. It is an excellent data source since the data can be plant-
specific and an unified approach is used to collect and process the
raw data. The defined physical component boundaries in the data book
constitute the frame-work for development of component fault trees
in Swedish PSAs.

Engineering judgement is a widely used data source in all PSAs. Generally, there is a wide spectrum of subjective estimates and they
need to be evaluated following the same standard. The review puts
emphasis on how the judgements were made and applied.

8   Treatment of Dependencies

Treatment of dependencies is obviously one of the critical issues in
the context of PSA. Dependencies may have a major impact on the
plant safety level and must be addressed at all stages of the analysis. This fact has been recognized in the Swedish PSAs, where as a
rule great emphasis has been put on the treatment of dependencies.
On the other hand, the differences between the performed analyses
are significant and may concern:

o   degree of detail
o   scope
o   choice of qualitative (identification) methods
o   representation of dependencies in the plant model
o   quantification models
o   sources of data
o   documentation.

Three types of dependencies have been consiered within the SUPER-
ASAR project, namely: Common Cause Initiators (CCIs) of transient
character, intersystem dependencies and intercomponent dependencies.
The two last mentioned groups are in turn divided into functional
and shared-equipment, physical interaction and human interaction dependencies. Due to their special nature and importance a particular
type of intercomponent dependencies, Common Cause Failures (CCFs),
have been treated separately.

Generally, due to the high degree of detail in modeling of accident
sequences (event tree analyses) and in modeling of safety systems

(fault tree analyses), the Swedish PSAs have been very successful in the task of identification of significant functional and shared-equipment dependencies. In several cases design deficiencies have been observed, leading to modifications of the plants.
The qualitative analysis of dependencies within the SUPER-ASAR project has resulted in:

o   identification of problems to be resolved, concerning analysis details, existence of background documentation and modeling issues (e.g. need of certain safety functions in specific accident conditions)

o   identification of issues for sensitivity studies (e.g. CCF-models and data, systematic misconfiguration of redundant components)

o   proposals for future research projects (e.g. collection of Swedish CCF-data, treatment of errors of commission)

o   proposals for supplementary studies (e.g. CCIs and dynamic effects for some of the plants, human interaction dependencies for all plants)

The planned sensitivity studies are expected to facilitate establishment of priorites for the recommended supplementary analyses and for research projects.

9   Treatment of Human Interactions

The qualitative review of human interactions is focused on which types of interaction (before, during and after accident conditions) have been considered and which models and methods have been used in the evaluation. A survey of all human interactions modeled in the PSAs was made resulting in an overall picture of modeling features in each PSA.

The subsequent evaluation of this material answers the following questions

1   Which types have been considered?
2   Which time frames have been used?
3   Which sources of information have been used?
4   How were the human interaction models integrated?
5   How were the human interaction models quantified?

The main conclusions of the review is that the treatment of human interactions in Swedish PSAs in most cases is rather superficial. Thus, supplementary analyses have been recommended to be carried out in parallel with continued research work on this subject.

After implementation of hardware modifications and improvements in the plant design, issues related to human interactions will become more significant (in relative terms) and future PSA-work will focus on this area.

10 Results and Conclusions from the Qualitative Part of the SUPER-ASAR Project

The results of the qualitative review of the Swedish PSAs present a long list of differences in assumptions, modeling and completeness of the different tasks included in a PSA. Among the identified qualitative discrepancies only some of the most significant have been mentioned here. Many issues will be subject of sensitivity analysis and other issues will initiate additional analyses. The quantitative phase of the SUPER-ASAR project will provide a more definite list of problem areas, hopefully supported by numerical results.

The goal for the second phase of the SUPER-ASAR project is (if possible) to quantify the most significant model discrepancies and to generate modified PSA results which can be used with greater confidence in the process of decision making. The ambition of the project is to demonstrate in practice how modifications of assumptions and models influence results of different PSAs. It is expected that this approach will facilitate the use of available PSAs in daily safety work.

Bibliography

1. SKI-ASAR-O1. Periodic Safety Review of Oskarshamn 1, 1983, Swedish Nuclear Power Inspectorate (in Swedish)
2. SKI-ASAR-R2. Periodic Safety Review of Ringhals 2, 1985, Swedish Nuclear Power Inspectorate (in Swedish)
3. SKI-ASAR-B1/B2. Periodic Safety Review of Barsebäck 1 & 2, 1985, Swedish Nuclear Power Inspectorate (in Swedish)
4. SKI-ASAR-R1. Periodic Safety Review of Ringhals 1, 1986, Swedish Nuclear Power Inspectorate (in Swedish)
5. Forsmark 3 Probabilistic Safety Analysis, 1986, AB ASEA-ATOM (in Swedish)
6. Oskarshamn 1 Probabilistic Safety analysis, 1987, OKG AB (in Swedish)
7. Oskarshamn 3 Probabilistic Safety Analysis, 1986 OKG AB (in Swedish)
8. Reliability databook, RKS 85-05. Second edition, 1985
9. SUPER-ASAR preproject study. Scope and Limitations of Swedish PSAs. SY-PM 4037-1. Gunnar Johanson, 1987, Systecon AB (in Swedish)
10. Retrospective Analysis of Dependencies in Swedish PSAs. Phase I: Qualitative Overview, Stefan Hirschberg, 1987, AB ASEA-ATOM (to be published)
11. Retrospective Analysis of Human Interactions in Swedish PSAs. Phase I: Qualitative overview. Marit Bengtz and Stefan Hirschberg, 1987, AB ASEA-ATOM, (to be published)

APPLICATION OF RELIABILITY ANALYSES OF VVER NPP SAFETY SYSTEMS TO PSA

Josef Dušek, Karel Dach
Nuclear Research Institute, Řež, Czechoslovakia

A short information on fault tree reliability analyses of the type-213 VVER-440 reactor ECCS (passive system and LPIS), spray system and bubbling depressurization system, performed in NRI Řež, is given. For these analyses several computing codes are available. The NRI activities in frame of the IAEA coordinated PSA research programmes and connection of the PSA with noise diagnostics are also mentioned.

1 Introduction

The reliability analyses carried out so far in NRI Řež have employed the fault tree method and were focused on the safety system of the Czechoslovak nuclear power plants (NPP) with the Soviet-type VVER-440 pressurized-water reactor of type 213 /1-3, 5-7/. These analyses were related mainly to the 3rd and 4th units of the Jaslovské Bohunice NPP (EBO), the results being applicable also to the NPP Dukovany (EDU). Such analyses are now carried out for the NPP Mochovce (EMO), where an antiseismic design will be used /8/. Preliminary reliability analysis of safety systems was carried out even for the NPP Temelín with VVER-1000 reactors in construction.

2 Reliability analyses

The loss-of-coolant accident (LOCA) following the rupture of main circulation piping (diameter of 500 mm) with double-sided outflow of coolant and the loss of in-site power with transition to emergency power supply are considered to represent the most severe possible accident for the 213-type VVER-440 reactor (EBO, EDU). The maximum rated earthquake (i.e. earthquake with power of six balls of MSK-64 scale with maximum acceleration of 0.25 m/s² is also taken into account in EMO. In order to localize these LOCA accidents, which are considered to be the design basis accidents (DBA), the NPPs are equipped with a number of safety systems (Fig.1).

Passive system (PS) of the emergency core cooling system (ECCS) is composed of two independent identical subsystems. Each of them has two similar pressure accumulators. Discharge lines lead from one accumulator to the upper plenum and from the second one to the lower plenum. Reliable operation (when pressure is decreased under 4 - 6 MPa) of at least one of them is sufficient for sucessful function in the Czechoslovak design. The discharge line is spontaneously closed by a float valve before the accumulator is emptied in order to prevent the nitrogen from penetrating into the core. Reliable function of this valve has been found during the first PS reliability fault tree analysis as the most serious problem /1/.

After the exhaustion of accumulators the low pressure injection system (LPIS) has to ensure removal of residual heat from the reactor during LOCA. It includes three mutually independent loops, one of them is considered to be sufficient

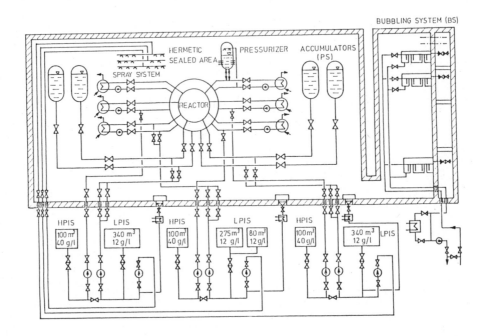

Figure 1: Type-213 VVER-440 safety systems

for a reliable intervention of LPIS. Two of the loops are connected to the accu-
mulator-reactor conduit; the remaining one is connected to the cold and hot legs
of one of main circulation loops. Water is delivered from the emergency tanks of
boric acid and, after their exhaustion, from the well in the floor of the hermetically sealed area through the emergency heat exchangers.

Reliability analysis of the LPIS evaluated its unavailability for the period
between two refuelings and the probability of failure of the operated LPIS in
the period of two weeks /1, 2, 3/. This analysis took into account sensitivity
of input data and rate and range of periodical tests. It was suggested to dupli-
cate motor-operated valves under sumps and level indicators and to verify the
input data of pneumatically operated valves (in hermetically sealed area) with
more precision. The similar conclusion was made for the spray system.

The bubbling depressurization containment (BS) reliability analysis /5-7/ was
carried out using the fault tree method too. The task of this system during
LOCA is to decrease temperature in the primary circuit hermetically sealed area
(HSA) and to establish there an underpressure relating the NPP ambient pressure.
The BS is connected with the HSA by the coupling corridor and comprises twelve
independent floors (for the condensation of the steam component of the steam-
-air mixture during the bubbling through the boric acid). Proper functioning of
six floors of BS is required for proper function of this system in the Czechoslovak design. The human errors during the NPP outage (the closing of some hermetic doors, the opening of auxiliary system valves - the ventilation of the BS
holding tanks) were identified as the most frequent causes of failures.

The results obtained, mainly their qualitative part, have turned out to be very
useful and contribute significantly to assurance and improvement of safety of
the Czechoslovak NPPs.

3 Computing codes

In NRI Řež, several computing codes are available for fault tree analyses /4,8/. The most often used codes are the SAFEDO-2 code (Monte Carlo simulation approach; periodical tests) and the CRAFT code (extended analytical technique of Bulgarian code KADO). The next computing codes used for reliability analysis are ALLCUT-2 (readjusting of the American code ALLCUTS), the LOTR-3 code (Bennet's algorithm with mutually excluding products; periodical tests), the SPOL-3 code (analytical approach with partial modularization) and the American code FRANTIC. For uncertainty analysis,the US computing codes SAMPLE, RANGE and COSMOS were implemented.

4 International cooperation

As far as PSA methods is concerned Czechoslovakia participates in IAEA coordinated research programmes through two contracts related to the problems of PSA.

The first of them is the contract No. 4032/RB within the frame of the programme "Development of risk criteria for the whole nuclear fuel cycle". Its subject is "Importance of independent and dependent human error to system reliability and plant safety" and the activity aims at selection and reliability analysis of a safety system with very few human interactions and of a safety system enabling more human interventions /8/. Passive system and LPIS of the NPP Mochovce ECCS were selected for analysis and an analysis using values with uncertainties is also carried out for both systems.

The reliability analysis of PS takes into account its function, ways of redundancy, in-service testing and operational conditions with preference given to the

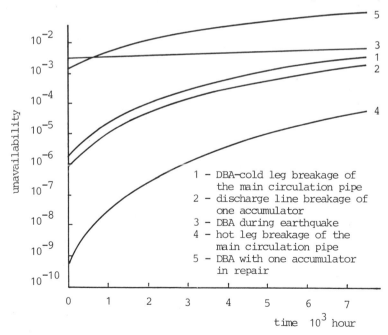

Figure 2: NPP Mochovce passive system unavailability

conservative reliability input data. Two variants of information transmission to the unit control room were analysed: direct transmission and transmission via computer. The results showed approximately by one order lower unavailability of PS with the new possibility of transmission via computer. The analysis also showed great importance of right and verified selection of top event of the fault tree (Fig.2) and very small possibilities of human factor to influence the PS and its function.

The second contract No. 4355/RB is a part of the programme "PSA for a research reactor" and its task is to prepare a partial PSA study for the reconstructed research water cooled and moderated research reactor LVR-15 with thermal power of 15 MW_{th} in NRI in Řež /9, 10/.

5 PSA in diagnostics

In the past years due to rapid development of instrumentation, control and diagnostics great effort was focused to the problem of establishing of expert systems, namely the necessary knowledge base for noise diagnostics expert system.

The block scheme of a noise diagnostic expert system can be seen in Fig.3. Technological process characterized by a state quantity {X} is regulated by a quantity of action {U}. The check out quantity {Y} gives information about technological process and the system itself. Quantities {N} characterize the failures. The proper diagnostics is realized by means of three blocks: Identification of state - Failure recognition - Risk assessment.

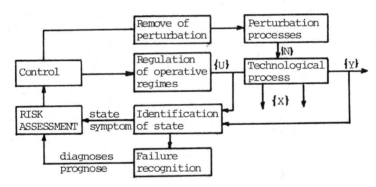

Figure 3: Noise diagnostic expert systems and risk assessment

The main requirements for an expert diagnostic system are:
. monitoring of equipment state in all operation situations,
. detection of deviations from "normal" operation conditions,
. classification of phenomenon significance - risk assessment,
. recommendation for solving the existing situation

In NRI Řež, an expert system for reactor interval behaviour is under development /11/.

6 References

/ 1/ Dušek, J., Reliability Analysis of Complex Systems in View of the VVER NPP, ECCS, PhD Thesis (1984) (in Czech)

/ 2/ Dušek, J., Dach, K., IAEA-SM-275/28, Vienna (1985) 217

/ 3/ Dušek, J., Hojný, V., Proc.Conf."Thirty Years of NRI", Řež, June 1985, Vol.1, p.27 (in Czech)

/ 4/ Dach, K., Dušek, J., Hojný, V., Briš, R., Poster IAEA-SR-111/47, Blackpool, March 1985

/ 5/ Dušek, J., Hojný, V., Briš, R., Operating Experience and Methods of Improvement of Performance of the NPPs with VVER Reactors (Int.Conf.Pleven, 1984) (in Russian)

/ 6/ Hojný, V., Dušek, J., Jaderná energie 32, No. 8-9 (1986) p.329 (in Czech)

/ 7/ Krett, V., Dach, K., Dušek, J., Workshop on Technological Risk in Modern Society, Laxenburg, March 1987

/ 8/ Dach, K., Dušek, J. et al., Progress Report to Contract No. 4032/RB (Dec. 84-March 87), NRI Řež, April 1987

/ 9/ Dušek, J. et al., Report NRI 7894 R,T, Řež, Nov. 1986

/10/ Hron, M., Dušek, J., Dach, K. et al., Progress Report to Contract No.4355/ RB (March 86-Nov.86), NRI Řež, Nov.1986

/11/ Dach, K. et al., SMORN V - Symp. on Reactor Noise, München, Oct. 1987

THE STATUS OF DEVELOPMENT AND PRACTICAL USE OF PROBABILISTIC
SAFETY ASSESSMENT METHODOLOGY IN CSSR.

Miroslav Hrehor
(Czechoslovak Atomic Energy Commission, Prague, CSSR)
Petr Babic
(Power Research Institute, Prague, CSSR)

Abstract

The first part of the paper gives a brief summary of the current status of the
nuclear energy programme and its regulatory background in CSSR emphasizing a
leading role of the State Nuclear Safety Inspectorate of CsAEC in the
development and practical use of probabilistic safety assessment methodology.
In the secund part a simple practical technique is presented enabling
calculation of MTBF and MTTR in the cases which cannot be directly modelled by
means of logical operators commonly used in fault treee models.

1 Review of Current Status

1.1 Czechoslovak Nuclear Energy Programme

At present Czechoslovakia is operating 7 nuclear power reactors WWER-440 on
the sites Jaslovske Bohunice and Dukovany. The 8th unit is in commissioning
and will be put into operation by the end of this year. Another 4 units of the
same type are under construction at Mochovce. Recently, construction work has
started at a new site - Temelin where four 1000 MWe WWER units are planed. By
the year 2000, the share of electric energy produced in nuclear power plants
in CSSR will exceed 50% of total electrical energy output.

1.2 Nuclear Safety Policy

Regardless of satisfactory operating results, the issues of nuclear safety are
under permanent review in CSSR. Compliance with safety regulations which have
been issued in accordance with IAEA Safety Series is controlled by the State
Nuclear Safety Inspectorate of Czechoslovak Atomic Energy Commission. Our
licensing procedure is based on deterministic approach. Reactor safety concept
is fundamentally in agreement with the international standard and as such it
is based on defence in depth.

1.3 R&D Activities

The intensive nuclear programme in CSSR is accompanied by adequate R&D
activities. In the early 1970's the important role of reliability engineering
was recognized and a special R&D programme oriented on a development of
probabilistic methodology and techniques for reliability evaluation of
engineering safety features was adopted. Under this programme a number of
foreign and domestic computer codes have been modified and developed as a tool
for practical use.

1.4 Reliability Evaluation Programme

In recent years, the reliability evaluation programme of reactor protection and safety-related systems promoted by the State Nuclear Safety Inspectorate of CsAEC has been initiated. Under this programme plant specific fault trees were developed and reviewed in close co-operation with designers, operators and maintenance personnel. Detail system fault tree logic of ECCS (pasive, high and low pressure), spray and barbotage systems and emergency feedwater system were developed in Nuclear Research Institute at Rez near Prague.
In Research Institute of Fuel and Power Complex at Bratislava system fault tree analyses ware oriented on emergency power supply of primary circulation pumps, reactor control and protection system and on fire protection in cable spreading rooms. Recently the first integration of event and fault tree models for LOCA accidents of different sizes resulting in preliminary core melt frequency estimates was carried out.
In Power Research Institute in Prague problems connected with reliability of the electrical supply for control and instrumentation system were thoroughly studied.
All these studies provided the better understanding of system functions and led to valuable insights into course of accident sequences, system dependencies, operator interactions etc. As a results of these analyses some components were duplicated, some operator information had to be monitored, periodical tests were made more stringent and certain measures against the possibility of common-cause failure were accepted. These analyses revealed possibilities to increase the reliability of the safety systems with no additional great effort and cost.

1.5 Future Trends

A number of PSA studies which have been completed in the world since 1975 confirmed that current NPP designs present low risk to the public compared to other risks in society. Due to this fact future PSA applications in CSSR should provide valuable benefits to the utilities rather than being solely the means addresing public risk. Manpower an computer resources will be concetrated on the development of a "living" PSA model for each nuclear unit which could be utilized as a plant computer model implemented on small computers to support design change process, technical specification evaluation and other operational problem evaluations and to streamline training of operating personnel, maintenance, testing of components atc. Paralelly we will concentrate our effort on the development of a plant specific component failure data base which is a must if one wants to improve the credibility of numerical PSA results.

2 Approximate Formulas for the Introduction of Non Boolean Relations Into a System Fault Tree

The technique described below has been developed to investigate the reliability of an electric supply system for the instrumentation and control system (I C) of the WWER 440 unit.
A relatively short power blackout (e.g. tenth of millisecond to two seconds) is able to violate normal functioning of 1 C system and cause the loss of information and/or produce an undesirable control device actuation. Thus, the focal point of interest is the blackout occurrence frequency or blackout duration rather than power supply system unavailability.
Several techniques for the calculation of the system up-state period (or MTBF) and the system failure duration (or MTTR), are available at present e.g., the American kinetic tree theory /1,2/, German approach /3/ deriving the system failure frequency expression from the system unavailability expression, and

French approach based on Markov processes /4/. All these techniques have been however developed for the case of continuously monitored components.
A generalized approach to fault tree modelling when non-boolean realation are to be dealt with is proposed as described below.

2.1 Non-Boolean Relations

Standard approach to fault tree quantification is based on the following two assumptions: /i/ both the occurrence probability and its consequence for any coincidence of basic events are independent of the occurrence sequence of the individual events, /ii/ processes underlying the occurrence of basic events are mutually independent (in probabilistic sense).
The case when any of these assumptions does not apply is called here "non-boolean relation" between events. The introduced concept is akin to the Type 2A of dependent failures specified in PRA Procedures Guide, NUREG/2300.

2.2 Proposed Approximations

I. Every basic (or composed) event placed in a fault tree model is to be specified in the way similar to the one used for the steady state of the renewal process discribing failures of a monitored component. Thus, an analyst is obliged to assign to every basic event at least two of the following characteristics:
T = MTBF (mean time between event occurrences)
t = MTTR (mean time to complete a recovery action)
$u = t/(t+T)$ = steady state unavailability
$w = 1/(t+T)$ = failure occurrences frequency
The following equation holds

$$w = \frac{u}{t} = \frac{1-u}{T} \qquad (1)$$

The same set of characteristics can be produced for the top of the fault tree if the top-event unavailability expression (obtained by means of any standard technique) is treated according to /3/.

II. The following approach to fault tree modelling can be used when functional dependency is to be dealt with:
/a/ Each non-boolean relation between events is appoximated by the boolean representation containing an auxiliary basic event (see Fig. 1)
/b/ Approximate formulas for characteristics of an subsystem of interest /u_S and w_S/ are to be derived for each type of relation. The formulas should express reliability characteristics as a function of analogous characteristics of the event A (see Fig. 1)/u_A, w_A/, of a random coincidence "A and B"/u_{AB}, w_{AB}/ and of other characteristics, which have been employed in the non-boolean relation model
/c/ The fault tree quantification is to proceed from basic events to the top of the fault tree. Every time an auxiliary event is met the appropriate subtrees are to be quantified to provide for calculation of the characteristics of the auxiliary event.

III. An analogy to the approach well known from PSA - level 1 studies, but aimed at only one subsystem of interest, can be adopted for the derivation of approximating formulas for non-boolean relations
/a/ Find all scenarios (event sequences) that can occur in the subsystem of interest
/b/ For each sequence determine the mean time to/between the occurrence of a specified coincidence of events and mean duration of the coincidence

/c/ Compute the resulting average reliability indices for the subsystem of interest (e.g. by weighting using the occurrence frequency of the individual sequences)

/d/ Compute such auxiliary event characteristics which provide for validity of the substitution delineated on Fig. 1 (or any other boolean representation, preserving the explicit expression of the input subtrees, A and B), e.g. by means of Eq. (1) to (3).

$$u_C = (u_S - u_{AB})/(u_A - u_{AB}) \qquad\qquad (2)$$

$$\frac{1}{t_C} = \frac{w_S - w_{AB}}{u_S - u_{AB}} - \frac{w_A - w_{AB}}{u_A - u_{AB}} \qquad\qquad (3)$$

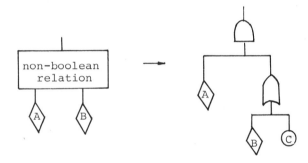

Figure 1: A possible representation of a non-boolean relation between loss of power supply via normal /A/ and reserve /B/ path. Event C is an auxiliary event, representing some additional /non-random/ coincidence of A and B events

References:

/1/ Fault Tree Handbook, NUREG-0492,1981
/2/ Vesely,W.E., A Time Dependent Methodology For Fault Tree Evaluation, Nuclear Engineering Design 13, 1970, p. 337-360
/3/ Schneeweiss,W.G., Computing Failure Frequency, MTBF and MTTR via Mixed Products of Availabilities and Unavailabilities
IEEE Transactions on Reliability, R-30, 1981, 4, p. 362-363
/4/ Pages, A - Gondran, M., Fiabilité des systémes, Collection de la Direction des Etudes et Recherches d Electricite de France, Paris, Eyrolles 1980

EXPERIENCES FROM PLANT SPECIFIC PRA FOR TVO NUCLEAR POWER PLANT

Mikko Kosonen, Risto Himanen, Tapio Saarenpää
(Industrial Power Company Ltd., SF-27160 Olkiluoto, Finland)

ABSTRACT

TVO nuclear power plant on the western coast of Finland is operated by
Industrial Power Company Ltd. The decision to begin PRA study for units I &
II was made by the utility in October 1984. The emphasis of the level 1 PRA
is put on human factors and detailed identification of dependencies. The
study is mainly performed by the utility due to educational purposes.

1 PLANT DESCRIPTION

TVO nuclear power plant is operated by Industrial Power Company Ltd. (TVO,
Teollisuuden Voima Oy). The plant is located in Olkiluoto on the western
coast of Finland and it consists of two identical BWR units, TVO I and TVO
II, supplied by ASEA-ATOM, Sweden. The net electrical power capacity of both
units is 710 MW. The first criticality of TVO I and TVO II was reached in
July 1978 and in October 1979, respectively.

The principle of using four half-capacity subsystems is applied in both
units to all important safety functions. Normal performance of two out of
four subsystems is sufficient to cope with possible incidents and accidents.
The four redundant circuits of safety-related systems are assigned to two
main groups, which are located in physically separated areas. Within these
areas a separation by distance or by means of barriers is used between the
redundant parts.

Station service power is supplied through three transformer units. Two of
them are connected to the 400 kV grid through the outdoor section of the
generator bus. The third one - startup transformer - is connected to an
independent 110 kV line. It acts as a back-up to the above mentioned two
plant transformers.

These two power sources are entirely independent. Divisioning into
safety-related and non-safety-related systems is in accordance with the
requirements on the process systems to be supplied with power.

The distribution network is divided into four separate sections, too. This
divisioning is consistently pursued for the power supply to motors, control
equipment, etc. throughout the power plant. Four diesel generators for each
unit provide onsite standby power supply, and battery-backed systems supply
no-break d.c. power and priority a.c. power across rotating converters.

2 BACKGROUND FOR THE TVO PLANT SPECIFIC PRA

The probabilistic analyses in TVO began during the licensing period when
safety systems were analyzed parallelly by the vendor Asea-Atom and by
Technical Research Centre of Finland.

After these system analyses the probabilistic approach was used in optimization for periodic tests according to Technical Specifications and preventive maintenance of safety systems during power operation /1, 2/. In the next step, the question of allowed outage times (AOTs) during plant operation was undertaken for systematic treatment. The first study was concerned with the diesel generators /3/. This analysis served mainly methodological development purposes. The insights obtained encouraged to continue with an analysis of the systems for residual heat removal /4/, which is still under work.

In 1980 it was decided to build a failure data system for the plant to aid both the maintenance work (planning) and reliability analysis. All failure reports since 1981 are included in the database (nowadays a total of 10000 reports). TVO's failure data system is also connected to the Swedish ATV system (Arbetsgrupp for Tillförlitlighet, Värmekraft)

The decision to begin a PRA study for TVO I and II was made by the TVO management in October 1984 - a couple of weeks before the Finnish authority STUK released the official requirement for PRA studies. The background for the decision included recognition of the following topics:

- Serious core damage of a nuclear power unit would be an economic catastrophe for any utility - even without significant environmental releases of radioactivity.

- Tens of PRAs have been made or are going on overall in the world including most Swedish NPPs similar to TVO I and II. Also it was anticipated that for a possible new plant a PRA study would be required.

- The most important factors of the core melt risk most often are not related to frontline safety systems and level 1 PRA is an efficient and systematic tool when mapping, evaluating and ranking different factors of the core melt risk.

The emphasis of the study was put on those areas that had been recognized as the most important in the earlier Swedish studies for similar multiredundant Asea-Atom units, namely human factors and detailed identification of dependencies. The utility has set several goals for the study, among them also the evaluation of the core melt frequency, and ranking of the most important core melt sequences. However, most important of the goals are related to mapping, ranking and optimization of improvements in system design, education, training, and procedures. Also the optimization of Technical Specifications is considered. The goal to increase the familiarization of the plant staff to the systems and safety features requires that the study is mainly performed by own personnel. The level 1 study has to be performed in such a way that its results are applicable both to higher level PRA studies and to cost-benefit analyses of the resulting modifications.

3 PROJECT ORGANIZATION AND MANAGEMENT

Both the requirement of the authority and the goal setting of the PRA required to perform the study mainly by the utility's own personnel. A pre-study during 1985 preceeded the PRA project including method education and training of the project staff by several consultants.

A significant effort in the project has been done in co-operation with consultants when developing practical applications of methods suitable for effective dependency identification, human error analysis and fault tree modelling.

The project is managed by a steering group (see Figure 1) consisting of the deputy managing director of the company and managers of several departments. The project work is done in five working groups. The composition of the working groups is flexible in order to allow the use of the best expertise within the company.

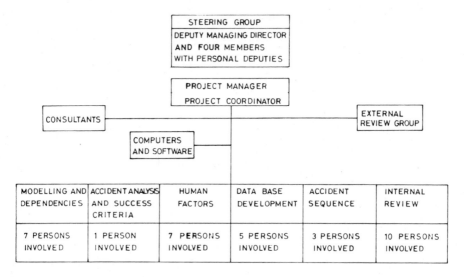

Figure 1: PRA project organization

4 METHODS OF ANALYSIS

Plant accident sequence analysis is based on thoroughly studied consequences of initiating event classes. These classes are determined by the plant's physical behaviour. All transient initiating events lead either to loss of feedwater or loss of condensor or loss of both feedwater and condensor. LOCA's are divided into three classes, namely large LOCA (steam line break greater than 300 cm^2), medium break LOCA (water line break above 25 cm^2 and steam pipe breaks between 150 and 300 cm^2) and small LOCA (a water line break between 2 and 25 cm^2, a steam line break between 2 and 150 cm^2, and all pressure vessel bottom leaks).

System success criteria are determined mainly by best estimate calculations (Swedish BISON and GOBLIN codes) and verifications. For the cases where they are not available the FSAR (Final Safety Analysis Report) criterias are used.

The PRA-study for a Swedish Asea-Atom type unit, Forsmark 3, showed that the CCFs (Common Cause Failures) cover a bulk of the core melt frequency. This is expected from plants having multiredundant, separated safety systems. This in mind the main resources in systems analysis is concentrated on the explicit modelling of automatic control signals and electric power supplies.

The Swedish SUPERTREE code /5/ with preprogrammed component subtrees is used in fault tree modelling. All designed functional dependencies like cooling, signals, and power supply on busbar level are referred to explicitly in the component subtree (see Figure 2). This facilitates the checking of fault tree models by persons who are not familiar with reliability analysis but who do know the plant well. The FMEA-form (Failure Mode and Effect Analysis) is an essential part of systems analysis and fault tree documentation. A direct access from SUPERTREE to FMEA would be useful, but because of restrictions in screen size it is not implemented in the code.

Reactor protection system was analyzed with success logic block diagrams, because it was recognized in a very early stage that fault tree models become too complicated for a pure signal system. For quantification the Finnish RELVEC code was used /6/.

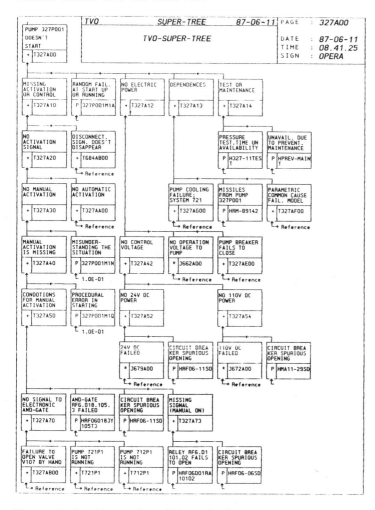

Figure 2: A subtree of auxiliary feedwater pump

The overall framework for the TVO Human Reliability Analysis Task is SHARP /11/. The main emphasis is put on Human Interaction (HI) types 1 (i.e. test and maintenance activities), 3 (accident termination by following procedures) and 5 (restoring initially unavailable equipment during accident sequences). The type 2 HIs (those resulting in initiating events) are not addressed explicitly, but the empirical initiating event data is assumed to include them. The type 4 (those that aggravate the accident) HIs were considered to be beyond the scope of the TVO PRA study.

The assessment of T & M —induced unavailability includes first of all the system downtime that performance of tests and preventive maintenance are causing. Besides that the restoration errors after completion of T & M activities are analyzed. For this purpose all the regular T & M activities causing components to be changed from their normal states, are identified. Also, the possible ways (and their completeness) of revealing the errors are considered. Combining these two aspects the systems analysts base their quantification on slightly modified procedures of "Shortened Version of THERP/Handbook" /11/.

Another broad class of type 1 HIs includes the various calibration errors. Identification and initial screening of these are achieved by structured sessions involving personnel familiar with the operation and maintenance of the equipment. Any other T & M related HIs possibly resulting in dependent errors in redundant trains are also searched for. The quantification of the HIs that survive the screening is performed with the Multiple-Sequential Failure (MSF) model /12/.

For the HIs during accident sequences (types 3 and 5, per SHARP) a two-step approach is adopted: first an initial screening is achieved by applying the "Shortened Version of THERP" approach /13/ and then for the selected HIs a final quantification is performed by a combined use of the Human Cognitive Reliability (HCR) correlation /14/ and the Human Reliability Handbook /15/.

In the TVO I/II PRA a thorough mapping of the dependency factors is performed. All dependencies through auxiliary systems, and the most significant other dependencies (maintenance, room, etc.) are modelled explicitly in system fault trees.

The analysis of dependencies has been planned in co-operation with Avaplan Oy and it is divided into seven main objectives: (1) All system-related dependencies are modelled in very detailled system fault trees. (2) Human-related dependencies due to erraneous, incorrect or missing maintenance are mapped with the maintenance personnel. The quantification is based on the Multiple-Sequential Failure model /13/. (3) Environment-related dependencies (floodings, fires, missiles, radiation, incorrect temperature) are mapped by walking through the rooms having vital or active components of safety-related systems or their auxiliaries including cables. They are quantified using normal fault-tree technique. The mapping form is in Figure 3. (4) Typical dependencies in auxiliary power supply systems are mapped applying Hazards and Operability study. (5) Plant protection system is talked through with emphasis on latent failures and completeness of tests. (6) Common cause initiators are not mapped as a specific task, but they are documented in connection with all phases of the study. (7) Engineering judgement together with several common cause studies /7, 8, 9, 10/ is used when evaluating the remaining implicitly modelled common cause probabilities. Although quite a lot of dependencies are explicitly modelled, there is no basis to decrease the parameters of this class dependencies.

```
┌─────────────────────────────────────────────┬──────────────┬──────────────┐
│ PRA TVO I/II                                 │ ROOM:        │ SIGN:        │
│ MAPPING OF ROOM RELATED DEPENDENCIES         │              │ DATE:        │
└─────────────────────────────────────────────┴──────────────┴──────────────┘
```

1. SENSORS   —press —temp   —leak   —fire   —rad   —other————————

2. LEAKAGES   —alarm   —switch   —circuit————————

leaking media	from room/system	effect on system/subsection	notes	degree of effect

3. FIRES Burnable material   type:————————————————
             amount:—lot   —significant   —small
          Distinquishing system
                    —CO2   —sprinkler   —none   —other————————
          effect   degree
          on system/——> [   ]   of——> [   ]
          subsection   effect

4. MISSILES (Explosions, hits, vibration, etc mechanical common cause)

cause	effect on system/subsection	notes	degree of effect

5. TEMPERATURE—alarm   —switch —circuit———————— Vent. system————————
                                                 Coolins syst————————

high/ low	cause	effect on system/subsection	notes	degree of effect

6. HUMIDITY—   MOISTURE—   IMPURITIES—   ELECTRIC PHENOMENA—

cause	effect on system/subsection	notes	degree of effect

7. RADIATION   zone classification: —green   —orange —red

cause	effect on system/subsection	notes	degree of effect

Figure 3: The mapping form for room related dependencies

5 SUMMARY

Level 1 PRA-study for TVO units I and II is being performed mainly by
utility's own personnel and it will be finished by the end of 1987. Main
goals of the study are identification and ranking of qualitative findings,
and educational purposes. The emphasis of the study is put on the areas
recognized as most important in the earlier PRA-studies for similar plants,
i.e. human reliability and dependencies.

Although only the qualitative part of the PRA is finished, the experiences
of such an intensive risk study are purely positive. Knowledge of the plant
safety features of those involved in the project has significantly
increased. In connection with the PRA the determination of realistic success
criteria has given important knowledge of the real capability of safety
systems. The essential problem related to the performance of the project is
the optimistic original planning of the resources available. On the other
hand, most of the findings are on the level of detailness not possible to
study by any consultant who is not initially familiar with the plant.

6 REFERENCES

/1/ Lehtinen E., Mankamo T. & Pulkkinen U., Optimum test interval of closing valves. Nucl. Eng. Dec 81 (1984) p.99-104.

/2/ Heinonen R. & Piirto A., Preventive maintenance of safety systems during normal operation of TVO's nuclear power plant. International symposium on Advantages in Nuclear Power Plant Availability, Maintainability and Operation, Munich May 20-23, 1985. proceedings IAEA, Vienna 1985

/3/ Mankamo T., Perhonen H., Pulkkinen U., Kosonen M. and Vanhala J., Experience from use of PRA methods in the re-evaluation of technical specification. ANS/ENS Topical Meeting on Probabilistic Safety Methods and Applications, February 24 - March 1, 1985, San Francisco

/4/ Kosonen, M., Saarenpää, T., Vanhala, J. & Mankamo, T., Operational Alternatives in Failure Situations, Application to residual heat removal system. SRE-symposium, Otaniemi October 14-16, 1986, Finland.

/5/ Ericsson, G., Knochenhauer, M. & Mills, R., Efficient fault tree handling -- The Asea-Atom Approach, ANS/ENS Topical Meeting ..., February 24 - March 1, 1985, San Francisco

/6/ Niemelä, I., Plant and Control System Reliability and Risk Model. 5th EuReDatA Conference, Heidelberg, April 9-11, 1986, Germany.

/7/ Hirschberg, S. & Pulkkinen, U., Common Cause Failure Data: Experience from Diesel Generator Studies. Nuclear safety, 26(1985)3.

/8/ Atwood, C. L., Common Cause Fault Rates for Diesel Generators, NUREG/CR-2098 (EG & G Idaho Inc. Report EA-5289), February 1983.

/9/ Fleming, K. N. & Mosleh, A., Classification and analysis of reactor operating experience involving dependent events. EPRI-NP3967, 1985.

/10/ Bongarts, Meessen & Kröger, Nutzung ausländischer Betriebserfahrungen zur Ableitung von Zuverlässigkeitskenngrössen - insbesondere für abhängige Ausfälle. Beitrag zur Phase B der DRS. KFA-ISF-IB-1/85, KFA Jülich.

/11/ Hannaman, G. W. & Spurgin, A. J., Systematic Human Action Reliability Procedure (SHARP), NUS Corporation, 1984. EPRI NP-3583.

/12/ Swain, A. D., Accident Sequence Evaluation Program Human Reliability Analysis Procedure, U.S. Nuclear Regulatory Commission, 1978. NUREG/CR-4772.

/13/ Samanta, P. K., O'Brien, J. N. & Morrison, H. W., Multiple-Sequential Failure model: Evaluation of and procedures for human error dependency, U. S. Nuclear Regulatory Commission, 1985. NUREG/CR-3837.

/14/ Hannaman, G. W., Spurgin, A. J. & Lukic, Y. D., Human Cognitive Reliability analysis for PRA analysis, NUS Corporation, 1984. NUS-4531.

/15/ Swain, A. D. & Guttman, H. E., Handbook of Human Reliability Analysis with emphasis on nuclear power plant applications, U.S. Nuclear Regulatory Commission, 1983. NUREG/CR-1278.

EXPERIENCE FROM PERFORMING PREOPERATIONAL PSA FOR AN NPP OF

THE VVER-440 TYPE IN POLAND

Mieczysław Borysiewicz, Maciej Kulig
  Institute of Atomic Energy, Świerk-Otwock, Poland

Abstract

The paper concerns an experience being gained from performing
Probabilistic Safety Analysis of Level 1 for the Żarnowiec NPP,
a two units VVER-440 station presently at the early stage of construction. The general idea for structuring the analysis is outlined. The study objectives, scope, organization and current
development are also reported.

1   Scope and Objectives of the PSA Project

In the fall of 1985 a PSA project for the Żarnowiec NPP was formulated. It met an assistance requirement under the IAEA Interregional Project on PSA, initiated also in 1985. Such an arrangement has impacted significantly the PSA study development in
Poland. In particular, the IAEA technical advice on task assignment, prioritatization and overall Project management has been
followed. Currently, the Project is being developed in the framework of the National Programme for Research and Development (NPRD)
on Nuclear Safety, that will insure basic financial resources for
such an activity.

The current study scope corresponds to the Level 1 PSA. It will
be developed, in the long term, into full scope risk assessment
analysis. The ultimate goal of the study is development of a
living PSA for NPP with VVER type reactors that would take form
of modular system of codes and data files for providing an assistance to the Regulatory Body, Designer and Utility to solve current safety and plant operation issues. The system would be continuously updated to follow plant specific documentation upgrading in plant design phase , data collecting and possible operation evaluation feedback to system configuration and operation
procedures during plant operation phase . Such a use of PSA
techniques is found to be particularly suitable for Poland where
the first NPP is at early stage of construction. The plant specific objectives are related to comperative studies for alternate
maintenance, surveillance, operating and start-up procedures and
possible design change. The outcomes of the Project finds immediate "on line" application in developing computer aids for the
plant operational staff for system status monitoring, technical
specification compliance estimation and defining risk oriented
optimal strategy of plant operation. System of codes for such
purposes is being developed in the framework of another NPRD on

methods ensuring safe plant operation. Another immediate use of
the Project activities is the training of the plant personel and
preparation of manuals for such training by the Project personel.

2   Staffing and Management

The Project involves all principal national organizations in the
field, namely:
* Central Laboratory of Radiation Protection, Warsaw, (Regulatory
  body)
* Institute of Atomic Energy (IAE), Świerk, (Project Technical Co-
  ordinator) and Institute of Power Systems and Automation, Wrocław
* NPP Żarnowiec (Utility)
* Energoprojekt (Architect-Endineer, Designer), Warsaw and Gdańsk
* Technical Universities from Gdańsk and Poznań.

The institutions participating in the PSA Project have different
structures and specific responsibilities. Therefore, for flexible
integration of the PSA teams the PSA Coordination Group has been
set up. The Group consists of group leaders from the participating
organizations responsible for specific task development. The technical overall management of the Project is done at the IAE. A desirable overall upgrading of the Project staff PSA capabilities has
been achived through participating in the IAEA training courses,
workshops and technical committee meetings on the PSA subjects. The
valuable IAEA assistance in acquiring recent selected PSA materials
should be also notified.

3   Metodology

There is a number of studies on PSA related problems (selected system reliability analysis, selected accident sequences delineation,
human reliability) that have been recently completed or being developed by the importers of VVER systems [1-2]. However, no PSA Level
1 study for a VVER system plant has been completed. Only recently
plans of joint extensive activity of CMEA countries for full scope
PSA studies of VVERs, coordinated by institution in USSR has been
reported. Thus, at the moment the PSA activities were initiated in
Poland the detail methodological guidance for the PSA Project had
to be concluded from selected PSA studies of PWRs of other design
and from a number of procedure guides, that synthetize the past experience of probabilistic studies to provide generic guidelines. As
the principal base study the IREP ANO-1 study [3] was selected. A
system by system comparison was done between ANO-1 and the Żarnowiec NPP in order to enforce the application of this base document
and in order to elaborate important differences between the two
NPPs which have to be considered when applying the document. It has
provided together with IREP Procedure Guide [4] detailed guidance
and it may give a sound base for the results of the study as well.
Additional materials, particulary German Risk Study [5] , Insight
into PRA Methodologies [7] , Catalog of Dominant Sequences Information and PRA Procedure Guide [6] have been serving as base documents for finding rationals for detail of methodological approach
and for relevance and officiency of a particular method in develop-

ing probabilistic model for a NPP of a given design.

4 Plant Familiarization

The preliminary Safety Analysis Report (PSAR) and available plant
system descriptions and drawings provided the information base for
the familiarization task. Several remarks should be made that bia-
se findings of this task:
* Details of Reactor Protection System (RPS), Engineered Safety
  Feature Actuation System (ESFAS) and Plant Balance Control System (PBCS) have not been completely fixed. There are general
  functional and design characteristics available, including parameter settings. However, they may change in the course of design
  development.
* Plant response to some of PSA relevant events are not sufficiently analyzed in licensing and other available documents e.g.:
  - required response of Emergency Feedwater System (E F S) and
    Decay Heet Removal System (DHRS) for mitigating small LOCAs
  - response of High Pressure Injection System (HPIS) and Chemical
    Volume Control and Water Make-up System (CVCMS) to the plant
    transients
* More realistic analysis of physical processes accounting for Engineered Safety Features feedback on accident progression should
  support present findings derived by engineering judgement, analyst intuition and an extrapolation from the licensing materials
  and other design PSA studies.
It is not expected that the future task iteration, accounting for
the above conclusions, will change dramatically the task results.
However, it may change some of functional dependencies displayed
in the event trees and impact on detailed fault tree structure.

4.1 Plant Design

The Żarnowiec NPP is a two units of 440 MWe VVER each, located on
Lake Żarnowiec near Gdańsk. The plant is going to enter commercial
operation in 1991. The design of the reactor coolant system is typical of VVER-440 plants currently in operation. There are 6 horizontal steam generators and 6 reactor coolant pump loops. The secondary side differs from the standard design by implementing one
turbine-generator unit.The safety systems designs is typical of
NPP with VVER-440 type 213. The safety envelope containment is
composed of hermitized compartments connected with a building that
locates a passive Reactor Building Pressure Suppression System
(RBPSS) designed to mitigate consequences of LBLOCAs, in conjunction with operation of the three train   Reactor Building Spray
System (RBSS). RBSS is basic system for performing Containment
Overpressure Protection (COP) and Radioactivity Removal (RR) functions for other LOCAs and plant transients.

Basically, Emergency Core Cooling during the injection phase (ECCI)
is accomplished by 3 train High Pressure Injection System (HPIS),
3 train Low Pressure Injection System (LPIS) and 4 train Core
Flood System (CFS). The Emergency Feedwater System - EFS (2 train
Auxiliary Feedwater Pump System - AFPS or 3 train Emergency Feedwater Pump System - EFPS, and 6 steam generator safety relief

valves and 6 pressure reduction station dumping steam to atmosphere) and Pressurizer 1 or 2 Safety Relief Valves (SRV) may operate during small break LOCAs to lower RCS pressure for effective
water injection by HPIS.

The long term recirculation phase of ECC begins when either high
pressure pumps are realigned to take suction from the containment
sump (HPRS) or when low pressure pumps are connected to this sump
(LPRS) or to RCS (Decay Heat Removal System - DHRS). For very small
LOCAs when DHRS can be implemented, decay heat removal can be also
provided by the secondary side Heat Removal Pump System - HRPS
(3 pumps, 2 trains).

There are three independent trains of HPRS, LPRS. The heat exchangers are common for DHRS, HPRS, LPRS and RBSR (recirculation configuration of RBSS).

For LOCAs and transients the fast shutdown of the reactor is performed by the Reactor Protection System (RPS) inserting into the
core 6 groups of control rod assemblies. Minor or slow reactivity
changes can be compensated by Chemical Volume Control and Water
Make-up System (CVCMS). This system is normally isolated given signal for diesel generators start up, that actuates ECCS, SWS, RBSI,
EFS and other Essential Power Supply (EPS) systems. The RPS must
operate to prevent a severe RCS overpressure transient. If the RPS
fails and RCS survive (it is still an unresolved issue) reactor
subcriticality can be achieved by injecting borated water into RCS
by HPIS.

Decay heat removal from RCS is accomplished normally by delivering
feedwater to the steam generators from the Power Conversion System
(PCS) boiling off the water to the turbine condenser or to the
technological condensers. One can distinguish the steam and water
phases of the secondary side heat removal process. During the steam
phase the required PCS function is performed by one of the systems:
* Turbine Condenser Pressure Reduction Station System - TCRSS (2
  pressure reduction stations, 5 main feedwater pumps AFPS, turbine
  condenser, deareator)
* Heat Removal Pressure Reduction Station System - HRRSS (2 pressure reduction station, 2 technological condensers, AFPS, deareator).
Given loss of PCS functions, the feedwater is delivered to the steam
generators by AFPS/EFPS. If the PCS and EFS are unavailable decay
heat removal may be accomplished via a "feed and bleed" operation
by injecting water to RCS by HPIS and boiloff of the coolant into
the containment through the SRVs.

If RPS immedietely scrams the reactor and core cooling via the secondary side is not delayed then it may be expected that the surge
capacity of the RCS overpressure protection by opening SRVs is not
demanded. In other cases the operability of one or both of SRVs
would be required. The SRVs that open to respond a transient must
all reclose to ensure the integrity of RCS. Otherwise the transient
would result in a small LOCA. Success of SRVs to prevent a small
LOCA does not eliminate a potential for slowly loosing RCS inventory
via smaller leaks and an eventual core uncovery within hours. The

function of RCS inventory is provided by operability of CVCMS or HPIS.

4.2 Initiating Events

With the exception of the loss of offsite power case only internal initiating events (IEs) are considered. Departing from generic lists of these events (e.g. [8]) a review of their applicability to the Żarnowiec NPP was made based on engineering judgement, PSAR and the plant system descriptions. Failures of normally operating support system components may cause reactor shut down and degrade safety systems. To identify such failures, dependencies between front line and support systems and among support systems were analyzed. The former are synthezed in Table 1.

	Offsite Power	EPS	ESFAS	Service Water System	High Pressure Air System	Ventilation and Air Conditioning System	Intermediate Cooling System
RPS							
CVCMS	x			x	x	x	
HPS		x	x	x	x	x	x
LPS		x	x	x	x	x	x
CFS							
RBSS		x	x	x		x	
RBPSS						x	
TCPRSS	x			x		x	
HRPRSS	x	x		x		x	
EFPS		x	x			x	
AFPS	x	x	x			x	
SRV							

Table 1: Żarnowiec Front Line vs. Support Systems Dependencies

Unavailability of sufficiently detail documentation of some of the support systems invalidated performance of FMEA on these systems. Therefore the obtained results concerning IEs must be updated in future.

A Master Logic Diagram technique was used to develop a hierarchical structure of functional grouping for selected set of IEs. With the purpose of systemic event tree development the groups were condensed into few macrogroups with a similar response of the plant. Five main macrogroups of LOCA were identified depending on front line systems response. These macrogroups described in approximate break size range are: breaks $<$ 4cmD (I), 4cmD-10cmD (II), 10cmD-25cmD (III), 25cmD-35cmD (IV) and breaks $>$ 35cmD (V). The 1-st LOCA range was divided into two subclasses Ia and Ib account-

ing for different possible accomplishment of core cooling by EFS,
DHRS, HPIS and HPRS depending on a break size and these systems capabilities. Precise lower and upper bounds for Ia and Ib break size
range require further investigations. The system success criteria
for Ia, Ib and II-V LOCA macrogroups are presented in Table 2. An-
ticipating low probability of failure of series valves arrangements
on the low pressure injection lines penetrating the boundary of the
hermitized compartments and on the low pressure suction line from
the RCS the interface type LOCA was not considered to important
contribution to risk.

With respect to different plant response that may differentiate
systemic event tree structure, transient IEs was grouped into:
• transient IEs which do not effect the front line systems significantly
• IEs interupting PCS normal mode decay heat removal capabilities
• loss of Service Water System.
The success criteria for systems responding to transients are
synthetized in Table 3.

LOCA size	RS	Injection			Recirculation		
		ECC	COP	RR	ECC	COP	RR
Ia	A	$(C1 \cdot G1)+(C1 \cdot B2)$	F2	F2	C3+B3+B4	F3	F3
Ib	↑	$(C2 \cdot G1)+(C1 \cdot B2)$	↑	↑	C3	↑	↑
II	↓	C1			C3		
III	↓	C1·D1	↓		D2		
IV	−	D1·E1	↓		D2		
V	−	D1·E2	F1·F2	↓	D2	↓	↓

Table 2: LOCA Success Criteria

RS	Core Cooling	RCS Overpressure Protection	RCS Integrity	RCS Inventory Make-up	COP	RR
A	B1+B2+(C1·G1)	G1	G1ʹ	H+C1	F2	F2
$\bar{A}$	$(B1 \cdot C1 \cdot G2)+$ $+(B2 \cdot C1 \cdot G2)$	G2	G2ʹ	C1	F2	F2

Table 3: Transient Success Criteria

Symbol description for Table 2 and 3
+ = or, • = and, A = 6 groups of control rod assemblies inserted
into the core with possibly one with the highest reactivity worth,
stuck outside the core, $\bar{A}$ = RPS failure to achieve Reactor Subcriticality, B1 = TCPRS or 1/2 HRPRS, B2 = 1/3 EFPS or 1/2 AFPS,
B3 = 1/3 DHRS, B4 = 1/3 HRPS, C1 = 1/3 HPIS, C2 = 2/3 HPIS, C3 =
1/3 HPRS, D1 = 1/3 LPIS, D2 = 1/3 LPRS, E1 = 1/4 CFS, E2 = 2/4 CFS
F1 = RBPSS, F2 = RBSI, F3 = RBSR, G1 = 1/2 SRV open, G1ʹ = 1/2 SRV

close after opening, G2 = 2/2 SRV open, G2´= 2/2 SRV close after
opening, H = CVCMS if not isolated by EFAS.

5   Event Tree Development and Fault Tree Design

Two functional event trees have been developed for LOCAs and transients by:
(1) making use of:
  • plant LOCA functions: Reactor Subcriticality, Emergency Core
    Cooling, Containment Overpressure Protection (COP) and Radio-
    activity Removal,during the injection phase and similiar func-
    tion during the recirculation phase,
  • plant transient functions: RS, COP, RR, RCS Overpressure Pro-
    tection, RCS Integrity and RCS Inventory Make-up,
(2) placing the functions of the event tree headings in the approxi-
    mate chronological order they will be performed to respond an IE
(3) incorporating the functional dependences into the tree structure
    by removing success failure decision branches at appropriate
    places in the tree.

Six LOCA and two transient systemic event trees have been developed.
They have been a direct consequence of the functional event trees
and the system success criteria given in Tables 2 and 3. The headings of the system event trees correspond only to front line system
events (see the note appended to Tables 2 and 3 for precise definition of these events). Neither support systems nor operator actions
are explicitly depicted in these trees.

The information needed for system fault tree development has been
assimilated from available plant documentation. To large extent,
this work has been performed by Energoprojekt - Gdańsk being involved in preparation of the technical plant design documentation.
To insure a level of information adequate for fault tree development
very detailed guidelines have been prepared at the IAE. They concern
both of the scope and format of information documentation and system
modeling recommended practices. In particular, it is emphasized to
apply a methodology that insures a hierarchical level structure of
fault trees with the intermediate events at each level corresponding
to superelements that can be developed (if sufficient information
are available) into finer resolution events or which can be assigned
a meaningful value of occurence probability otherwise. The top level
of the tree is developed to the extent necessary to portray all the
superelements (of the lowest resolution) whose failure is sufficient
to fail the system for the given application. Local events and possible support system interfaces are analyzed within each superele-
ment. This approach facilitates permanent accounting for changing
details of instrumentation, control, operator action affecting a system and other information that may alter with system design, and
operational and emergency procedures development. Making use of the
above described methodology the groups participating in the PSA Project are developing front line system fault trees for each event
tree failure definition. Support system fault trees is being developed only for all the interfaces identified by the front line systems and for the interfaces with the other relevant support systems.

For fault tree and accident sequence quantification both of in-house developed and adapted codes (FTAP2, IMPORTANCE, SETS and FRANTIC II) are utilized. The microcomputer work stations are also used for fault tree designing, data handling and input preparation for main frame computer codes.

Since there is actually no NPP in operation in Poland, the PSA team has made an investigation concerning reliability data for similar components and subsystems in the conventional, non-nuclear industry in Poland. Only a few data could be found and the available data turned out to be not applicable because the characteristics of the components or the operational conditions were too different. Nevertheless a computerized data-base system is being set up in order to systematically collect generic and plant specific data. This work is complemented by reviewing available sources of data used for PSA studies. Reliability data has been tabulated. A hierarchical structure for this data base has been developed. The data is structured by major component type headings, subclasses and failure modes. A mean value, variance, median and error factor, and remarks concerning data source, where appropriate are provided for each failure mode. Initiating events occurence rates are also included.

6   Conclusion

The current Project development suffers from many defficiencies induced by lacking sufficiently complete materials concerning plant design and operational procedures. No PSA study of a reference plant available is also an important factor that impacts on the Project. However, the structuring of PSA methods, that have been implemented, provides means for easy assimilation of possible changes and/or development of plant data, so that the Project may provide a matured probabilistic model before the plant start up. It is expected that the Project intermediate results will be reviewed by the IAEA expects and the Project technical capabilities enhanced by the planned CMEA cooperation in this field.

References

1. Collection of papers on national PSA and System Reliability Analysis programmes in Bulgaria, CSSR, GDR, Hungary and Poland, Proc., IAEA Workshop on Advances in Reliability Analysis and PSA, Budapest, 7-11 October 1985.
2. R.Virolainen, S.Vuori, Finnish Experiences in the Risk Assessment and Reliability Analysis of NPPs, ibidem.
3. Interim Reliability Evaluation Program Analysis of the Arkansas Nuclear One-Unit 1 NPP, NUREG/CR-2787.
4. IREP Procedure Guide.
5. GRS, Deutsche Risikostudie Kernkraftwerke, Verlag TUV Rheiland, 1981.
6. PRA Procedure Guide, NUREG/CR-2300 Vol. 1.
7. Insights into PRA Methodologies, NUREG CR-3852.
8. ATWS: A Reappraisal - Part II, Frequency of Anticipated Transients, EPRI NP-801.

GERMAN RISK STUDY, PHASE B
RESULTS OF THE EVENT TREE AND FAULT TREE ANALYSES

H. Hoertner
(Gesellschaft fuer Reaktorsicherheit (GRS) mbH,
Forschungsgelaende, D-8046 Garching, Federal Republic of Germany)

Abstract

This paper deals with the most important results of the level 1 analysis performed
in Phase B of the German Risk Study and with the insights it provided. The
question is raised, to what extent the results of risk analyses can be verified
against available operating experience. In this respect the results of the German
Risk Study will be compared with the estimates of the German Precursor Study.
Finally, the results of the German investigations are briefly compared with the
results of recent U.S. risk analyses.

1. Results and Insights from the German Risk Study

Table 1 shows the most important results of the event tree and fault tree analyses
performed in Phase A [1] and Phase B [2] of the German Risk Study. The reference
plant for these anayses is the Biblis nuclear power plant, Unit B, which has a KWU
pressurized water reactor and a gross electrical output of 1300 MW.

Initiating Event	Phase A [$^1/a$]	Phase B [$^1/a$]
Small leak in a reactor coolant loop	$5.7 \cdot 10^{-5}$	$3 \cdot 10^{-6}$
Small leak at the pressurizer during loss of preferred power	$7 \cdot 10^{-6}$	ε
Small leak at the pressurizer during other anticipated transients	$2 \cdot 10^{-6}$	$3 \cdot 10^{-6}$
Loss of preferred power	$1.3 \cdot 10^{-5}$	$2 \cdot 10^{-7}$
Loss of main feedwater	$3 \cdot 10^{-6}$	$3 \cdot 10^{-6}$
Loss of main heat sink (without loss of main feedwater)	ε	$1 \cdot 10^{-6}$
Large and medium leak in a main steam line	- [1]	$8.5 \cdot 10^{-6}$
Small leak at the pressurizer during a leak in a main steam line	- [1]	$7.5 \cdot 10^{-6}$

ε means negligible
1) according to WASH-1400 not quantified

Table 1: German Risk Study, Frequencies of Event Sequences not
Successfully Coped With

The frequencies of event sequences not successfully coped with by the design basis
safety systems are listed for various initiating events. If, in the case of a

failure of these safety systems, no further measures can be taken which will still prevent a core melt, then the frequencies indicated correspond to core melt frequencies caused by the initiating events in question.

For the frequencies assessed in Phase A, a core melt was assumed to have occurred if the minimal requirements for the safety systems as determined on the basis of the pessimistic assumptions in the licensing procedure could not be met. System modifications in the reference plant which were performed after the completion of Phase A as well as the consideration of realistic minimal requirements for the design basis safety systems led to lower frequencies in Phase B of the study.

In Phase A, the largest contribution to core melt frequency was the uncontrolled "small leak in a reactor coolant loop". Meanwhile, as a result of the installation of a semi-automatic cooldown with 100 K/h, it has been possible to reduce this contribution by about one order of magnitude to approximately 3×10^{-6}/a.

The second largest contribution in Phase A was the uncontrolled "loss of preferred power" (emergency power case). In Phase B, the corresponding frequency is 2×10^{-7}/a, i.e., it is lower by almost two orders of magnitude and thus of minor significance. This improvement is mainly due to the installation of a standby grid connection and the possibility of switching back the 10 kV emergency busbars to the 10 kV busbars of the in-house power supply, after return of power to the in-house power supply; this switching back can also now be performed in the case of a failure of the emergency power diesel generators.

Another important contribution to core melt frequency was in Phase A the "small leak at the pressurizer during a loss of preferred power". In Phase B, this contribution could be neglected. During a "loss of preferred power" there will be an immediate and automatic partial cooldown of the plant, preventing a demand of the pressurizer relief valves. Furthermore, much longer dry-out times for the steam generators were evaluated on the basis of realistic values for the residual heat. Consequently, a demand of the pressurizer relief valves needs no longer be expected in case of a "loss of preferred power".

The most important system modifications with respect to the results are:

-   the installation of a semi-automatic system for the controlled cooldown with 100 K/h in the case of a "small leak";

-   automatic partial cooldown in the case of a "loss of the main heat sink";

-   the control of the position of the different valves of the pressurizer relief system by means of various additional isolating signals;

-   the improvements in the main steam relief station, i.e. installation of
    •   15 % safety valves which can be blocked,
    •   quick-closing main steam isolation valves (disc-type) instead of gate-valves;

-   the installation of a standby grid connection;

-   the possibility of switching back the 10 kV emergency busbars to the 10 kV busbars of the in-house power supply, in the case of the failure of the emergency power diesel generators.

In addition to the initiating events dealt with in Phase A, analyses have been made in Phase B regarding further initiating events, in particular:

- large and medium-sized leaks in a main steam line, and

- leaks in steam generator heating tubes.

At the generally improved level of safety achieved with the system modifications, a dominant contribution has been assessed for "leaks in a main steam line". This contribution of nearly 10^{-5}/a results mainly from leaks inside the steel containment.

A similar contribution has been determined for an uncontrolled "small leak at the pressurizer during leak in a main steam line". However, this contribution is drastically reduced when the monitoring of process variables for the activation of the pressurizer relief valves will be modified to be able to withstand LOCA conditions. This system change will be performed in summer 1987.

The investigations with regard to "leaks in steam generator heating tubes" are not yet completed. Important contributions are to be expected here if, after the failure of the auxiliary spray system of the pressurizer, the activation criteria for high-pressure safety injection are fulfilled and as a consequence the injection of the defective steam generator cannot be isolated on the secondary side. In this case, however, there are still alternative measures which can be taken by manual intervention of the operating personnel.

An important aspect of Phase B refers to the evaluation of realistic minimal requirements for the safety systems. Minimal requirements on the basis of best-estimate investigations were evaluated for the whole spectrum of "leaks in a reactor coolant loop". Table 2 contains these minimal requirements for emergency core cooling and residual heat removal [3].

Leak cross section (cm²)	System functions required					
	High pressure injections	Accumulator injections	Low pressure injections	Low pressure recirculations	Admissible delay of secondary side cooldown (min)	Feedwater supplies
> 500	−	−	1	1	∞	−
200–500	1	−	1	1	∞	−
300–500	−	2	1	1	∞	−
80–200	3 or 4	−	2	2	∞	−
	2	−	1	1	60	1
	1	−	1	1	30	main
50–80	2	−	1	1	60	feedwater
	1	3	1	1	60	supply
	1	−	1	1	30	or
25–50	2	−	1	1	90	2
	1	−	1	1	60	aux. / emerg.
2–25	1	−	1	1	> 120	feedwater
	−	−	1	1	30	supplies

large leak
medium leak
small leak

Table 2: Minimal Requirements for the System Functions for Emergency Core Cooling and Residual Heat Removal in the Case of Leaks in a Reactor Coolant Loop

If a cooldown of the plant will be started within 30 minutes after a LOCA occurred, 1-out-of-4 HP and 1-out-of-4 LP injections are sufficient to cope with the LOCA for the whole leak spectrum. In the case of large leaks (> 500 cm²), no HP injection is necessary. This also applies in the case of small leaks (< 25 cm²) if the cooldown is initiated within 30 minutes.

The accumulator injections serve for rapid refilling of the reactor pressure vessel in the case of large and medium leaks. However, only for medium leaks (300 - 500 cm^2) do they represent a redundancy to the HP injections in order to prevent a core meltdown.

For leaks via stuck-open pressurizer valves, principally the same minimal requirements apply as for leaks in a reactor coolant loop. But, for a valve cross section of about 40 cm^2 and availiability of 1 HP injection, there exists an admissible delay of at least 2 hours for the initiation of a 100 K/h cooldown.

On the whole, the table shows that substantially fewer system trains are sufficient to cope with a LOCA than the 2-out-of-4 injections which were generally assumed in the investigations for Phase A.

Significant contributions to core melt frequency were only found for leaks smaller than 50 cm^2. The frequencies of larger leak cross sections were considerably overestimated in Phase A. In Phase B very low occurrence frequencies have been assessed for these leaks, i.e. they are of minor importance.

According to the results of Phase B, the frequency of event sequences not sufficiently coped with by the design basis safety systems amount in total to about 3×10^{-5}/a. Event sequences resulting from transients and from small leaks yield approximately the same contributions to this value.

The frequency of transients not sufficiently coped with is mainly determined by failure of heat removal via the steam generators, i.e. the loss of the feedwater supply by the 3 main feedwater pumps as well as by the 6 auxiliary feedwater and emergency feedwater pumps, respectively.

Failures of the control signals or of the circuit breakers which may lead to a failure of the auxiliary feedwater supply, will in many cases be corrected within the available time frame. Furthermore, a redundant and diverse measure of the secondary heat removal is the complete secondary pressure relief and an injection via the fire protection system. The corresponding accident management measures could be performed during the initial period of slow changes in the conditions of the primary system, which are characteristic for these event sequences.

Figure 1 shows the histories for pressure and water inventory in the primary system for the transient "loss of the main feedwater" if the steam generators are not supplied with auxiliary feedwater and via the fire protection system [3]. In the case of this initiating event the steam generators will have dried out relatively quickly, i.e. after approximately 35 min. In the case of other anti-cipated transients, e.g. "loss of main heat sink" or "loss of preferred power", a dry-out of the steam generators occurs after approximately 70 min.

After the dry-out of the steam generators, the primary circuit heats up. The increase of the primary pressure will be limited by the pressurizer relief valves (PORVs). About 70 min after the occurrence of the initiating event "loss of main feedwater" the collapsed water level drops to the core zone, if a feedwater supply of the steam generators has not been established by this time. For the other likely transients the available time period will be about 120 min.

In the case of no feedwater supply of the steam generators, a core meltdown can still be prevented by means of emergency measures taken on the primary side, i.e. by "bleed and feed". For this purpose, the pressure in the reactor coolant system must be reduced before the water level drops to the core zone, so that the HP safety injection pumps with a design head of 110 bars can supply coolant from the borated water storage tanks to the reactor pressure vessel. This can be achieved by opening of one or both of the pressurizer relief valves.

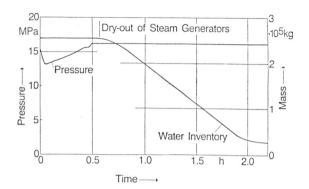

Figure 1: Loss of Main Feedwater and Loss of Aux. Feedwater Supply.
         Pressure and Water Inventory in the Reactor Coolant System

With respect to the initiating event "loss of main feedwater", Figure 2 shows pressure and water inventory in the primary system as function of time dependent on the relief valve with the larger cross section (approx. 40 cm^2) being opened about 70 min after the occurrence of the initiating event. All 4 HP safety injection pumps will be started automatically. In the example given in Figure 2 the calculations are based on 2 HP injections. Below a pressure of 30 bar, the accumulators also feed in their water inventories.

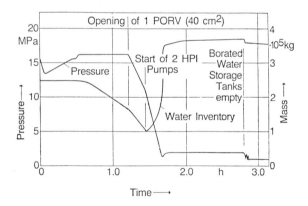

Figure 2: Loss of Main Feedwater and Loss of Aux. Feedwater Supply.
         Pressure and Water Inventory in the Reactor Coolant System,
         With Bleed and Feed

After a short period of time the primary system is completely flooded again. At the same time, the pressure in the system stabilizes at about 20 bar. Some 3 hours after the occurrence of the initiating event "loss of main feedwater" the borated water storage tanks are empty. The system reaches saturated conditions at a pressure of about 10 bar. The LP systems can now remove the decay heat in the recirculation mode of operation.

This example shows that in many cases a core meltdown can still be prevented even if the design basis systems fail. In order to perform "bleed and feed", intervention by the control room personnel is necessary for opening one or both of the pressurizer relief valves. Such an intervention is an unplanned manual action, i.e. a measure which is not described in the operating manual. If this measure has an unavailability of about 10^{-1}, it reduces the contribution to core melt frequency as a result of uncontrolled transients to about $2 \times 10^{-6}/a$.

Consequently, the overall core meltdown frequency is less than $2 \times 10^{-5}/a$. Excluded in this value is the contribution resulting from an uncontrolled leak in a steam generator heating tube, because the corresponding investigations have not yet been completed.

With respect to the event tree and fault tree analyses carried out in Phase B of the German Risk Study, the following overall insights have been obtained:

- with the system modifications carried out in the reference plant, the dominant contributions to core melt frequency as assessed in Phase A are considerably reduced;

- additional initiating events investigated in Phase B yield important contributions to core melt frequency on the improved level of safety;

- the overall core melt frequency assessed in Phase B is lower than the value estimated in Phase A;

- realistic minimal requirements for the system functions are based on so-called best-estimate analyses;

- in order to get realistic results, unplanned measures, i.e. measures not described in the operating manual, should also be taken into account for prevention of core melt.

2.   Evaluation of Operating Experience

In Phase A of the German Risk Study, it was necessary to use generic reliability data, mainly taken from non-nuclear operating experience [4]. Therefore, the results of the reliability analyses were not plant-specific but valid for a PWR plant of the type of Biblis B.

During the last years, evaluations of operating experience have increased in importance. The operating experience can be used to establish component reliability data needed for probabilistic analyses. The corresponding work done within Phase B of the German Risk Study was reported at the SMIRT conference [5]. Mainly plant-specific reliability data were used for the failure behavior of individual components. These data were obtained in the Biblis B plant over an observation period of several years. In cases where plant-specific operating experience was not sufficient on its own, it was referred to the operating experience in Germany or to the worldwide experience with LWR plants.

Operating experience can also be evaluated more directly in relation to observed incidents. So-called precursor studies provide an useful approach in order to support reliability estimates with the available operating experience as far as possible. "Precursors" are operationally observed events which either actually led to severe core damage or which, in conjunction with the failure of further systems, could have led to severe core damage. In precursor studies frequencies of severe core damage as well as trends can be assessed on basis of the operating experience.

The first comprehensive precursor study was the U.S. Accident Sequence Precursor Study. It evaluated the operating experience in U.S. PWR and BWR plants during 1969-79 with a total of approximately 430 years of operation [6]. A mean frequency of severe core damage of $4.5x10^{-3}$ per reactor year was estimated as average for all plants. This value is extremely high but more than 80 % of this value is due to just 3 events, with more than 50 % due to the Three Mile Island (TMI) accident. In reference [6] this is the only accident which actually led to severe core damage.

In a further evaluation for the years 1980-81, a considerably lower frequency of core damage of to $1.6x10^{-4}$ per reactor year was estimated [7]. This result took into account the insights and system improvements gained from the TMI accident.

The discrepancy between the two figures indicates, however, that there is considerable uncertainty in the estimates and that they can be strongly influenced by just a few events. Furthermore, differences between various plants were generally not taken into account. Therefore, results of the U.S. Accident Sequence Precursor Study cannot be directly applied to individual plants.

The German Precursor Study was the first plant-specific precursor investigation [8]. It is based on the operating experience in Biblis nuclear power plant which has two similar Units, A and B, and a total of approximately 16 years of reactor operation. In comparison with the U.S. study this operating experience is very limited, but it has the considerable advantage of being directly applicable to a specific plant, which is the reference plant of the German Risk Study.

As an example of results of the German Precursor Study (GPS), Table 3 shows the frequency of initiating events as directly derived from the operating experience in the Biblis plant, Units A and B. The frequencies of the initiating events from operating experience are given separately for the years 1975-79 and 1980-83. They show a distinct reduction in the data with increasing operating time. The reasons are system improvements and the increasing experience of the operating personnel.

Initiating Event	Frequency [1/a]			
	GPS 1975-79	GRS-A	GPS 1980-83	GRS-B
Loss of main feedwater	3.5	0.8	0.25	0.3
Loss of main heat sink	1.5	0.3	- 1)	0.3
Loss of preferred power • Unit A • Unit B	0.7 - 1)	0.1	0.25 0.25	0.03
Pressurizer Relief Valves • Demand of 1 PORV • Demand of both PORVs	0.9 0.25	0.5	0.5 0.25	0.4 - 2)

1) no occurrence
2) in the case of loss of aux. feedwater supply

Table 3: German Precursor Study (GPS) and German Risk Study (GRS), Frequencies of Initiating Events

Also given in Table 3 are the frequencies from the German Risk Study (GRS), Phases A and B. The frequencies of the initiating events used in Phase A of the German Risk Study are average values of the German nuclear experience with PWR plants till end of 1978. The frequencies of Phase B are plant-specific frequencies for Biblis nuclear power plant, Units A and B, taking into account both, operating experience and system modifications till end of September 1986.

The German Precursor Study estimated a frequency of severe core damage of 5×10^{-5} per reactor year as an average over the 16 years of operation, with a 95 % upper confidence limit of 5×10^{-4} per reactor year. Figure 4 shows the results of the German Precursor Study as well as the core melt frequencies of the German Risk Study, Phase A and Phase B. The estimate for Phase B is still provisional, the 90 % confidence limits have not yet been calculated. Both, the precursor evaluations and the investigations of Phases A and B of the Risk Study, clearly show a distinct decrease in the estimated frequency of severe core damage/core melt with increasing operating time.

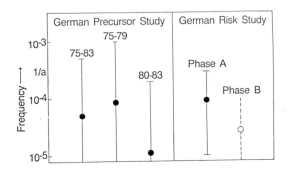

Figure 3: German Precursor Study and German Risk Study, Frequencies of Severe Core Damage/Core Melt

Evaluations from precursor studies and the results of analytical risk studies cannot be compared in all details. Precursor studies - as opposed to risk studies - do not aim at completely covering all possible sequences of events. They only cover those events which have actually occurred in the operating experience investigated. Therefore, the German Precursor Study does not contain contributions to the frequency of severe core damage resulting from "leaks in a reactor coolant loop" or "main steam line breaks" or other unlikely events which have not been observed.

Nevertheless, the good agreement between the overall results, and also between the partial results which have not been discussed here, is an indication that important contributions to core melt frequency result from initiators closely related to operational events.

3.   Comparison with Other Studies

At the beginning of this year, the U.S. Nuclear Regulatory Commission published the Reactor Risk Reference Document NUREG-1150 as a Draft for Comment [9]. In this report the results of risk analyses carried out for 3 PWR and 2 BWR plants of different design are discussed. Some of the results of these studies with respect to the frequency of core damage accidents will be commented on briefly.

Figure 4 shows the mean values and - as far as has been calculated - the uncertainty bounds of core damage frequencies estimated as base cases for the Surry, Zion and Sequoyah PWR plants and for the Peach Bottom and Grand Gulf BWR plants. Also shown in this Figure are the core melt frequencies for Biblis B PWR plant as assessed in Phase A and Phase B of the German Risk Study.

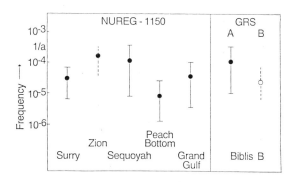

Figure 4: Core Damage Frequencies
          Assessed in Different Risk Studies

All the mean values lie within a range from just below 10^{-5}/a to about 2×10^{-4}/a. Although the overall values for core damage frequency for the individual plants differ by only about one order of magnitude, the major contributions can be explained to a great extent on a plant-specific basis, see Figure 5.

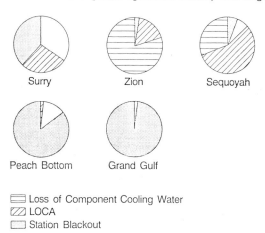

Figure 5: Contributions to Core Damage Frequencies
          Assessed in Different Risk Studies

In the Zion plant, for example, the failure of the component cooling water system contributes 79 % to the core damage frequency. The failure of this system leads to a loss of coolant via seal leaks of the reactor coolant pumps. Such leaks play no part in the German Risk Study. In Biblis B, as in the other German plants, there are additional seals which are automatically inserted when the primary coolant pumps are shut down, e.g. as a result of the failure of the seal water supply.

The contribution of a "station blackout", i.e. the total failure of the electrical supply, is remarkably high in 3 of the U.S. plants. For Grand Gulf, the core damage frequency is almost entirely caused due to the "station blackout". In the case of Surry this contribution is 38 %. Apparently, these high contributions result from a low redundancy and diversity in the electrical power supply.

For Biblis B, the total failure of the power supply is only of minor significance. This is a result of the additional installation of a standby grid connection and the possibility of switching back the four 10 kV emergency busbars. Therefore, these busbars can also be supplied either from the main grid connection, the standby grid connection, from Unit A or from a medium voltage grid via a cable connection. Furthermore, the emergency feedwater pumps are supplied from Unit A. As a consequence, the "loss of preferred power" (loss of offsite power and failure of the turbine generator to run back to house load) contributes only about 1 % to the core melt frequency. This is important in view of possible accident management measures: In many cases an electrical power supply is available in order to perform such ultimate measures to prevent core melt.

4.   Conclusion

In a very early stage of Phase A of the German Risk Study it was recognized that a substantial contribution to core melt frequency can result from a leak via pressurizer valves [10, 11]. This led to several improvements in the pressurizer system before the TMI accident occurred.

The safety concept and the high standard of safety requirements for nuclear power plants in the Federal Republic of Germany have not been challenged by the Chernobyl accident. However, this accident has remarkably affected the discussions of the question "how safe is safe enough".

Based on the operating experience and the results of probabilistic risk analysis the safety measures installed in nuclear power plants are subject to further development to reduce the probability of accidents and to limit the possible consequences.

The points discussed in this paper can be summarized as follows:

-   Probabilistic risk analysis methods are a useful instrument for the examination of the safety design of nuclear power plants. A main advantage of these methods is their applicability to the area of accident prevention. With this respect the German Risk Study has shown that the system changes performed in the reference plant have led to a considerably improved level of safety.

-   Risk analyses are increasingly used to identify accident management measures as has been shown for the case of accident prevention.

-   As risk analyses become more detailed, the results become increasingly plant-specific. The detailed evaluation of operating experience for the individual plants investigated is therefore of increasing significance.

LITERATURE

[1] Gesellschaft für Reaktorsicherheit:
     Deutsche Risikostudie Kernkraftwerke, Hauptband.
     Verlag TÜV Rheinland, Köln, 1979

[2] H. Hoertner:
     Zuverlässigkeitsuntersuchungen für Sicherheitssysteme und
     ihr Vergleich mit Auswertungen von Betriebserfahrungen
     10. GRS-Fachgespräch "Ergebnisse neuerer Sicherheitsanalysen"
     Köln, 12.-13. November 1986, Report GRS 64

[3] F.W. Heuser, H. Hoertner, E. Kersting:
     Risikountersuchungen zur Sicherheitsbeurteilung von Kernkraftwerken
     Jahrestagung Kerntechnik '87
     Karlsruhe, 2.-4. Juni 1987

[4] Gesellschaft für Reaktorsicherheit:
     Deutsche Risikostudie Kernkraftwerke, Fachband 3,
     Zuverlässigkeitskenngrößen und Betriebserfahrungen.
     Verlag TÜV Rheinland, Köln, 1980

[5] H. Hoertner, J. von Linden:
     German Risk Study - Influences of Data Base, Minimal Requirements
     and System-Changes
     9th International Conference of Structural Mechanics in Reactor Technology,
     Session M15; Lausanne, August 17-21, 1987

[6] J.W. Minarick and C.A. Kukielka:
     Precursors to Potential Severe Core Damage Accidents: 1969-1979.
     A Status Report. NUREG/CR-2497, June 1982

[7] W.B. Cottrell, J.W. Minarick, P.N. Austin, E.W. Hagen and J.D. Harris:
     Precursors to Potential Severe Core Damage Accidents: 1980-1981.
     A Status Report. NUREG/CR-3591, ORNL/NSIC-217,
     Volume 1: July 1984, Volume 2: February 1984

[8] H. Hoertner, W. Frey, J. von Linden and G. Reichart:
     German Precursor Study - Methods and Results.
     International ANS/ENS Topical Meeting on Probabilistic Safety Methods
     and Applications
     San Francisco, February 24 - March 1, 1985

[9] USNRC:
     Reactor Risk Reference Document, Vol. 1-3
     Draft for Comment, February 1987

[10] H. Hoertner:
     Ausgewählte Probleme und Ergebnisse der Störfallablauf- und
     Zuverlässigkeitsuntersuchungen für die Deutsche Risikostudie
     1. GRS-Fachgespräch "Kernenergie und Risiko - Fachvorträge"
     München, 3./4. November 1977, Report GRS 10

[11] W. Bastl, H. Hoertner, P. Kafka:
     Influence of Probabilistic Safety Analysis on Design and Operation
     of PWR Plants
     Topical Meeting on Probabilistic Analysis of Nuclear Reactor Safety
     Los Angeles, May 8-10, 1978

NUREG-1150 RISK ASSESSMENT METHODOLOGY AND RESULTS*

A. S. Benjamin
[Sandia National Laboratories, Albuquerque, NM]

G. J. Boyd and S. R. Lewis
[Safety & Reliability Optimization Services, Knoxville, TN]

C. N. Amos
[Technadyne Engineering Consultants, Inc., Albuquerque, NM]

M. A. Cunningham and J. A. Murphy
[U.S. Nuclear Regulatory Commission, Washington, DC]

Abstract

NUREG-1150 constitutes a full-scope reassessment of the risks to the public from several light water reactor plants with various containment types. Emphasis has been placed on determining the magnitude and character of the uncertainties, rather than focusing upon a point estimate. The risk-reduction potential of proposed plant modifications (backfits and procedural changes) has also been studied, and their costs and benefits have been evaluated. It has been found that the risks from internal events are generally lower than previously evaluated in the Reactor Safety Study (RSS). However, certain unresolved phenomenological issues cause the tops of the uncertainty bands to appear at levels that are comparable to or higher than the RSS point estimates. The issues that are important vary from plant to plant. Most of the postulated plant modifications do not appear to be cost-effective, although a few procedural changes are possible exceptions. Several reviews of this work are in progress, and a second iteration is being performed to include external events, incorporate new technical information, and address comments.

1. Background and Methodology

Shortly after the accident at Three Mile Island, Unit 2, the NRC initiated a Severe Accident Research Program to develop an improved understanding of severe accidents and to provide a sound technical basis to support regulatory decisions in this area [1]. A key product of this program is NUREG-1150, which provides estimates of risk for several nuclear reactors of different design [2]. The principal technical analyses for NUREG-1150 have been performed at Sandia National Laboratories under the Severe Accident Risk Reduction Program (SARRP) [3-5] and the Accident Sequence Evaluation Program (ASEP) [6]. Most of the reports documenting this work have been prepared as drafts-for-comment, reflecting the fact that the current analyses are subject to reevaluation and revision. The final reports will be completed in the summer of 1988.

*This work is supported by the United States Nuclear Regulatory Commission and performed at Sandia National Laboratories which is operated for the U.S. Department of Energy under contract number DE-AC04-76DP00789.

A major aspect of the work has been the development of a methodology which improves upon previous full-scale probabilistic risk assessments in several areas:

• The results of previous PRAs have been used to help direct the application of resources for the core damage frequency evaluation. Common mode failures have been treated more comprehensively than in many previous PRAs.

• Containment event trees have been developed to a degree of detail never attempted before, because of the recognition of the complexity of the containment loads and performance aspects of the analyses.

• Base estimates of radioactive release have been obtained from calculations performed with the Source Term Code Package (STCP), the methodology developed for NUREG-0956 [7]. Using parametric models, uncertainties have been examined which included phenomena not currently modeled in the STCP.

• Uncertainties in the estimates of severe accident frequency, containment loading and performance, and radioactive source terms have been treated through a stratified Monte Carlo (i.e., Latin hypercube) sampling procedure [8] which uses input from a group of experts augmented by the results of experiments and analyses available to date.

• Consequences have been calculated using both the current baseline consequence code (CRAC2) [9] and an improved code (MACCS) [10] which incorporates the latest health effects models.

• The same methods have been utilized to examine the cost-benefit trade-offs for proposed safety option backfits and operating procedure modifications. Uncertainties in both the benefits and the costs have been treated more thoroughly than previously.

• A computerized processing capability has been developed to facilitate the integration of the various parts of the analyses and interpretation of the results.

The uncertainty analysis has had two primary objectives. The first is to provide, for each of several measures of risk, a credible and realistic range in which the analysts have a reasonable confidence that the correct answer lies. The second is to highlight the particular sources of uncertainty which have the greatest influence on the overall risk uncertainty range. The procedure that was developed to accomplish these objectives utilized a group of experts selected from various laboratories and other organizations to represent various areas of severe accident phenomenology. With the aid of these experts, a set of issues was defined for each plant to cover the known or suspected principal sources of uncertainty. (An example of an issue is the pressure rise in containment occurring from direct heating.) Some issues were decomposed into several subcases to represent varying sets of preconditions corresponding to different accident scenarios. Then a range of possible outcomes was generated for each subcase of each issue, based on the experts' judgment in light of the available analyses and experiments. Next, the range was decomposed into discrete outcomes, or levels, and the experts assigned weighting factors to each level. Roughly, the weighting factor assigned by an individual to a level represented his degree of belief that the outcome of the issue was correctly represented by that level. The individual weighting factors for each level were averaged over the group to obtain a weighting factor for the sampling. Correlations between issues or between separate subcases within an issue were

identified and the sampling was constrained to satisfy the specified correlations. The Latin hypercube method was utilized to obtain a set of sample
members for the risk evaluation. The risk was calculated and displayed for each
sample member, and the potential reduction in risk achievable through implementation of various safety options was also evaluated and displayed. Finally,
various statistical methods were utilized to evaluate the relative importance of
the various issues. The overall procedure is referred to as a "limited" Latin
hypercube (LLH) application and is displayed schematically in Figure 1. The
issues considered for each plant are listed in Table I.

Because of the large number of possible combinations of different accident
sequences, containment release pathways, issue levels, and meteorological
conditions to be considered, it was necessary to develop an integrated code
capability for calculating risk. The following codes were developed for this
purpose:

- TEMAC (Top Event Matrix Analysis Code) [11], which evaluates the frequencies
  of the cut sets and calculates several importance measures for the base
  events. Both point estimates and uncertainties are evaluated.

- TEMAC3 (postprocessor for TEMAC), which groups the cut set results into plant
  damage states for purposes of the containment event tree analysis.

- EVNTRE, which calculates the conditional probabilities for the pathways
  through the containment event tree and provides a preliminary binning of the
  results. The program can operate in a point estimate or sampling mode.

- POSTSM (postprocessor for EVNTRE), which provides the final binning of
  containment event tree results for purposes of the source term analysis.

- XSOR and RELTRAC [12], a set of plant-specific parametric codes which
  estimate fission product source terms. These codes are used when STCP
  calculations are not available for a particular scenario or when an issue
  being sampled is not modeled in the STCP.

- CLUSTER (postprocessor to XSOR and RELTRAC), which maps the source terms
  obtained from the sampling onto a smaller number of centers. The source term
  centers are subsequently input to the consequence evaluation codes, CRAC2 and
  MACCS.

- RISQUE (Risk Integration, Sensitivity, and Quantitative Uncertainty
  Evaluation), which calculates and displays the mean risk, complementary
  cumulative distribution functions, and safety option averted risk for each
  sample member in the LLH process and performs statistical analyses of the
  results.

These codes were used to calculate the risk for the plant both with and without
the proposed safety option backfits. When a safety option was included, the entire procedure was repeated with the input modified to reflect the influence of
the safety option on the sequence frequencies, containment responses, and/or
fission product source terms. The benefit of the safety option was calculated
as the difference in risk with and without the option in place. This risk
difference, or "averted risk," was calculated and displayed for each of the
sample members in the LLH sample.

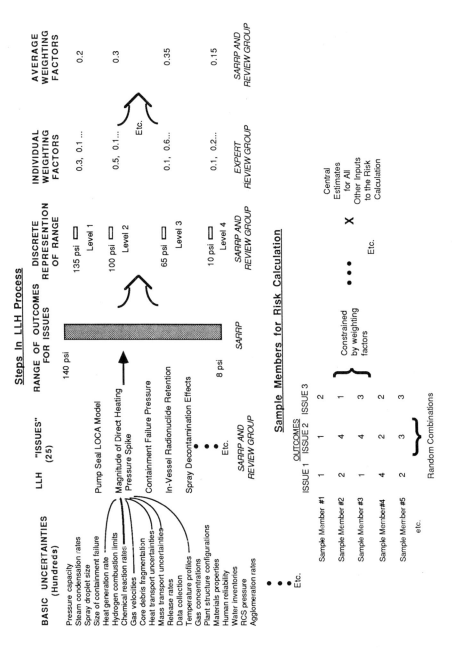

FIGURE 1.   OVERVIEW OF THE LIMITED LATIN HYPERCUBE (LLH) APPLICATION TO RISK ASSESSMENT

SYSTEM BEHAVIOR ISSUES

	SURRY	SEQUOYAH	PEACH BOTTOM	GRAND GULF
1. LIKELIHOOD AND SIZE OF RCP SEAL LOCA	X	X		
2. CREDIT FOR GAS TURBINE GENERATOR	X			
3. BETA FACTORS FOR COMMON MODE ANALYSIS	X	X	X	
4. INTERFACING CHECK VALVE FAILURE RATE	X	X		
5. ECCS OPERABILITY AFTER CONTAINMENT FAILURE	X	X		
6. STEAM BINDING OF AUXILIARY FEEDWATER PUMPS		X		
7. SUCCESS CRITERIA FOR FEED-AND-BLEED COOLING		X		
8. USE OF SPARE BATTERY			X	
9. OPERATOR FAILURE TO ACTUATE SLC SYSTEM			X	
10. OPERATOR FAILURE TO VENT DURING ATWS			X	X
11. POWER RECOVERY UNCERTAINTY				
12. HPCS OPERABILITY AT HIGH TEMPERATURE				X
13. DIESEL GENERATOR RELIABILITY				X

CONTAINMENT ISSUES

	SURRY	SEQUOYAH	PEACH BOTTOM	GRAND GULF
1. LOCATION AND SIZE OF INDUCED RCS LOCA	X	X		
2. LIKELIHOOD AND EFFECTS OF IN-VESSEL STEAM EXPLOSION	X	X		
3. PRESSURE RISE FROM DIRECT HEATING AND STEAM SPIKE	X	X		X
4. PRESSURE RISE FROM HYDROGEN BURN AT VESSEL BREACH	X			
5. CONTAINMENT FAILURE PRESSURE	X	X	X	
6. CONTAINMENT FAILURE SIZE	X		X	(X)*
7. CONTAINMENT SPRAY OPERABILITY IN SEVERE ENVIRONMENT	X	X		
8. PROBABILITY OF BREAK SUBMERGENCE FOR V SEQUENCE	X			
9. PRESSURE RISE FROM H₂ BURNS BEFORE VESSEL BREACH		X		
10. EX-VESSEL DEBRIS BED COOLABILTY		X		
11. IMPAIRMENT OF ICE CONDENSER FUNCTION		X		
12. CONTAINMENT FAILURE BY DIRECT CORE DEBRIS CONTACT		X	X	
13. LIKELIHOOD/AREA OF STUCK-OPEN SRV VACUUM BREAKER			X	
14. USE OF HIGH PRESSURE SERVICE WATER DRYWELL SPRAY			X	
15. OPERATOR ABILITY TO VENT CONTAINMENT AFTER CORE DAMAGE				

CONTAINMENT ISSUES (CONTINUED)

	SURRY	SEQUOYAH	PEACH BOTTOM	GRAND GULF
16. CONTAINMENT FAILURE LOCATION			X	
17. REACTOR PRESSURE VESSEL FAILURE MODE			X	
18. CONTAINMENT PRESSURE PRIOR TO VESSEL BREACH			X	
19. CONTAINMENT PRESSURE RISE AT VESSEL BREACH			X	
20. REACTOR BUILDING BYPASS DUE TO HYDROGEN BURNS				
21. LIKELIHOOD OF DRYWELL FLOODING				X
22. PRESSURE RISE FROM EX-VESSEL STEAM EXPLOSION				X
23. LIKELIHOOD OF HYDROGEN DETONATION				X
24. LIKELIHOOD/AREA OF INDUCED DRYWELL LEAKAGE				X
25. LIKELIHOOD OF REACTOR PEDESTAL FAILURE				X

SOURCE TERM ISSUES

	SURRY	SEQUOYAH	PEACH BOTTOM	GRAND GULF
1. AMOUNT OF IN-VESSEL RELEASE FROM FUEL	X	X	X	(X)
2. AMOUNT OF CsI DECOMPOSITION IN THE RCS	X	X	X	(X)
3. AMOUNT OF DEPOSITION IN THE RCS	X	X	X	(X)
4. DECONTAMINATION FACTOR FOR V-SEQUENCE RELEASE	X			
5. FRACTION OF RCS SPECIES RELEASED FROM CONTAINMENT	X	X	X	X
6. AMOUNT OF RELEASE FROM CORE-CONCRETE INTERACTIONS	X			
7. FRACTION OF CCI SPECIES RELEASED FROM CONTAINMENT	X	X		
8. DECONTAMINATION FACTOR FOR CONTAINMENT SPRAYS	X	X		
9. AEROSOL AGGLOMERATION UNCERTAINTIES	X	X		
10. AMOUNT OF LATE IODINE RELEASE FROM CONTAINMENT	X	X	X	X
11. REVOLATILIZATION OF Cs AND I AFTER VESSEL BREACH	X	X	X	X
12. AMOUNT OF RELEASE DURING HIGH-PRESSURE EJECTION	X	X		
13. AMOUNT OF RELEASE DURING DIRECT HEATING	X	X		
14. DECONTAMINATION FACTOR FOR ICE CONDENSER		X		
15. DECONTAMINATION FACTOR FOR WATER IN REACTOR CAVITY	X	X		X
16. DECONTAMINATION FACTOR FOR SUPPRESSION POOL			X	
17. DECONTAMINATION FACTOR FOR REACTOR BUILDING			X	(X)

*(X) REFERS TO ISSUES WHICH ARE NOT INCLUDED IN THE CURRENT RESULTS BUT WILL BE EVALUATED IN THE NEXT ITERATION.

TABLE I.   SUMMARY OF ISSUES CONSIDERED IN THE LLH UNCERTAINTY ANALYSIS

2. Results and Discussion

The analyses provided in the Sandia drafts-for-comment have been completed so far for four reference plants: (1) a pressurized water reactor (PWR) with a dry, subatmospheric containment (Surry Unit 1), (2) a PWR with an ice condenser containment (Sequoyah Unit 1), (3) a boiling water reactor (BWR) with a Mark I containment (Peach Bottom Unit 2), and (4) a BWR with a Mark III containment (Grand Gulf Unit 1). A fifth NUREG-1150 plant, a PWR with a large, dry containment (Zion Unit 1), has been evaluated separately by Brookhaven National Laboratory [13] and is not considered in this paper. Because of the changes being planned before final publication of NUREG-1150, the results shown here should be considered preliminary.

Table II presents a comparison of the mean core damage frequencies for the four plants together with a summary of the highest contributing sequences. It may be observed that station blackouts (loss of all ac power) are the only important contributors for the BWRs. This is a reflection of the wide diversity of water delivery systems that are available to BWRs provided ac power is available. However, while station blackouts are important contributors for the PWRs as well, other sequences, including other transients and small-break loss-of-coolant accidents (LOCAs), are also important. Accident sequences initiated by external events (e.g., earthquakes, fires, and floods) have not been included in the present analysis but will be included for two of the plants (Surry and Peach Bottom) during the next iteration.

Figure 2 presents the conditional probability of early containment failure or bypass, given the occurrence of a core melt. The term "early" is taken here to include all cases for which significant radionuclide releases to the environment occur before or within a short time after the time of reactor vessel breach. Thus, interfacing system LOCAs or steam generator tube ruptures that result in a direct release path from the primary system to the environment are included as early containment bypasses, and failures occurring soon after vessel breach due to rapid pressurization of containment or direct core debris attack on the structure are included as early failures. On the other hand, failures resulting from long-term gradual pressurization or basemelt meltthrough are not considered early failures, nor are releases resulting from intentional containment venting in accordance with written procedures. The results in Figure 2 are based on a weighted average of all accident sequences (the sequences are weighted by their frequencies).

Two separate evaluations are depicted. The one labeled as "central" utilizes point estimates from the ASEP and SARRP programs wherein the inputs to the containment event trees are intended to represent the median viewpoint of the reactor safety community. For these estimates, the judgments as to what comprises the median view for each containment event tree question were made, subject to internal consistency constraints, by the SARRP analysts after careful review of all the information available from previous analyses and experiments. The second display illustrates the results of the LLH uncertainty analysis obtained by sampling the selected set of severe accident issues over their ranges of belief. Each sample member is depicted by a horizontal dash having an associated value of risk on the ordinate, and a box is used to designate the range between the 5th and 95th percentiles of the distribution. As mentioned earlier, the inputs for the sampling of issues were provided by the expert review group; all parameters which were not sampled were kept at their central estimate values.

SURRY (2x10⁻⁵)	SEQUOYAH (1x10⁻⁴)	PEACH BOTTOM (8x10⁻⁶)	GRAND GULF (3x10⁻⁵)
1. STATION BLACKOUT WITH REACTOR COOLANT PUMP (RCP) SEAL LOCA	1. SMALL LOCA AND FAILURE OF HIGH PRESSURE RECIRCULATION	1. STATION BLACKOUT WITH COINCIDENT FAILURE OF STATION BATTERIES	1. STATION BLACKOUT WITH EVENTUAL FAILURE OF HIGH PRESSURE INJECTION PUMP SEALS
2. LOSS OF BUS, FAILURE OF PILOT OPER. RELIEF VALVE (PORV) TO RECLOSE, FAILURE OF LOW-PRES. RECIRC.	2. LOSS OF COMPONENT COOLING WATER LEADING TO RCP SEAL LOCA AND FAILURE OF ECC AND SPRAY PUMPS	2. STATION BLACKOUT WITH EVENTUAL DEPLETION OF STATION BATTERIES	2. STATION BLACKOUT WITH COINCIDENT FAILURE OF STATION BATTERIES
3. LOSS OF OFFSITE POWER, FAILURE OF AUX. FEEDWATER AND PORVs	3. STATION BLACKOUT WITH REACTOR COOLANT PUMP SEAL LOCA		
4. STATION BLACKOUT WITH EVENTUAL BATTERY DEPLETION	4. STATION BLACKOUT AND FAILURE OF AUXILIARY FEEDWATER		
5. STATION BLACKOUT AND FAILURE OF AUXILIARY FEEDWATER	5. SMALL LOCA AND FAILURE OF RECIRCULATION FOR EMERGENCY CORE COOLING AND CONTAINMENT SPRAYS		

TABLE II. SUMMARY OF CORE DAMAGE FREQUENCIES AND PRINCIPAL CORE DAMAGE SEQUENCES

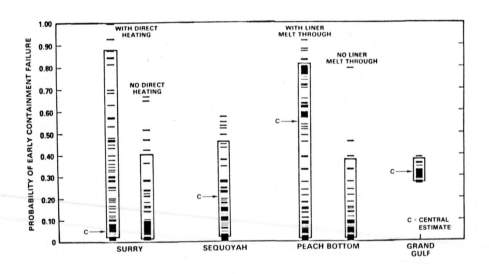

FIGURE 2. CONDITIONAL PROBABILITIES OF EARLY CONTAINMENT FAILURE OR BYPASS (SUMMED OVER ALL SEQUENCES WEIGHTED BY THEIR FREQUENCIES)

The results in Figure 2 illustrate that a relatively high conditional probability of early containment failure cannot be ruled out for any of the plants. However, in some cases (e.g., Surry), the preponderance of estimates is near the low end of the bar. This indicates that the experts consider it unlikely that the issue outcomes would be sufficiently adverse to cause an early containment failure. The governing issues vary from plant to plant. For Surry, direct containment heating has the largest effect on the results. However, if the calculation is redone assuming that direct heating does not occur (illustrated by the second bar for Surry), a set of secondary issues including interfacing system LOCAs, steam generator tube ruptures, and hydrogen burns become important. For Peach Bottom, the principal issue is containment failure by core debris attack on the drywell shell. When this issue is deleted, containment pressurization during the blowdown at vessel breach becomes important. The results for Sequoyah and Grand Gulf are governed by hydrogen burns, especially during scenarios where the hydrogen igniters are not available for at least a part of the accident (e.g., station blackouts). In the case of Grand Gulf, failure occurs most often when ac power is recovered after core damage but prior to vessel breach, causing ignition of a detonable mixture. The uncertainty in the probability of early failure is known to be understated for Grand Gulf because the issues selected for sampling emphasized source term rather than containment uncertainties (owing to the importance of source term uncertainties on risk for that plant). The range of issues considered for Grand Gulf will be broadened in the next iteration.

Figure 3 provides examples of results obtained for the fission product releases to the environment. In this display, the sample members are not shown individually as in Figure 2; only the box depicting the range between the 5th and 95th percentiles is displayed. For early containment failures at Surry (Figure 3a), environmental releases obtained from the STCP tend to fall in the lower part of the LLH uncertainty range. This occurs because many of the issues which are not modeled in the STCP have the potential for increasing the source term. Such issues include decreased fission product deposition in the reactor coolant system (RCS) due to natural convection flows, decomposition of cesium iodide due to high RCS radiation and temperature levels, revolatilization of cesium and iodine from the RCS after vessel breach due to decay heating of the surfaces, oxidation releases caused by high pressure ejection of core debris from the RCS and by direct heating, and late reevolution of iodine from the containment due to radiolysis in water pools, organic iodine formation, and other sources.

A comparison between environmental release fractions predicted by the Industry Degraded Core (IDCOR) program [14] with those from the present study is given in Figure 3b for a late containment failure at Peach Bottom. For three of the radionuclide groups (cesium, tellurium, and barium/strontium), the IDCOR values appear near the upper end of the LLH uncertainty range, and for one (ruthenium), the IDCOR value far exceeds the uncertainty range, which falls below 10^{-6}. The latter effect reflects the experts' view that fission product releases due to oxidation were previously overstated. On the other hand, the IDCOR iodine release is near the bottom of the corresponding uncertainty band and the IDCOR lanthanum release is very much lower than the band. The higher values for iodine in the LLH uncertainty analysis are the result of the experts' beliefs concerning increased releases due to CSI decomposition and late iodine sources, whereas the higher lanthanum values are associated with the experts' views on core-concrete thermochemistry.

Figure 4 provides results for the risk of latent cancer fatalities and of early fatalities. The central estimates, denoted by "C", were obtained by utilizing

(A) SURRY STATION BLACKOUT, EARLY CONTAINMENT FAILURE

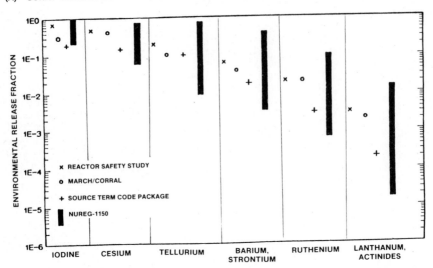

(B) PEACH BOTTOM STATION BLACKOUT, LATE CONTAINMENT FAILURE

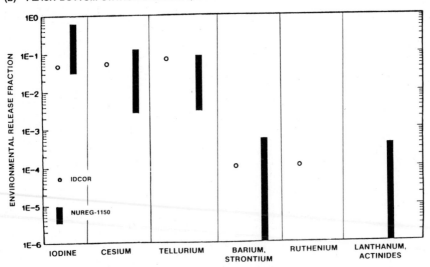

FIGURE 3.   COMPARISONS OF ENVIRONMENTAL RELEASE FRACTIONS

(A) LATENT CANCER FATALITIES

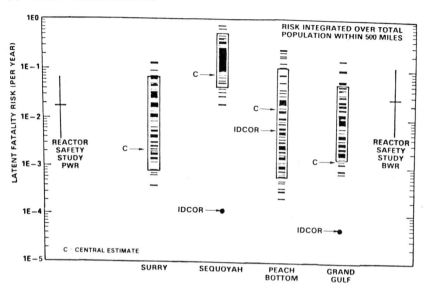

(B) EARLY FATALITIES

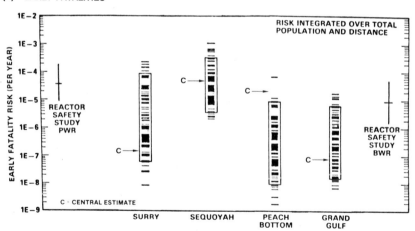

FIGURE 4.   RISK OF LATENT CANCER FATALITIES AND EARLY FATALITIES

the central values for containment response (defined above as roughly representing the median view of the reactor safety community) together with fission
product releases based on STCP code results. The fact that the central
estimates in some cases fall very low with respect to the uncertainty band and
in other cases fall very high reflects the experts' view that the STCP predic-
tions were very conservative in some areas (e.g., in the lack of modeling of
late revolatilization and late iodine sources) and very optimistic in others
(e.g., in the treatment of refractory releases from core-concrete interactions). The principal issues affecting the sizes of the LLH uncertainty bands
are listed in Table III.

Figure 4 also shows a comparison of results from the present study with results
from the IDCOR program [14] and from the earlier Reactor Safety Study (RSS)
[15]. In making these comparisons, it should be noted that each set of analyses
utilized different models and assumptions that make a direct comparison difficult. For example, the CRAC code was used to obtain consequence results for
the RSS, CRAC2 was used for IDCOR, and MACCS was used for the results of the
present study illustrated in Figure 4. The RSS assumed that there would be no
evacuation 30 percent of the time, IDCOR assumed 100 percent evacuation, and the
present study assumed that 5 percent of the population would never evacuate.

In general, the RSS estimates tend to be near the upper ends of the LLH uncertainty ranges, reflecting the fact that current evidence tends toward lower
source terms overall than used in that study. For two of the plants (Sequoyah
and Grand Gulf), IDCOR's estimates of latent cancer fatality risk tend to be
much lower than the LLH uncertainty bands. This emanates primarily from the
lesser importance in the IDCOR study of station blackouts and other sequences
leading to failure of containment safeguards, together with the lower assessed
threat from issues such as hydrogen burning, direct heating, and late fission
product releases. For the other plant having comparative calculations (Peach
Bottom), IDCOR's estimate of the latent cancer fatality risk is comparable with
the present estimates but the principal contributing accident scenarios are
different. Anticipated transients without scram followed by overpressure or
overtemperature failure of the drywell are more important in the IDCOR
analysis. Note also that IDCOR predicted zero early fatalities in their base
analysis owing to the assumption of 100 percent evacuation; thus the IDCOR
result is not shown in Figure 4b.

The last major element of the risk reassessment involves the determination of
costs and benefits for postulated safety options. The safety options addressed
in the study include both preventive options (i.e., those intended to reduce the
overall core damage frequency) and mitigative options (i.e., those designed to
reduce the consequences). Both hardware changes and procedural changes have
been considered.

Figure 5 provides a set of cost-benefit results for one of the plants. Both the
benefits and the implementation costs are illustrated as bars on a horizontal
scale, with the former representing the 5th to 95th percentiles from the LLH
distributions, and the latter representing the results of a three-point uncertainty evaluation. Areas where the bars overlap indicate potential cost effectiveness. Where this occurs, the option is subject to more detailed
investigation of competing risks and other cost impacts.

To address the needs of various interests in the reactor safety community, which
include regulators, licensees, and the public, four different measures of benefit were employed:

REACTOR PLANT	SYSTEM ISSUES	CONTAINMENT ISSUES	SOURCE TERM ISSUES
SURRY	CHECK VALVE FAILURE FREQUENCY (L)	DIRECT HEATING (E, L) INDUCED RCS LOCA (L) H$_2$ BURN/STEAM SPIKE (L) CONT. FAILURE PRES. (L)	AEROSOL AGGLOMERATION (E)
SEQUOYAH	COMPONENT COOLING WATER COMMON MODE MODEL (L)	ICE CONDENSER BYPASS (E, L) HYDROGEN BURNING AT VESSEL BREACH (E)	LATE IODINE RELEASES (L) RCS DEPOSITION (L) CORE-CONCRETE RELEASES (E)
PEACH BOTTOM	DC POWER COMMON MODE MODEL (E, L) AC POWER RECOVERY MODEL (E, L)	MELTTHROUGH OF DRY-WELL SHELL (E, L)	REACTOR BUILDING DECON-TAMINATION FACTOR (E, L) CORE-CONCRETE RELEASES (E)
GRAND GULF	DIESEL FAILURE RATE (E, L)	REACTOR PEDESTAL FAILURE (L)	REVOLATILIZATION OF CESIUM AND IODINE (L) LATE IODINE RELEASES (L)

TABLE III.   SUMMARY OF PRINCIPAL ISSUES CONTRIBUTING TO UNCERTAINTY IN RISK OF EARLY FATALITIES (E) AND LATENT CANCER FATALITIES (L)

(1)   Actual averted offsite cost, consisting of the financial impact of early fatalities, early injuries, latent cancer fatalities, medical attention, relocation, lost wages, decontamination, lost property, and interdiction of land and farm costs;

(2)   Averted population dose calculated at $1000 per person-rem (a surrogate for offsite costs);

(3)   The combination of (1) and the actual averted onsite costs, consisting of the capital cost of the plant, cleanup costs, power replacement costs, and the costs of onsite personnel health effects; and

(4)   The combination of (2) and the actual averted onsite costs.

The algorithm did not include costs that are normally referred to as secondary costs, e.g., the economy-wide costs associated with adverse public opinion, concern in the financial community, and increased regulatory constraints placed on the industry.

The costs of implementation included installation costs, continuing maintenance costs, and the costs of radiation exposure during both installation and continuing maintenance. The cost of replacement power during installation was estimated separately but not shown on the cost-benefit comparison because of its great dependency on such unknown factors as the specific schedule mandated for implementation, the status of other projects in progress at the utility, the financing arrangements of the utility, and the availability of power at the time of the modification.

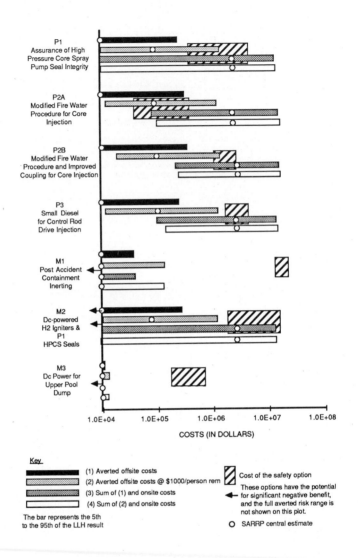

FIGURE 5. COMPARISON OF COSTS AND BENEFITS (MONETIZED AVERTED RISKS) FOR PREVENTIVE AND MITIGATIVE OPTIONS -- GRAND GULF

Most of the safety options investigated in this study proved to be not cost-effective; i.e., the bar representing the implementation cost exceeded the bars representing the benefit over the entire range of uncertainty. Options which were found to be potentially cost-effective (i.e., for which there was significant overlap between costs and benefits) are listed in Table IV. In general, these modifications are procedural in nature and therefore have low implementation cost.

REACTOR PLANT	SAFETY OPTIONS
SURRY	NONE
SEQUOYAH	PROCEDURE TO PROLONG ECCS INJECTION BY LIMITING CONTAINMENT SPRAY INJECTION IMPROVED MAINTENANCE PROCEDURE FOR COMPONENT COOLING WATER PUMPS AUTOMATIC SWITCHOVER TO RECIRCULATION PROCEDURES TO ENHANCE AVAILABILITY OF STATION BATTERIES
PEACH BOTTOM	STAGGERING OF STATION BATTERY TESTING AND MAINTENANCE USE OF DIESEL-DRIVEN FIRE PUMP TO PROVIDE WATER TO DRYWELL SPRAYS
GRAND GULF	PROCEDURE TO ALIGN DIESEL-DRIVEN FIRE PUMP TO REACTOR CORE ISOLATION COOLING LINE ASSURANCE OF SEAL COOLING FOR HIGH PRESSURE CORE SPRAY PUMP USE OF SMALL DIESEL GENERATOR TO DRIVE CONTROL-ROD DRIVE PUMP

TABLE IV.   SUMMARY OF SAFETY OPTIONS FOUND TO BE POTENTIALLY COST-EFFECTIVE

3. Conclusions and Limitations

The risk from all of the plants was found to be low; that is, all of the plants meet the proposed safety goals of the U.S. Nuclear Regulatory Commission (NRC) for early and latent cancer fatalities. The factors influencing the risk and the issues driving the uncertainty in risk tend to be highly plant-specific. However, station blackouts appear to be important for all the plants. The probability of early containment failure given a core melt may not be low, although there appears to be more confidence in the performance of the large, dry containment than in the other types. Source term phenomena not modeled in the severe accident codes may be very important, and may lead to significantly higher or lower source terms than predicted by the codes, depending on the specifics of the accident scenario.

The limitations associated with probabilistic risk assessment in general have been discussed in many forums and need not be reiterated here. However, there are a few specific limitations of importance that should be recognized when interpreting the results of this paper:

• The results apply to only four reactor plants and should not be inferred as being generally applicable to other plants.

• The results are based on internal initiating events only, as external events were not considered. External events will be incorporated into the next iteration for two of the plants.

• The number of issues considered was limited and, while an attempt was made to focus upon important issues, there is no guarantee that all the important ones have been considered. For example, uncertainties associated with consequence evaluation modeling were not included.

• The consideration of operator actions was limited to actions associated with written procedures. During severe accidents, operator actions outside the formal procedures, both positive and negative, could occur.

- For two of the plants (Surry and Sequoyah), accident sequences resulting in core damage were assumed to proceed to core melting and subsequent breaching of the reactor vessel. It is anticipated that some of the sequences would be arrested prior to reactor vessel breach.

- The effects of assumptions and simplifications used in the mechanics of the analyses have not been fully explored. Follow-on activities will include a more thorough examination of the impacts of such assumptions and simplifications.

- The composition of the expert review groups was limited principally to NRC contractors. As a result, the viewpoints of other interests such as the utility industry and intervenor groups may be underrepresented. Other limitations apply to the manner in which expert opinion was solicited.

Between the times of the completion of the drafts-for-comment in 1987 and the final publication in 1988, several reviews are being conducted and a series of improvements are being implemented. Contacts are being made with plant and utility personnel to verify the representation of the plant configuration and procedures. The reports have been distributed to several hundred persons representing various organizations and interests domestically and abroad, and many of them will be providing their comments. An external peer review committee has been formed under the chairmanship of Prof. William Kastenburg of the University of California at Los Angeles. Other committees have been formed to evaluate the procedures for performing uncertainty analysis utilizing expert opinion. Comments and recommendations from these various sources will be assessed and the analyses will be modified as deemed appropriate.

In addition, new technical information pertinent to the NUREG-1150 issues is being generated through analyses and experiments sponsored by NRC. These will be incorporated together with new technical information from other sources, including foreign organizations, into the database for reconsideration by the experts.

Analyses have been initiated for a BWR with a Mark II containment, LaSalle Unit 1. These analyses include several methodological improvements, including the use of continuous sampling distributions and consideration of consequence modeling uncertainties.

Finally, a quality assurance review of all inputs and outputs is being conducted to verify, as rigorously as possible, that the results are free from error.

Acknowledgments

Too many people have contributed to this study for it to be practical to list them all. However, the authors would particularly like to recognize the efforts of the following people, without whose accomplishments this paper would not have been possible: V. L. Behr, S. E. Dingman, J. M. Griesmeyer, F. E. Haskin, R. L. Iman, D. M. Kunsman, M. J. Shortencarier, and D. C. Williams (Sandia National Laboratories); W. B. Murfin (Technadyne Engineering Corporation); L. N. Smith (Science Applications International Corporation); J. C. Helton (Arizona State University); and R. S. Denning (Battelle Columbus Laboratories).

References

1. "Nuclear Power Plant Severe Accident Research Plan," NUREG-0900, U.S. Nuclear Regulatory Commission, 1981.

2. "Reactor Risk Reference Document," NUREG-1150 (Draft-for-Comment), U.S. Nuclear Regulatory Commission, 1987.

3. Benjamin, A. S., et al., "Evaluation of Severe Accident Risks and the Potential for Risk Reduction," NUREG/CR-4551, Vol. 1-4 (Drafts-for-Comment), Sandia National Laboratories, 1987.

4. Benjamin, A. S., et al., "Containment Event Analysis for Postulated Severe Accidents," NUREG/CR-4700, Vol. 1-4 (Drafts-for-Comment), Sandia National Laboratories, 1987.

5. Denning, R. S., et al., "Report on Radionuclide Release Calculations for Selected Severe Accident Scenarios," NUREG/CR-4624, Vol. 1-5, Battelle Columbus Laboratories, 1986.

6. Harper, F. T., et al., "Analysis of Core Damage Frequency from Internal Events," NUREG/CR-4550, Vol. 1-7 (Drafts-for-Comment), Sandia National Laboratories, 1986.

7. "Reassessment of the Technical Bases for Estimating Source Terms," NUREG-0956, U.S. Nuclear Regulatory Commission, 1985.

8. Iman, R. L., et al., "A Comparison of Uncertainty and Sensitivity Analysis Techniques for Computer Models," NUREG/CR-3904, Sandia National Laboratories, 1985.

9. Ritchie, L. T., et al., "CRAC2 Model Description," NUREG/CR-2326, Sandia National Laboratories, 1984.

10. Alpert, D. J., et al., "The MELCOR Accident Consequence Code System," Proc. CEC Workshop on Methods of Assessing the Off-Site Radiological Consequences of Nuclear Accidents, 1986.

11. Iman, R. L. and M. J. Shortencarier, "A User's Guide for the Top Event Matrix Analysis Code (TEMAC)," NUREG/CR-4598, Sandia National Laboratories, 1986.

12. Helton, J. C., et al., "Incorporation of Uncertainties into Reactor Accident Source-Term Estimates," Sandia National Laboratories, to be published.

13. Khatib-Rahbar, M., et al., "Evaluation of Severe Accident Risks and the Potential for Risk Reduction: Zion Power Plant," NUREG/CR-4551, Vol. 5 (Draft-for-Comment), Brookhaven National Laboratory, 1987.

14. "IDCOR Task 21.1: Risk Reduction Potential," Technology for Energy Corporation, 1984.

15. "Reactor Safety Study," WASH-1400, U.S. Nuclear Regulatory Commission, 1975.

SOME OBSERVATIONS ON NUREG-1150

Richard C. Vogel and Ian B. Wall
[Electric Power Research Institute, Palo Alto, California, U.S.A.]

Abstract

The U.S. Nuclear Regulatory Commission (USNRC) requested comments on their
recently published draft "Reactor Risk Reference Document" (NUREG-1150). The
report concludes that the risk from internal initiators meets USNRC's safety
goals. Furthermore, backfitting of U.S. plants is not cost-effective. Although
the methodology is basically sound, EPRI believes that the execution was flawed
primarily in its use of expert opinions and in providing inadequate time for the
performance of supplementary calculations of important physical phenomena. This
paper provides an overview of EPRI's comments and recommendations to USNRC for
preparation of the next edition of NUREG-1150.

Introduction

The U.S. Nuclear Regulatory Commission has recently published the "Reactor Risk
Reference Document" (NUREG-1150) [1] in draft form for comments. This document
provides the results of risk analyses for five different U.S. light-water reactor
(Surry, Zion, Sequoyah, Peach Bottom and Grand Gulf). The draft document points
out that the data base and insights may be used in a number of regulatory actions
such as (1) implementation of the NRC Severe Accident Policy Statement,
(2) implementation of the NRC safety goal policy, (3) consideration of the NRC
backfit rule, (4) evaluation and possible revision of regulations and regulatory
requirements for emergency preparedness, plant siting and equipment qualification, and (5) establishment of risk-oriented priorities for allocating NRC
resources. Clearly, it is an important piece of work whose results have manifest
implications to reactor safety.

NUREG-1150 updates the "Reactor Safety Study (WASH-1400) [2] by re-baselining the
analyses of the Surry and Peach-Bottom power plants. The Risk Assessment Review
Group [3] faulted the Reactor Safety Study for understating the error bounds on
the estimated risks. A major objective of NUREG-1150 was to quantify the
uncertainties associated with risk parameters. The NRC should be complimented
for tackling the problems of uncertainty since it is appreciated that the problem
is a difficult one. However, we believe that, although the methodology is
basically sound, its execution was flawed primarily due to insufficient resources
in time and money for supporting calculations, and a lack of breadth in the
expertize of the expert group. In the following sections, we make some observations on selected aspects of NUREG-1150 and offer some suggestions to NRC for
improvements in the final report.

The Delphi Process

Many of the physical phenomena which contribute to public risk have not been
thoroughly measured so expert opinion was used to supplement the sparse
database. For example, the 26 issues considered in the uncertainty analysis for

the Surry plant, are shown in Table 1 [4]. Unfortunately, it seems to us that the outcome of this study is, to a large extent, dominated by "expert" opinion. As we all by now appreciate, the various outputs have quite wide uncertainty bands of factors of 100 or more. When the analysis for a given reactor scenario has to refer 26 issues to experts for their opinion, it is clear how large uncertainty bands can develop.

The experts themselves felt uncomfortable with the procedure as can be appreciated by reading Appendix F of "Evaluation of Severe Accident Risks and the Potential for Risk Reduction: Surry Power Station, Unit 1" [5] which gives the experts' opinions of the procedure. A typical comment was that, "in general, the reviewers felt that the uncertainty approach being pursued by SARRP was about the best that could be done within time and budget constraints."

Table 1

ISSUES CONSIDERED IN SURRY UNCERTAINTY ANALYSIS

Systems

- Reactor Coolant Pump Seal LOCAs

- Credit for Gas Turbine Generator

- Beta factors for Common Mode Analysis

- Interfacing Check Valve Failure Rate

Containment

- ECCS Operability After Containment Failure

- Induced Reactor Coolant System LOCA

- In-Vessel Steam Explosions

- Direct Heating and Steam Spike

- Hydrogen Burning at Vessel Breach

- Containment Failure Pressure

- Containment Failure Size

- Spray Operability in Containment Environment

- V Sequence Submergence

Source Term

- In-Vessel Release from Fuel

- CsI Decomposition in RCS

- RCS Deposition

- Scrubbing DF for V Sequence

- RCS Species Released from Containment

- Core-Concrete Release from Fuel

- CCI Species Released from Containment

- Scrubbing DF for Containment Sprays

- Aerosol Agglomeration

- Late Iodine Releases from Containment

- Late Revolatilization from RCS

- High Pressure Ejection Release from Fuel

- Direct Heating Release from Fuel

The above discomfort was emphasized by one of the reviewers who said (p. F-5), "The participants were forced to provide unsubstantiated guesses as input on many issues that could at least have been based on calculations had budget and schedule allowed." Another reviewer said (p. F-6) that "there is a significant amount of unmitigated guessing during the collection of input for the Limited Latin Hypercube (LLH) that could have been prevented if participants abstained on issues about which their qualifications were limited."

In the summarizing statement in ref. 5 (p. F-13), it was pointed out that

"(1) The LLH input process involved substantial guessing at parameters or outcomes that could have been avoided had more time been available.

(2) The results will need to be carefully characterized in terms of what they mean and what they do not mean. The semantics are very important. The group was split in their advice on this issue, however, since some wanted the results to be presented as a characterization of uncertainty, while others thought that they should be presented as the outcomes of sensitivity studies."

Expert judgment has been used to supplement sparse databases in other scientific disciplines. For example, EPRI has recently completed a probabilistic reassessment [6] of the seismic hazard in the Eastern United States (east of Rocky mountains). Since the incidence of moderate or larger earthquakes at any location within this region is relatively low (e.g., $<10^{-3}$ per year) and only one hundred or so years of recordings exist, the database is very sparse. Building upon previous efforts [7], EPRI developed a very structured and disciplined approach to the use of expert opinion including the following innovations:

- Earth science expertise was provided by six independent teams formed specifically to promote interaction among different disciplines (geology, geophysics, seismology). This avoided a too narrow disciplinary focus.

- A single, common database was compiled and distributed to each team. This database was reviewed and accepted by all participants. No "private" data was used.

- Each team were required to document and to justify their interpretations of the data. A professional facilitator assisted the group decision making.

- Workshops and seminars were conducted at which major technical issues were discussed and each team received feedback both from their peers and from the results of the calculations.

USNRC and U.S. Geological Survey (USGS) geoscientists attended the workshops to ensure familiarity with the work. EPRI's probabilistic seismic hazard was submitted to USNRC in July 1986; a Safety Evaluation Report is expected soon.

EPRI believes that the above approach to using expert judgment to supplement a sparse database and to assess the uncertainty bands on risk parameters was quite successful. For its next version of NUREG-1150, we recommend that USNRC establish a similar process and involve experts from industry organizations.

Scrutability of Calculations

The use of a Limited Latin Hypercube (LLH) is an efficient way to estimate the mean (median) values of risk parameters and their uncertainty bounds. However, only the aggregation of the samples is reported which impedes a full peer review of the work. There is another way to gain insight into the "sensitivity" of a given answer to input assumptions. This procedure is to use an integrated methodology, such as used by IDCOR [8] or in Level 3 PRAs, to define the risk-dominant scenarios, do best-estimate evaluations of the resulting radioactive releases and consequences, and then to vary key parameters and determine the change in answers. This approach makes it possible to identify what is important. However, it does require a modest number of calculations with STCP (or MAAP). It also points out where beneficial work can be done to improve understanding. It is appreciated that this was done in this manner in QUEST [9]. However, we believe that the spread of the input values used in QUEST was too broad. Furthermore, the source term community is now more knowledgeable which should narrow the spread of results in any study of this type.

EPRI has applied this approach, with MAAP, in analyses of the Peach Bottom and Sequoyah plants. For Peach Bottom, some 60 separate MAAP calculations were made, analyzing both ATWS and station blackout scenarios. Variations included those related to sequence description and those related to phenomenological behavior. This was possible since MAAP incorporates features that are conducive to making this type of study. Tables 2 and 3 qualitatively state some of the more important findings for sequence variations and phenomenological variations respectively.

Use of STCP Code

The Source Term Code Package (STCP) has the potential for user input to substantially affect the output results. What were the governing rules issued by NRC to assure that such user inputs were qualified and:

a. were applied in a self-consistent manner by all users for all analyses for all plants related to the NUREG-1150 effort (e.g., analyses in NUREG/CR-4624 by BCL and NUREG/CR-4629 by BNL);

b. represented realistic descriptions of the plants and best estimate values for the many physical constants that must be user defined;

c. were selectively and realistically parameterized to evaluate, in a consistent manner, a range of results based on known areas of high uncertainty?

It is claimed that the Source Term Code Package (STCP) results provided the basis for source term evaluations although, in reality, the package was apparently not used extensively. The methodology actually used instead of STCP should be verified and validated to the maximum possible extent. The documentation that describes the verification process should be available. Also, the comparisons of the key models against relevant experiments should be available. As far as we know, this is not the case.

We are puzzled by the suggestion of a new phenomena for concern -- that is the revolatilization of iodine from the suppression pool. We would expect that iodine would slowly (over a period of days) revolatilize if the suppression pool were acid. However, it seems to us that the pH of the pool can be estimated so that this matter could be settled in a deterministic sense rather than subjected to expert opinion.

TABLE 2

IMPACTS OF SEQUENCE DESCRIPTION - VARIATIONS FOR PEACH BOTTOM

<u>VARIATIONS</u>	<u>MAJOR IMPACTS</u>
Venting through wetwell	Decreased release to RCB because drywell integrity retained for many hours
Cooling of debris in drywell	Lower release of Tellurium to RCB and some reduction in cesium iodide release
Throttling of ECCS pumps during an ATWS event	Slows accident progression
Suppression pool cooling with RHR during an ATWS event	Extends time to drywell failure
Realistic power versus time criterion for ATWS analysis	Realization that more accurate methodology required for treating uncovered core
Drywell failure time	Release inversely proportional for ATWS and directly proportional for blackout
Drywell failure area from excessive temperature (ATWS)	Release inversely proportional to area
Drywell failure area from over-pressurization (blackout)	Release directly proportional to failure area

TABLE 3

IMPACTS OF PHENOMENOLOGICAL PARAMETER VARIATIONS FOR PEACH BOTTOM

VARIATIONS	MAJOR IMPACTS
Core nodalization and power factors	Sensitivity to power peaking factors diminished when more nodes used
Increase fuel melting temperature	Significantly increases hydrogen production in-vessel, increases CsI release fraction, increases ex-vessel release fractions, but deposition in drywell and RCB dominant
Fission product release and transport behavior	Cesium iodide release sensitive to vapor pressure. If tellurium is released in-vessel, it is transported similar to cesium iodide
Heat transfer from RPV to containment (convective heat loss)	Releases to RCB are reduced for large heat losses
Ex-vessel heat transfer	Releases to RCB reduced for low values of emissivity or for low concrete liquefaction temperature
Suppression pool scrubbing decontamination factors	Releases not sensitive when pool is bypassed. Releases are sensitive for wetwell venting cases, but releases are low
Disable aerosol impaction model for secondary containment	Other deposition mechanisms, particularly gravitational settling proved to be nearly as effective in aerosol removal processes

Treatment of Common Cause Failures

In the area of common cause failures, there is an important inconsistency of
treatment. In Appendix J (p. 13-36) of ref. 1, the NRC staff acknowledge that
common cause failures are plant-specific and are important to estimation of core
damage frequency but conclude that current (generic) approach is adequate given
the range of uncertainties. However, chapter 3 of Main Report [1] states that
common cause failures are the critical issue for many dominant accident
sequences. A correct treatment of common cause failures can drastically change
the risk perspective. For example, page 3-37 of Main Report shows station blackout contributes 86% of core damage frequency at Peach Bottom. Page 3-39
acknowledges "the (ccf) model may be somewhat conservative" and recommends "a
detailed plant-specific analysis of dependent failures of batteries before any
significant regulatory actions are proposed". A separate USNRC study has applied
EPRI's common cause failure methodology to this problem and has concluded a ten-
fold reduction in the station black-out probability [10]. If correct, this
change would reduce the Peach Bottom core damage probability from 8.2E-6 to
1.5E-6 and the station black-out contribution from 86% to 47%. It should be
noted that correct treatment of common cause failures may not always be this
significant and could increase probabilities in some cases.

We recommend that the common cause failure analysis be completely redone by using
EPRI/USNRC plant-specific methodology [10,11].

Assumed Containment Failure Mode

The Industry Degraded Core Rulemaking (IDCOR) program concluded that the dominant
containment failure mode would be leak-before-break, which would occur as a
result of a large strain in the containment boundary [12]. In Appendix J.10 [1]
the USNRC staff acknowledge that the mode and timing of containment failure is
very important in determining accident consequences but do not concur with the
IDCOR conclusion. The consequences calculated in NUREG-1150 generally assumed
that (a) no significant leakage would develop for internal pressures less than a
"capability pressure" which is that associated with membrane yield in steel
containments, yield of rebar, or one percent tendon strain in prestressed
containments and (b) sudden loss of integrity for higher internal pressures.
Since 1981, EPRI has been conducting a major experimental and analytical research
project to determine the failure mode of steel-lined concrete containments. Work
to date provides strong evidence for relatively high weighting, e.g., 50% or
more, for leak-before-break mode of containment failure. For accident scenarios
having a slow containment pressure rise, incorporation of such a weighting would
radically modify the risk profile for plants with concrete containments and
provide a more realistic perspective of their risks and of the risk-dominant
accident sequences.

The EPRI research was triggered by a detailed structural analysis [13] of the
Surry containment. It was postulated that local stress concentrations in the
steel liner would cause tearing and leakage prior to failure of rebar. This
postulate has been confirmed by a series of full-scale tests of lined prestressed
concrete slabs and corners [14,15]. The concrete and liner were biaxially
stressed to represent internal pressure and punching loads were applied in the
z-direction to the penetrations. Excess air pressure was applied to the liner in
order to monitor leakage. Breaks opened-up and propagated in the liner and
provided pressure relief; crack propagation was limited by the interaction
between liner and concrete. Additional experiments have been performed for full-
scale lined reinforced concrete slabs and will be reported shortly. In parallel
with the experiments, EPRI's ABAQUS code [16] has been modified to represent the
behavior of the concrete and liner with a special emphasis on slippage between

liners and concrete as well as rebar and concrete [17,18]. The code has been validated against the experiments and can be used to analyze actual containments.

It is unclear what weighting was assigned in NUREG-1150 to containment leakage-before-failure especially considering the assumed rapid pressure rise due to direct containment heating. However, the NRC staff in Appendix J have concluded that the dominant failure mode is not leak-before-break. In conjunction with the forthcoming test of a 1/6-scale steel-lined concrete model at Sandia National Laboratories, we recommend that the weighting assigned to containment leakage-before-failure be reconsidered.

Conclusion

From the utilities' viewpoint, the conclusion in NUREG-1150 that the risk from internal initiators meets USNRC's safety goals [19] is comforting. Furthermore, it was concluded that back-fitting of plants in the United States to lower the risk is not cost effective.

In the broader sense, our concern with the documents is that those who are so inclined will read only tops of the bar graphs for latent fatalities, for example, and conclude that these latent fatalities are indeed a possibility for most serious consideration. One is battling the public syndrome of concluding that what might possibly happen will indeed happen, no matter how low its probability.

In conclusion, we think that NUREG-1150 was an enormous undertaking. The methodology may be as good as can be developed at this time, but the use of expert opinions was flawed because the experts did not always have expertise in the field under discussion and because inadequate time was given for them to perform supplementary quantitative evaluations of phenomena.

References

1. "Reactor Risk Reference Document," NUREG-1150 (Draft), February 1987.

2. "Reactor Safety Study--An Assessment of Accident Risks in U.S. Commercial Nuclear Power Plants," WASH-1400 (NUREG-75/014), October 1975.

3. H. W. Lewis, et al. "Risk Assessment Review Group Report to the U.S. Nuclear Regulatory Commission," NUREG/CR-0400, September 1978.

4. A. S. Benjamin. Presentation at NRC Workshop on NUREG-1150 Methodology, April 21-22, 1987, Rockville, Maryland.

5. A. S. Benjamin, et al. "Evaluation of Severe Accident Risks and the Potential for Risk Reduction: Surry Power Station, Unit 1," NUREG/CR-4551, Vol. 1 (DRAFT), February 1987.

6. "Seismic Hazard Methodology for the Central and Eastern United States," Vol. 1, EPRI NP-4726, July 1986.

7. D. L. Bernneutes, et al. "Seismic Hazard Characterization of the Eastern United States," Vol. 1, UCID-20421, April 1985.

8. "Nuclear Power Plant Response to Severe Accidents," IDCOR Technical Summary Report, November 1984.

9. R. J. Lipinski, et al. "Uncertainty in Radionuclide Release Under Specific LWR Accident Conditions," SAND84-0410, Vol. I-III, 1985.

10. K. Fleming, A. Mosleh, G. Parry, H. Paula, M. Bohn, D. Rasmusson, and D. Worledge. "Procedures for Treating Common Cause Failures in Safety and Reliability Studies: Vol. 1, Procedural Framework and Practical Guidelines; Vol. 2, Analytical Background and Techniques," Joint EPRI NP/NUREG report to be published in 1987.

11. K. Fleming, A. Mosleh, and D. Worledge. "Development of a Systematic Approach for the Analysis of System-Level Dependent Failures," International Topical Conference on Probabilistic Safety Assessment and Risk Management, Zurich, August 1987.

12. IDCOR Technical Report 85.2, "Technical Support for Issue Resolution," Atomic Industrial Forum, July 1985.

13. Rashid, Y.R. "Review of the Wash-1400 Surry Containment Capability Assessment." Appendix B of EPRI Report NP-4096, June 1985.

14. Julien, J.T. et al. "Concrete Containment Structural Element Tests." EPRI Report NP-3774, Vols. 1, 2, and 3, November 1984.

15. N. W. Hanson, et al. "Concrete Containment Structural Element Tests: Second Phase." EPRI Report NP-4867, August 1987.

16. H. D. Hibbitt, B. I. Karlsson, and E. P. Sorensen. "ABAQUS-EPGEN: A General-Purpose Finite Element Code," EPRI NP-2709-CCM, Vol. 1 (Rev. 1), June 1983; Vol. 2, April 1985; Vol. 3, March 1983; Vol. 4, June 1985.

17. Dunham, R.S. et al. "Methods for Ultimate Load Analysis of Concrete Containments." EPRI Report NP-4046, June 1985.

18. Dameson, R.A. et al. "Methods for Ultimate Load Analysis of Concrete Containments: Second Phase." EPRI Reports NP-4869M and NP-4869-SP, March 1987.

19. U.S. Nuclear Regulatory Commission. Federal Register, 51, 28044 (August 4, 1986) [republished with corrections, ibid, p. 30028 (August 21, 1986)].

GENERAL ELECTRIC EXPERIENCE IN PRA APPLICATION

K. W. Holtzclaw, Principal Engineer, Advanced Boiling Water Reactor Program
R. J. McCandless, Manager, Reliability Engineering
Nuclear Energy Business Operations
General Electric Company
San Jose, California USA

KEYWORDS: PRA APPLICATION
STANDARD PLANT RISK ASSESSMENT
GESSAR II PRA
SEVERE ACCIDENT PREVENTION & MITIGATION
STANDARD PLANT RISK REVIEW
GENERAL ELECTRIC PRA ANALYSIS

INTRODUCTION

At General Electric Probabilistic Risk Assessment (PRA) techniques have been
utilized by plant designers and analysts in all phases of the plant design through
plant operation. PRA has enabled the designers to select plant configurations
that achieve a specified level of safety while optimizing the design in other
areas. For plants in construction and operation, PRA methods have been used to
identify procedures, training and hardware modifications that are most cost
effective in meeting new regulatory requirements and design and operational
objectives. The techniques have also been used to optimize plant preventive
maintenance programs that have demonstrated the benefit of producing simultaneous
safety improvements and operating cost reductions.

While the applications of PRA are broad and useful in many areas of the design
process, a key application remains the integrated assessment of overall plant
risk. The accident at Three Mile Island focussed United States industry and
regulatory consideration on accidents beyond the design basis. (The accident at
Chernobyl is having the same impact.) Consequently, the role of PRA has increased
in significance in recognition of the usefulness of PRA methodology to evaluate
plant risk for the total spectrum of potential accident sequences. The United
States Nuclear Regulatory Commission (NRC) has recognized this use in requiring
the performance of PRA's for all new plant license applications and PRA-based
analyses for operating plants via the NRC's Severe Accident Policy.

The purpose of this paper is to provide an overview of GE experience in the
application of PRA to GE Standard Plant Designs in response to the Severe Accident
Policy requirement. The process was effectively demonstrated in the licensing of
the GESSAR II standard plant design, a process which took place between 1982 and
1986. This is the example case used in this paper. GE is undertaking a similar
program with the NRC under US Department of Energy sponsorship for the Advanced

Boiling Water Reactor design. Application of PRA to operating plants consistent
with expected detail NRC requirements emanating from the Severe Accident Policy
are provided in another paper co-authored by GE for PSA `87.

THE GESSAR II SEVERE ACCIDENT REVIEW

In response to the NRC request for a severe accident review of the GESSAR II
Standard Plant design, General Electric produced appendices to the licensing
documentation which discussed the features of the design that prevent severe
accidents from leading to core damage or that mitigate the effects of severe
accidents should core damage occur. The quantification of the accident prevention
and mitigation features was provided by means of a comprehensive PRA. Because the
formulation of the NRC's Severe Accident Policy was progressing in parallel with
the GESSAR II review, the NRC initially requested an evaluation scope essentially
limited to internal event initiators. However, further NRC requirements revised
the severe accident review scope to include the following:

  o   Detailed consideration of seismic, internal fire and internal flood
       events
  o   Internal event uncertainty analysis
  o   Seismic event uncertainty analysis
  o   Deterministic assessment of sabotage
  o   Demonstration of the technical resolution of NRC unresolved safety
       issues and generic safety issues
  o   Detailed analysis of station blackout
  o   Evaluation of NRC-proposed design modifications

THE GESSAR II PRA

The GESSAR II PRA was performed using the general approach typical to most
detailed PRAs - fault tree and event tree methodology to evaluate the frequency of
core damage and phenomenological models to assess accident consequences. Some
assumptions had to be made due to the fact that the GESSAR II design was a
reference standard plant which had not as yet been constructed. This was a major
difference from previous full scope PRAs. Site-related inputs were established
based on a reference site, and operational data for analysis inputs were based on
previous BWR experience.

Consistent with the risk assessment approach, realistic success criteria were
utilized. Human performance evaluations were aided by the recognition of the BWR
Owner's Group/GE Emergency Procedure Guidelines; however, consistent with the
state-of-the-art at that time, virtually no credit was taken for potential
accident recovery actions.

A number of modifications were made to the typical PRA methodology in terms of the
development and detail of accident classes and sequence analyses. In addition,
special analyses were performed to address specific phenomenological issues. The
basis was developed and documented to demonstrate that steam explosions were

effectively precluded by design. GE also established a model for fission product retention by the BWR suppression pool based on experimental testing by GE, and verified in a separate test program sponsored by the Electric Power Research Institute. A separate containment analysis was performed to assess the Mark III multiple-barrier containment response to severe accident loadings.

THE GESSAR II PRA RESULTS

The detailed GESSAR II PRA resulted in a calculated core damage frequency of ~5×10^{-6}/reactor year, and demonstrates the BWR prevention capability. By provisions for the multiple and diverse methods of water injection to the reactor vessel, coupled with the capability to rapidly depressurize the reactor, the probability of core damage due to inadequate core cooling is minimized. Accident sequences associated with loss of decay heat removal were found to be minimal contributors to plant risk due to the GESSAR II design capability for heat removal through either the power conversion system to the main condenser, the residual heat removal system heat exchangers or by release through the safety/relief valves to the pressure suppression pool. The heat sink capacity of the suppression pool and containment structures was found to provide significant time for operator action to assure other post-accident vital functions such as maintenance of adequate reactor pressure vessel water level and depressurization of the reactor pressure vessel if necessary.

Due to the GESSAR II plant severe accident mitigation features, particularly the multiple-barrier containment design and the fission product retention capability of the pressure suppression pool, no early fatalities were calculated. Furthermore, the latent fatality risk was calculated to be as much as four orders of magnitude below the NRC interim safety goal guideline.

The impact of seismic events and other external initiators were found to be small contributors to overall plant risk (approximately 10% of internal event risk).

THE NRC REVIEW

The NRC and its consultants reviewed in detail all of the GE submittals, and in many instances performed independent verification analyses. The review is documented in the NRC Safety Evaluation Report which concluded that:

o   The GESSAR II design provides substantial severe accident prevention capability

o   The risk of an early fatality for the GESSAR II design is negligibly small. The level of risk is low when compared with the levels predicted in other PRAs for other plant designs

o   Fire and internal flooding were determined to contribute insignificantly to GESSAR II core damage frequency o   The risk from seismic events could be much larger than the GE prediction due to uncertainties associated with the analysis approach and severe accident source terms.

CONCLUSIONS

The NRC granted General Electric a Final Design Approval for the GESSAR II design on September 22, 1986, signifying the successful completion of the severe accident review. This is the only standard plant design that has completed this level of review to date.

The NRC is currently working on a document that will aid in standardizing the process for future standard plant applications by specifying the PRA form and content. The lessons learned from the review of the GESSAR II PRA are being included in the NRC guidance document.

Utilization of the PRA in the design and licensing process was a significant factor in helping to successfully resolve 73 design issues with the NRC.

On-going plant-specific PRA work is making use of the GESSAR PRA experience. ABWR design and licensing activities are making daily use of PRA models to assist in resolving design and licensing issues. Numerous PRA applications programs for operating plants are being performed including recent work to optimize over 50,000 equipment surveillance intervals resulting in significant safety and operating cost improvements.

CURRENT CORE DAMAGE INSIGHTS REGARDING BOILING WATER REACTORS IN THE UNITED STATES

Mary T. Drouin, Walter L. Ferrell, Alan M. Kolaczkowski, Jeffrey L. LaChance, and Bonnie J. Shapiro
[SCIENCE APPLICATIONS INTERNATIONAL CORPORATION, 2109 Air Park Road SE, Albuquerque, New Mexico, USA, 87106, (505) 247-8787]

ABSTRACT

This paper addresses the latest insights obtained from Probabilistic Risk Assessments (PRAs) of Boiling Water Reactors (BWRs). A look at past PRAs indicates that "station blackout" type accidents were one of many dominant contributors to the overall core damage frequency at BWRs. However, recent analyses are concluding that this accident type is the dominant contributor. These latest insights are discussed in this paper and are based on the findings of two BWR studies done as part of NUREG/CR-4550.

INTRODUCTION

Since the publication of WASH-1400, the first United States (US) PRA for Light Water Reactors (LWRs), accident sequence insights -- specifically regarding BWRs -- have significantly changed. More detailed knowledge regarding system and plant operation during an accident, more sophisticated thermal-hydraulic analyses, more refined PRA methodology techniques and an increased data base have greatly improved BWR accident sequence insights. This is perceptively demonstrated from results of NUREG/CR-4550, [1,2].

PRAs based on internal initiators were conducted on a number of reference plants in order to provide the Nuclear Regulatory Commission (NRC) with updated information about LWRs. The results of these analyses have been used by the NRC to prepare NUREG-1150 which will examine risk from a selected group of nuclear power plants. These results provide the bases for updating our perception of risk from selected plants, developing methods for extrapolation to other plants, comparing NRC research to industry results, and resolving numerous severe accident issues. Grand Gulf and Peach Bottom were chosen as the two BWR reference plants.

The results (published as NUREG/CR-4550) indicate that transients and not Loss of Coolant Accidents (LOCAs) dominant the core damage risk. Of the significant transient accidents, loss of all AC power (Loss of Offsite Power, LOSP, and onsite power commonly referred to as "station blackout") is the significant contributor. Loss of all containment heat removal and Anticipated Transients Without Scram (ATWS) sequences are not the significant contributors once thought.

BACKGROUND

Starting with the results of WASH-1400, the core damage frequency for BWRs appeared to be dominated by both transients and LOCAs; specifically, ATWS type sequences and LOCAs or transients followed by either a loss of long term heat removal or a loss of injection. In the last twelve years there has been a multitude of PRAs covering the spectrum of BWRs (BWRs 1 to 6 reactor types and Mark I to III containments). A representation of these studies is presented in Table 1 as an example. Table 1 shows that the results of these PRAs identify three accident types that tend to be dominant: (1) those involving loss of injection (TQUV), (2) those involving loss of long term heat removal (TW), and (3) those involving anticipated transients without scram (TC). The contribution of these accident types varies from study to study. The older studies found the TW type accident to be dominant and some of the later studies show more contribution from TC and TW. However, combined these three accident types account for almost all the core damage frequency found in these studies. Two recent PRAs, done on the Grand Gulf and Peach Bottom BWR plants as part of NUREG/CR-4550, show that this trend may be changing.

CURRENT RESULTS

Unlike past PRAs, NUREG/CR-4550 identified station blackout as the major accident type dominating the core damage frequency at BWRs. Two other types of core damage accidents with frequencies greater than 1.0E-7 per reactor year were also identified. These are summarized below in Table 2.

ACCIDENT TYPE	GRAND GULF		PEACH BOTTOM	
	MEAN FREQUENCY	% CONTRIBUTION TO CORE DAMAGE	MEAN FREQUENCY	% CONTRIBUTION TO CORE DAMAGE
Station Blackout	2.8E-5	99%	7.0E-6	86%
ATWS	1.8E-7	1%	1.0E-6	12%
All Others	<1.0E-8	<<1%	2.0E-7	2%

Table 2: Summary of NUREG/CR-4550 BWR Results

The mean core damage frequencies at Grand Gulf and Peach Bottom are calculated to be 2.9E-5 and 8.2E-6, respectively. These frequencies fall well into the range calculated in the past PRAs; however, the dominant accidents have significantly changed. Both studies conclude that station blackout is the dominant contributor, making up 99% of the core damage frequency for Grand Gulf and 86% of the frequency for Peach Bottom. ATWS scenarios are of moderate importance and all other accident types relatively insignificant.

The major station blackout contributors in the two analyses include both short and long term sequences. Long term sequences (those in which core cooling is initially provided but lost in four to eight hours or longer) dominate the core damage frequency at Grand Gulf (~84%). At Peach Bottom, long term and short term (those in which core cooling is lost immediately) sequences are of comparable contribution. Results between the two plants differ because Grand Gulf has an independent High Pressure Core Spray (HPCS) system that is

STUDY (AND DATE)	REACTOR/ CONTAINMENT TYPE	TOTAL CORE DAMAGE FREQUENCY	ACCIDENT TYPE FREQUENCY	ACCIDENT TYPE [see note (a)]	% CONTRIBUTION TO CORE DAMAGE
WASH-1400 [3], Peach Bottom (1975)	BWR4/MARKI	2.7E-5	1.7E-5 1.0E-5 4.9E-7	TW TC TQUV	62% 36% 2%
IREP [4] -- Browns Ferry (1982)	BWR4/MARKI	2.0E-4	1.4E-4 5.5E-5	TW TC	72% 28%
Millstone (1982)	BWR3/MARKI	3.0E-4	2.4E-4 3.9E-5 2.0E-5	TQUV TW TC	80% 13% 7%
RSSMAP [5], Grand Gulf (1981)	BWR6/MARKIII	3.6E-5	2.8E-5 2.3E-6 5.4E-6	TW TQUV TC	78% 6% 15%
IDCOR [6] -- Peach Bottom (1984)	BWR4/MARKII	3.6E-5	3.3E-5 2.3E-6 6.0E-7	TC TQUV TW	92% 7% 1%
Grand Gulf (1984)	BWR6/MARKIII	8.3E-6	1.4E-6 1.9E-7 6.7E-6	TQUV TW TC	16% 2% 81%
Limerick PRA [7], (1981)	BWR4/MARKII	1.5E-5	1.2E-5 6.8E-7 1.0E-6	TQUV TW TC	87% 5% 8%
Shoreham PRA [8] (1983)	BWR4/MARKII	5.5E-5	3.2E-5 8.5E-6 1.4E-5 1.0E-6	TQUV TW TC S	58% 15% 25% 2%

(a) Accident type is defined as a combination of accident sequences which generally display similar characteristics regarding effects of the accident on the plant. This combination has no specific technical use for either the sequence or containment response analyses. It serves as a convenient way to discuss similar accident scenarios.

Table 1: Summary of Select BWR PRAs

relatively reliable and has its own dedicated AC/DC support system. This feature tends to reduce the chances for a short term failure of all core cooling, thereby increasing the relative contribution of long term blackout accidents for plants like Grand Gulf. In contrast, Peach Bottom has a High Pressure Coolant Injection (HPCI) system which, though AC independent, does not have its own dedicated DC support. This system tends to be less reliable than the HPCS system. Table 3 summarizes the station blackout frequencies, the relative percentages calculated, and the dominant contributors in both analyses.

Although ATWS type accidents were calculated to be dominant in NUREG/CR-4550, their relative contribution to the overall core damage frequency at BWRs when compared with previous studies has decreased. Both the studies show a large uncertainty range bounding the ATWS frequencies, thus their contribution could increase or decrease.

Other accidents types were calculated to be insignificant in both their frequency and relative contribution to core damage in NUREG/CR-4550.

CONCLUSIONS AND INSIGHTS

The results from the two NUREG/CR-4550 analyses and those of previous studies do differ. Several differences in approach are the reason. These are summarized below.

o   NUREG/CR-4550 incorporated long term failures into the analysis by allowing systems to operate initially and then fail later in the accident. Many previous studies have only considered short term failures; that is, immediate failure of HPCS/HPCI and Reactor Core Isolation Cooling (RCIC).

o   An examination of the effects of pool heatup on injection systems was included in NUREG/CR-4550. This issue can have a significant effect on station blackout, thereby the core damage, frequency. For BWRs 6s, this can be an important issue because even if the HPCS dedicated electrical AC division is available, HPCS may eventually fail because of pool heatup. Of the previous studies that have tended to consider long term failures, only battery depletion (failing either HPCI or RCIC) has been considered.

o   NUREG/CR-4550 treated ATWS in more detail than any previous analysis. It used a detailed Human Reliability Analysis (HRA) and event tree analysis coupled with improved thermal-hydraulic analyses. The HRA indicates that with the improved procedures and training, today's operators are better prepared and there is _little_ reluctance to inject boron. The thermal-hydraulic analyses reveal that failure to initiate boron does not necessarily lead directly to core damage. Low pressure injection systems, can for some period of time, give operators sufficient opportunity for a variety of corrective actions. These issues indicate that ATWS contribution has decreased and not the significant contributor once thought.

o   NUREG/CR-4550 gave considerable credit for alternate injection systems when the emergency systems failed to function. This credit was given because improved procedures have included instructions for alternate injection systems such as condensate, cross-ties from the Service

STATION BLACKOUT PLANT DAMAGE STATE (PDS) DESCRIPTIONS	MEAN FREQUENCY	PERCENT CONTRIBUTION (PDS/Total Core Damage)	DOMINANT CONTRIBUTORS
Grand Gulf:			
TB - Long term with HPCS providing coolant makeup	2.0E-5	71%/69%	o Recovery of LOSP o HPCS long term failure from seal failure o Diesel hardware failure
TBVW - Long term with HPCS providing coolant makeup and RHR not available with LOSP recovery	1.1E-6	4%/4%	o Recovery of LOSP o HPCS long term failure from seal failure o SW common mode failure
TBU1 - Long term with HPCS failure and RCIC providing coolant makeup	2.4E-6	9%/8%	o Recovery of LOSP o Diesel hardware failure
TBU - Short term with HPCS and RCIC failure	9.4E-7	3%/3%	o Recovery of LOSP o Diesel hardware failure o RCIC hardware failure
TBUX - Short term with HPCS with RCIC failure and no DC	3.8E-6	13%/13%	o Recovery of LOSP o Battery common mode failure
Peach Bottom:			
TB - Long term with HPCI and RCIC providing coolant makeup (battery depletion)	2.3E-6	33%/28%	o Recovery of LOSP and Diesel o Diesel hardware failure o Diesel maintenance o Operator failure to start SW pump
TBP - Same as TB but with stuck open SRV	1.2E-7	2%/1%	o Same as TB o SRVs stuck open
TBU - Same as TBU but with HPCI and RCIC failure and no DC	1.6E-7	2%/2%	o Recovery of LOSP o RCIC failure to start o Recovery of Battery hardware o Battery hardware of Division 2 o HPCIs' failure to start
TBUP - Same as TBU but with stuck open SRV	2.0E-7	3%/3%	o SRV sticks open o Battery common mode failure o Recovery of LOSP
TBUX - Short term with HPCI and RCIC failure and no DC	4.2E-6	60%/51%	o Battery common mode

Table 3: Grand Gulf and Peach Bottom NUREG/CR-4550 Station Blackout Results

Water (SW), and Control Rod Drive (CRD). Additionally, updated thermal-hydraulic analyses have indicated that the CRD can provide sufficient makeup for transient type accidents if its capacity is $\geq$ 200 gpm. Credit for these many alternate injection systems has greatly decreased the contribution of loss of injection type accident sequences to the core damage frequency. Previous studies have normally only given credit for the emergency core cooling systems, power conversion system and reactor core isolation cooling system for coolant makeup to the reactor. Some credit has been given for the condensate system, but is has been fairly minimal.

o   NUREG/CR-4550 examined the issue of continued survivability of equipment after containment failure in detail; that is, whether some systems would continue to operate after containment failure. Previous studies assumed that containment failure resulted in loss of injection. This conclusion was arrived at because it was assumed that (1) the pumps could not pump saturated water (pool goes to saturated conditions upon containment failure) or there were net positive suction head problems (loss of pool inventory -- flashing --- after containment failure) or (2) containment failure resulted in deformation of injection lines. Neither of these assumptions are always correct. Previous studies tend not to give credit for containment venting with makeup to the suppression pool. Incorporation of these issues has significantly reduced the contribution of loss of long term heat removal type accident sequences to the core damage frequency.

In summary, because of the considerable redundancy and diversity of coolant injection and heat removal features at both Grand Gulf and Peach Bottom, it is not surprising that common features of the plant tend to drive the core damage frequency. These include failure of common support systems (AC power and service water), common cause failures of equipment, and to some extent, human error. The above insights can be considered applicable to other BWRs of similar design to the extent that the redundancy arguments are true for other BWR plants of interest.

REFERENCES

[1]   M.T. Drouin, et al., Core Damage Frequency from Internal Initiators at Grand Gulf, Unit 1, NUREG/CR-4550, Volume 6 of 10, SAND86-2084, November 1986.

[2]   A.M. Kolaczkowski, et al., Core Damage Frequency from Initial Initiators at Peach Bottom, Unit 2, NUREG/CR-4550, Volume 4 of 10, SAND86-2084, October 1986.

[3]   United States Nuclear Regulatory Commission, Reactor Safety Study, WASH-1400, October 1975.

[4]   Interim Reliability Program: Analysis of the Millstone Point Unit 1 Nuclear Power Plant, NUREG/CR-3085, SAND82-7212, Volumes 1-4, May 1983.

[5]   S.W. Hatch, et al., Reactor Safety Studies Methodology Applications Program: Grand Gulf #1 BWR Power Plant, NUREG/CR-1659/4 of 4, SAND80-1897/4 of 4, October 1981.

465

[6] "Technical Report, IDCOR Task 21.1, Risk Reduction Potential," Energy Incorporated, November 1984.

[7] Probabilistic Risk Assessment: Limerick Generating Station, Philadelphia Electric, Co., Rev 4, June 1982.

[8] Probabilistic Risk Assessment Shoreham Nuclear Power Station, Science Applications, Inc., SAI=372-83-PA-01, June 24, 1983.

PROBABILISTIC SAFETY ASSESSMENT APPLICATIONS AND INSIGHTS

M.J. Hitchler, N.L. Burns,N.J. Liparulo
(Westinghouse Risk Assessment Technology)
Pittsburgh, Pennsylvania, USA

F.J. Mink
(Westinghouse)
Brussels, Belgium

Summary

    The insights gained through a comparison of seven PRA
studies (Italian PUN, Sizewell B, Ringhals 2, Millstone 3, Zion
1 and 2, Oconee 3, and Seabrook) included insights regarding the
adequacy of the PRA technology utilized in the studies and the
potential areas for improvement and insights regarding the
adequacy of plant designs and how PRA has been utilized to
enhance the design and operation of nuclear power plants.

1.0 INTRODUCTION
    Since the United States Nuclear Regulatory Commission's
publication of the "Reactor Safety Study" (Wash-1400) in 1975,
the use of probabilistic risk assessment (PRA) by the nuclear
power industry has increased dramatically. Approximately 30 PRA
studies of varying degrees of scope have been or are being
performed in the United States alone. Many European studies
have also been performed. Through comparison of the studies,
numerous insights and conclusions can be drawn. These insights
can then be applied to enhance the design and operation of all
nuclear power plants. The intent of this paper is to compare
the internal events results of several PRA studies, namely
Italian PUN, Sizewell B, Ringhals 2, Millstone 3, Zion 1 and 2,
Oconee 3, and Seabrook, to determine these insights and to gain
information about the important contributors to risk.

2.0 RESULTS OF PRA STUDIES
    The plants utilized in the PRA studies vary widely across
plant characteristics. The number of reactor coolant loops, the
power of the reactor, the reactor supplier and the architect
engineer are characteristics that make each plant unique and can
affect the results of a PRA study. Also the time frame in which
the PRA study was performed can have varying impacts on the
results of the study. For example, the degree of development of
PRA technology or the use of operating experience at the time of
the study can greatly affect the results.

The PUN and Sizewell B plants are in the design stages while Seabrook is scheduled to start operation in the near future. Millstone 3 began power operation in 1986. Zion, Oconee 3, and Ringhals 2 have been in operation for over ten years.

2.1 Core Damage Frequencies

The core damage frequencies for internal initiating events range from 1E-06 to 2E-04 per reactor year for the studies examined. The core damage frequencies for each of the PRA studies are shown in Figure 1. Seabrook, a newer plant, has an unusually high core damage frequency compared to the other PRA studies. This may be attributed to plant design, operation, PRA methods, analytical assumptions, or the scope of the study. Generally, the core damage frequency alone is not a good representation of plant characteristics. The dominant contributors to the core damage frequency yield more valuable information concerning a plant's vulnerabilities.

2.2 Dominant Accident Sequences

For the Ringhals 2 PRA, most of the dominant sequences involve a loss of coolant accident coupled with a failure of recirculation. This implies that the Ringhals 2 plant has a good main and auxiliary feedwater system because no transient events appear in the top ten sequences.

The Sizewell B dominant accident sequences include LOCAs with failure of injection or recirculation, an anticipated transient without scram and LOCAs with a loss of component cooling water. The failures of recirculation and injection are hardware failures and not operator errors. This is due to the design of the Sizewell B plant which attempts to limit the amount of operator action required during normal and abnormal operation.

The most important sequences in the Oconee 3 study involve a loss of low pressure service water which results in reactor coolant pump seal LOCAs. Other dominant sequences involve operator errors in failure to achieve cooling by recirculation or injection. Oconee 3's sequences also include a plant specific initiator - a loss of instrument air.

In the Millstone 3 study, the dominant accident sequences are more widely distributed with no sequence being greater than ten percent and the most dominant sequence being a medium LOCA with failure of recirculation. Other sequences include some type of loss of vital power - either vital AC power, vital DC power or a loss of offsite power.

FIGURE 1
CORE DAMGE FREQUENCIES
FOR INTERNAL INITIATING EVENTS

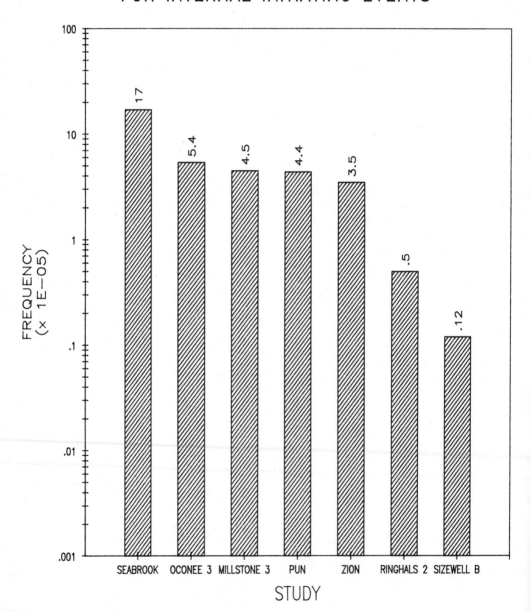

A small LOCA with failure of recirculation is the most dominant sequence for the Zion plant contributing approximately 46 percent to the total core damage frequency. Also the top four sequences for Zion involve operator errors in failure to achieve recirculation.

A loss of offsite power event with failure to recover offsite power or failure of continued onsite power (the "station blackout" accident sequence) dominates the accident sequences for the Seabrook study. Other sequences involve a loss of support system such as component cooling, service water and vital DC power.

For the Italian PUN design, a small LOCA with a failure of recirculation is the dominant accident sequence. Failure of accumulators and loss of support systems (component cooling and AC/DC power) also dominate the accident sequences.

The common sequences found throughout the studies include:
1. Loss of Coolant Accidents with failure of recirculation.
2. Station Blackout with failure to recover power.
3. Loss of coolant accidents with failure of injection.
4. Steam generator tube rupture with failure to depressurize.
5. Interfacing Systems LOCA.
6. Transients with feedwater available.
7. Transients without feedwater available.
8. Events with a loss of a support system (SW, CCW, Vital power).
9. Anticipated Transients without Scram (ATWS) events.
10. Loss of Offsite power events.

These sequences are contributors to the core damage frequency regardless of plant design.

If these contributions are tabulated to give a general overview of the types of dominant accident sequences as shown in Figure 2, the major contributors are small LOCAs with failure of recirculation, other LOCAs with failure of recirculation, events that result in a loss of service water or a loss of component cooling water, LOCAs with failure of injection and station blackout. If future designs take into account these types of accident sequences, the core damage frequency due to these sequences could be reduced. Also operating plants can utilize this information to develop and train operating personnel for response to these types of accidents.

FIGURE 2
GENERAL SEQUENCE CONTRIBUTORS

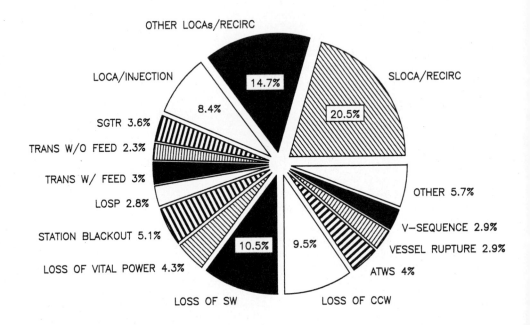

2.3 Initiating Event Frequencies

The events leading to the largest contribution to the core damage frequency vary across the PRAs. Oconee 3's largest contribution comes from a loss of service water, Millstone 3 and Seabrook from a loss of offsite power, Sizewell B, Ringhals 2 and Zion from a small LOCA and PUN from a Turbine Trip.

For a small LOCA event, the range of initiating event frequencies is 9E-04/year to 3.54E-02/year. The Zion frequency (3.54E-02/year) accounts for a small LOCA event that occurred at the Zion plant which was included in the calculation of the small LOCA initiating event frequency. The frequency for a loss of offsite power event ranges from 3.5E-02/year for Sizewell B to 7E-01/year for Ringhals 2 with most PRAs using a frequency of 0.1 events per year. The other initiating event frequencies are fairly consistent in the number of events per year for the given initiators.

The total number of initiating events considered in the seven PRA studies examined is roughly about 10 events per year. This number is relatively consistent regardless of whether or not the PRA study utilized plant specific data or PWR population data or whether or not Bayesian techniques were used to calculate the frequencies.

3.0 INSIGHTS

The insights that can be gained from a review of these seven PRA studies and other studies fall into two general categories - the adequacy of the technology utilized in the PRA studies and the adequacy of the plant designs. Each of the insights gained is discussed below.

3.1 Adequacy of PRA Technology

The level of maturity of the various elements of a PRA study depends on the desired end uses of the analysis. However, the PRAs examined utilized state of the art methodology at the time the PRA was performed. The studies appear to be complete in terms of the events considered and the systems analyzed. The utilization of experimental data and operating experience in the PRA studies appears to enhance the validity of the study and the representativeness of plant behavior. The following describes some of these elements.

Initiating Events Determination

The initiating events identified from operating experience are included in most of the PRAs. Also the detailed review of possible plant specific initiators that have occurred in the plants with operating experience have yielded a complete list of possible accident events.

The method used to calculate the initiating event frequencies varies across the PRAs. Zion and Oconee utilized generic PWR plant population data that was updated by plant specific operating experience using Bayesian techniques. Sizewell, due to no plant specific information, used the Zion initiating event frequencies in its study. Millstone 3 used surrogate plant operating experience to determine the frequencies of most of its initiators as did PUN and Seabrook. Ringhals 2 estimated the frequencies from plant specific data and data from other sources. Although different methods were used, the frequencies for the events are comparable.

Most of the initiating events utilized in each of the studies are similar. However, some plant specific initiators are incorporated into the Ringhals 2, Seabrook, PUN, Millstone 3, and Oconee 3 PRAs. Also, in the more recent PRAs the loss of support systems as initiating events were examined more closely and more event categories were utilized to determine their effects on the plant. These events such as loss of instrument air, DC power buses, service water or component cooling water may cause many frontline systems to fail and may also cause a reactor trip. The inclusion of support system failures as initiators in a PRA study leads to a more complete evaluation of plant responses.

Inclusion of RCP Seal LOCAs in Modeling

During station blackout accident sequences, most PRAs postulate that cooling would be lost to the RCP seals and these seals would begin to leak and lead to a LOCA condition. This was assumed to eventually lead to core uncovery and core damage if no AC power was restored.

Early PRA models of RCP seal performance following a loss of all cooling to the RCP seals were simplistic because the response of the seals was not well understood. The model assumed that a 300 gpm/ pump leak occurred 30 minutes after a loss of all cooling. This assumption lead to an estimated time for recovery of AC power before core damage of approximately 2 3/4 hours. This allowed for little time in which to recover AC power by the operators and maintenance personnel. Thus the probabilities for power recovery used in the PRA models were very low and this led to station blackout sequences with failure to recover power and RCP seal LOCAs becoming dominant sequences.

Because of these assumptions and the inclusion of this type of accident in the dominant accident sequences of most PRAs, the NRC conducted tests on the RCP seals. The tests determined that the leakage rate from the seals was dependent on the quality of the O-rings and the conditions of the plant (i.e., whether or not cooldown was possible). Utilizing this new information has lead to a refinement and the removal of some of the conservativeness of the previous PRA models. With the new model, the time to core uncovery following a station blackout accident and loss of all cooling could be increased to approximately 5-6 hours with a high probability of the core not being uncovered. This allows for higher probabilities of recovery of AC power because the time frame for operator response is greater. Thus the station blackout sequence accident sequence frequencies would decrease and possibly the core damage frequency would be reduced.

0300x:1D/072487

Human Error Modeling

The development of a detailed analysis of the operator actions involved in the prevention of core damage given an initiating event is an important consideration in a PRA study. Many actions must be taken by the operator during the course of an accident. Also plant testing and maintenance procedures could severely limit the availability of mitigation systems. Operator recovery actions given a system has failed are included in most PRAs and significantly reduce the core damage frequency.

3.2 Adequacy of Plant Design

Some vulnerabilities of a plant's design have arisen from a PRA study performed for that plant. Some of these vulnerabilities can apply to other plants also. If these considerations are accounted for by either operating procedures or through plant modifications, the availability and safety of the plant may be increased. The following describes some of the vulnerabilities determined in the studies.

Loss of Offsite Power / Station Blackout

The ability of a plant design to handle an extended loss of offsite power or a prolonged station blackout is currently a major issue in the regulatory environment. It is currently a NRC unresolved safety issue. Many frontline and support systems are dependent on AC power or DC power. The loss of offsite power requires that the emergency power diesel generators operate and are of sufficient power to supply all the major systems needed to achieve shutdown conditions. Several plants have included diversity and more redundancy in their designs to account for long periods without offsite power.

Ringhals 2 identified that the frequency of a loss of offsite power is greater than in other PRAs due to high frequency of salt storms in the winter months. The Ringhals 2 plant has four onsite dedicated diesel generators and several gas turbine generators to ensure that AC power would be available to the plant. Oconee 3 utilizes hydro units that are onsite in the event of a loss of offsite power. These hydro units are more reliable than diesel generators.

Recirculation Failures

The failure of recirculation following a loss of coolant accident is the largest contributor to the core damage frequency for the PRAs examined. Operator error in failing to initiate recirculation by switching the suction from the RWST to the containment sump is the dominant failure mode. Because operator errors were determined to be extremely important to the prevention of core damage in the PRAs, modifications to procedures and designs have been incorporated to lessen the impact of operator errors in the initiation of recirculation.

474

        Some newer designs have taken recirculation failures into
account. More alarms that alert the operator of a low water
level in the RWST have been added at some plants. Also
operating procedures have been improved along with the training
of the plant operators. More advanced designs have incorporated
automatic switchover devices to take the action out of the hands
of the operator. Another design utilizes the refilling of the
RWST from the containment sump. This eliminates the need to
initiate recirculation.
        Some of these designs would most likely decrease the
failure probability in achieving recirculation. This would in
turn decrease the contribution of the LOCA with failure of
recirculation accident sequences to the overall core damage
frequency and would also decrease the possibility of core damage.

4.0 CONCLUSIONS

        Numerous insights, both generic and plant specific, can be
determined through the use of a PRA study. These insights can
lead to modifications to plant design and improved reliability
of the plant as a whole. Modeling insights can be utilized
during the development and implementation of a PRA study to
yield a more complete and more widely accepted PRA study. The
performance of a PRA can lead to significant improvements in the
understanding of the design and operation of the plant.

5.0 REFERENCES

1.   Seabrook Station Probabilistic Safety Assessment, Public
        Service Company of New Hampshire and Yankee Atomic
        Electric Company, Pickard, Lowe and Garrick, Inc.,
        December 1983.

2.   Oconee PRA, A Probabilistic Risk Assessment of Oconee Unit
        3, Duke Power Company, Nuclear Safety Analysis Center,
        Electric Power Research Institute, NSAC-60, June 1984.

3.   Ringhals 2 PRA Summary Report, MITRA-Slutrapport, Swedish
        State Power Board, NUS Corporation, dated April 25,1985.

4.   Millstone Unit 3 Probabilistic Safety Study, Northeast
        Utilities Company, August 1983.

5.   Sizewell B Probabilistic Safety Study, Westinghouse, 1983.

6.   Italian PUN Probabilistic Safety Study, ENEL,
        Ansaldo/NIRA, and Westinghouse, 1984.

7.   Zion Probabilistic Safety Study, Commonwealth Edison
        Company, 1981.

COMBINED QUANTITATIVE-QUALITATIVE RISK AND SAFETY EVALUATIONS
FOR SPACE FLIGHT SYSTEMS

Dr. Christian PREYSSL
European Space Agency
ESTEC-Product Assurance and Safety Departement
P.O.Box 299 NL-2200 AG Noordwijk   Netherlands

ABSTRACT

The traditional approach towards risk and safety evaluations
for space flight systems has been based mainly on qualitative
analysis methods because of the lack of statistical data. Within
"fuzzy risk analysis" the spectrum of data that ranges from
statistical data to qualitative expressions from expert judgement
is treated. This combined quantitative-qualitative method is
based on the characterization of an undesirable event by the
"degrees of consequence, occurrence rate, uncertainty and type of
information", which are the constituents of "fuzzy risk". Risk
results are the basis for decisions during all phases of space
flight programs.

I. INTRODUCTION

Manned space flight programs incorporate systems comprising hardware, software and man-machine interfaces of extremely high complexity. The evolution of such systems involves the elimination,
or minimization and control of potential threats to system safety
i.e. hazards. Each remaining hazard requires systematic investigation of the associated risks by performing a safety analysis
So far mainly qualitative analysis methods have been used by the
space industry, known as "Hazard Analysis" and "Failure Mode
Effects and Criticality Analysis".Hazards are classified according to the severity of the consequences they might induce without considering explicitly the occurrence rate of such an event.
Little use has been made of existing quantitative risk analysis
approaches. The main reason for not applying quantitative safety
analysis techniques is the lack of statistical data on space
flight systems. Existing related qualitative data so far have not
been used in a systematic way in order to perform a risk assessment. Within the concept of "fuzzy risk analysis" it becomes
possible to make use of all types of data in the same model.

II. "FUZZY RISK ANALYSIS" METHOD

The spectrum of generally available data ranges from

- quantitative data based on objective statistical information
  -expressing randomness-obtained from tests and previous
  experience, to
- qualitative data based on subjective specialist judgement-
  expressing fuzziness-where no statistical experience or test
  data exists.

In a typically practical situation one will always have a mixture
of objective and subjective data.

Each undesirable event induced by a hazard in a system can be
characterized by the

- severity of the consequence of the event
- occurrence rate of the event
- uncertainty in the data and the model of the event
- type of information on the event.

"fuzzy risk analysis" is based on the following set of measures

- degree of severity of the consequence C
- degree of occurrence rate S
- degree of uncertainty U
- degree of objectivity of information I

which are the constituents of "fuzzy risk" as represented in
figure 1.

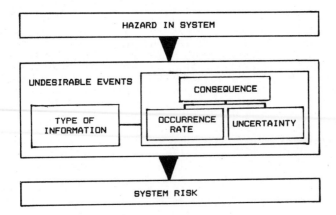

Figure 1

The concept of "degree" d of a characteristic A of an event E is based on "fuzzy mathematics" and "fuzzy logic", where

$$A(E) \longrightarrow d(A(E)) \in [0,1]$$

To each numerical value of the unity interval a qualitative attributive expression is associated and vice versa. As an example, in table 1, the "degree of occurrence" S of an event E — measured by either the probability P or possibility Q — corresponds to a defined set of ranked qualitative expressions. For all other degrees such a table can be defined.

P(E)	QUALITATIVE EXPRESSION	Q(E)
1.0	CERTAIN	1.0
10^{-1} - 1.0	MOST PROBABLE	0.9-1.0
10^{-2} -10^{-1}	QUITE PROBABLE	0.7-0.9
10^{-3} -10^{-2}	PROBABLE	0.5-0.7
10^{-4} -10^{-3}	RATHER PROBABLE	0.3-0.5
10^{-5} -10^{-4}	IMPROBABLE	0.2-0.3
10^{-7} -10^{-5}	HIGHLY IMPROBABLE	0.1-0.2
10^{-8} -10^{-7}	EXTREMLY IMPROBABLE	0.01-0.1
0.0 -10^{-8}	NEXT TO IMPOSSIBLE	0.0-0.01
0.0	IMPOSSIBLE	0.0

Table 1

A specific algebra is associated with each of the degrees which allows the modelling of event combinations.
In order to distinguish between randomness and fuzziness, possibility theory is used for the modelling of subjective information and probability theory is used for the modelling of objective information. The combination of events yields the use of the applicable algebra associated with the logic operators AND, OR, NOT and IF. In probability theory the following applies

$$P(A"AND"B) = P(A).P(B)$$
$$P(A"OR"B) = P(A)+P(B)-P(A"AND"B)$$
$$P(A)+P("NOT"A) = 1$$
$$P(A"IF"B) = P(A|B)$$

whereas in possibility theory

$$Q(A"AND"B) = \min\{Q(A),Q(B)\}$$
$$Q(A"OR"B) = \max\{Q(A),Q(B)$$
$$\max\{Q(A),Q("NOT"A)\} = 1$$
$$Q(A"IF"B) = Q(A|B)$$

In "fuzzy risk analysis" emphasis is put on the display and propagation of uncertainty i.e. the associated degrees."Data uncertainty" of an event is either displayed as a probability distribution of the probability of occurrence or as a possibility distribution of the possibility of occurrence. "Model uncertainty"
measures the sensitivity of the model of event combination to the
"degree of objectivity".
The "degree of objectivity" indicates where, between the probabilistic and possibilistic quantitative results, the "degree of
occurrence" of an event, originating from the combination of
other events, has to be allocated.
The "risk" R of a system can then be defined as the set of resulting "uncertainty distributions" s´ of the "degrees of occurrence" S induced by the "degree of objectivity" I associated with
the discrete "degrees of consequence" Cj

$$R = \{I:s´[S(Cj)],j \in N\}$$

and can be translated into a set of qualitative expressions
addressing each consequence-severity level separately.
As an example the "risk" of a system asscociated with the "degree
of consequence" C = 1.0, and the "degree of objectivity" I = 0.2
is displayed as the curve in figure 2.

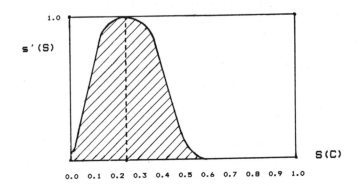

Figure 2

This quantitative representation corresponds to the qualitative
formulation:

  "Based on mainly subjective information it is more or less
  certain that the event with the worst consequence is
  improbable"

The objective of generating risk results is in their use for:

- the ranking of alternative system-configurations by ranking
  the risks
- the optimization of systems by reducing the risks
- the evaluation of compliance of residual system risks
  with risk standards or safety goals

The use of qualitative expressions facilitates the interpretation
and application of results in the decision making process during
all space-flight project phases.

III. CONCLUSION

The "fuzzy risk analysis" method provides a combined quantitative
-qualitative risk assessment concept which is based on the optimized use of models and the full range of existing data. Risk
results represent a suitable basis for supporting decisions at
all phases of space flight programs.

REFERENCES

1. C.Preyssl, "Risk Assessment Based on 'Fuzzy Mathematics'"
   presented at Conference on "Development of Risk Criteria for
   the Nuclear Fuel Cycle" - IAEA - Prague 1987

2. C.Preyssl, "Fuzzy Risk Analysis - Theory and Application"
   presented at "Society for Risk Analysis Conference 1986"
   - Boston 1986

3. D.Dubois,H.Prade, "Fuzzy Sets and Systems" - Academic Press
   - 1980

4. Y.Nishiwaki,C.Preyssl et al., "Optimization of Radiation
   Protection and the Possible Application of Fuzzy Set Theory"
   presented at "International Symposion on the Optimization of
   Radiation Protection" - IAEA SM 285/36 - Vienna 1986

5. Documents of the "European Space Agency" and "NASA"

SYSTEM MODELLING TECHNIQUES AND
INSIGHTS FROM THE DARLINGTON
PROBABILISTIC SAFETY EVALUATION STUDY

V.M. Raina, F.K. King, K.S. Dinnie, P.A. Webster, D.G.R. Anderson, E.M. Chan,
P.C. Chow
Ontario Hydro
Toronto, Ontario

KEY WORDS: Accident Sequence Identification, CANDU risk assessment

1.0   Introduction

Perhaps the most important task in the probabilistic safety assessment of a
nuclear power plant is the identification of sequences of events that can lead
to the release of radioactivity to the environment, and the calculation of their
frequencies of occurrence. Although almost all such assessments use the event
tree and fault tree techniques to carry out this task, it is probably fair to
say that no two PRAs are exactly the same in terms of the detailed application
of these techniques. The differences arise due to factors such as the purpose
for which the assessment is being undertaken, the specific nature of the reactor
design being analyzed, whether the study is pre- or post-operational, etc. It
is the purpose of this paper to describe how the general principles of nuclear
power plant risk assessment were applied in the conduct of the Darlington
Probabilistic Safety Evaluation (DPSE) Study. The paper presents examples of
accident sequences uncovered by the application of the adopted methodology,
which could not have been detected by any other means. It is such results and
insights that are felt to be the most useful products of a probabilistic safety
assessment.

2.0   DPSE Risk Assessment Process

The primary objectives of the DPSE study were to provide a thorough safety
design verification of the Darlington Station using probabilistic methods and to
identify those accident sequences that dominate public health risk and economic
risk to the utility. The following tasks were undertaken as part of the process
to achieve these objectives:

(a)   Identification of potential initiating events.

(b)   Development of event trees to identify those mitigating system failures
whose occurrence coincident with the various initiating events could
lead to core damage and release of radioactivity outside containment.

(c)   Development of fault trees for the various mitigating system failure
modes.

and

(d)   Integration of event tree and fault tree models to identify accident
sequences of concern.

The highlights of each of these activities are presented next. Containment analysis, and public health and economic consequence analyses are described in Reference 1.

3.0   Initiating Events

The initiating events considered in the DPSE study fell into one or more of the following categories.

3.1   Loss of Coolant Events

Four major subclasses of loss of coolant events were chosen based on the capabilities of systems and equipment provided to mitigate the effects of LOCAs. These systems and equipment are the D_2O feed system, the high pressure emergency coolant injection pumps and the low pressure emergency injection pumps. Also included were breaks that could lead to flow stagnation in the horizontal fuel channels and consequent fuel damage. Of particular interest in an analysis of the CANDU reactor are pressure tube failures, end-fitting failures and losses of coolant induced by fuelling machine failures.

3.2   Loss of Heat Transport Pressure Control

The list of initiating events included those events that could lead to either excessive heat transport pressurization or depressurization since either of these can lead to a breach in the heat transport system.

3.3   Loss of Moderator and End-Shield Cooling

The moderator and end-shield cooling systems are unique to the design of the CANDU system. Failures of these cooling systems, if not mitigated, can affect the structural integrity of the calandria, thereby potentially causing pressure tube and calandria tube failures.

3.4   Interruption in Steam Generator Heat Removal

A number of malfunctions in the normal feedwater system, steam system and heat transport circulation that could disturb the normal function of heat removal via the steam generators were identified. Among these were initiating events such as feed and steam line breaks, turbine trips and heat transport pump trips.

3.5   Reactivity Control Failures

Losses of reactivity control leading to neutron overpower were considered because of the possibility of impairment of fuel channel integrity.

3.6   Support System Failures

Failure modes and effects analyses were carried out for the electrical power, instrument air and the various service water systems to determine which malfunctions of these should be treated as initiating events. The criterion chosen was that the initiating event should not only cause the plant to be disturbed to the extent that a reactor shutdown was likely, but also affect one or more functions required for post trip heat removal. The list of initiating events thus identified was supplemented subsequently by a review of the mitigating system fault trees to determine if any events therein could initiate a transient. Special attention was paid to the various types of control power supplies provided in the station design.

The Darlington generating units will each be controlled by a dual digital computer control (DCC) system. The DCC system controls reactor and turbine power, heat transport pressure and inventory, and steam generator level and pressure. Certain malfunctions of the digital computer control system can thus cause a plant upset, and these were considered as initiating events.

Events such as severe earthquakes, tornadoes, aircraft crashes, widespread internal fires and flooding were not considered. It was felt that because of the extremely low probability of these events, coupled with the fact that thorough deterministic safety assessments were made for these phenomena, there was little to be gained by including them in the study, especially since probabilistic methods for handling these are not well-developed.

A complete list of the initiating events considered in the study may be found in Reference 1. A total of 38 event categories were identified.

4.0   Event Tree Analysis

The primary objective of the event tree analysis was to identify those mitigating system failure modes following an initiating event that could alter the course of an accident sequence enough to significantly affect the degree of fuel damage. Thus, the event tree top events were essentially failures of the various functions required to maintain fuel integrity. Service system failures, specific component failures or human errors were, in general, not shown in the event trees.

Event trees for two types of initiating events, viz, losses of coolant and the occurrence of a reactor shutdown, due to whatever reason, were developed in some detail, as it was felt that these would lead to the identification of all generic sequences causing fuel damage due to any one of the following three fundamental mechanisms.

(a)   Failure to shutdown

(b)   Uncontrolled loss of coolant

(c)   Failure to remove decay heat.

Thus, almost all mitigating functions that needed to be further analyzed were identified in these event trees. Event tree analysis was also carried out for other initiating events to identify any additional mitigating functions and to determine how, if at all, they affected the reliability of the mitigating functions shown in the event trees for losses of coolant and reactor shutdown. A convenient way of doing so was to incorporate these effects in the high levels of the fault tree logic for the mitigating functions, or the detailed system fault trees, as appropriate.

An example of an event tree taken from the study is shown in Figure 1. The initiating event is a small loss of coolant with a discharge rate beyond the capacity of the D_2O feed pumps. The top line of the event tree shows the expected sequence of events which comprises:

(a)   An automatic reactor trip on low pressurizer level or heat transport (HT) pressure (SD).

(b)   Automatic cooldown of the HT system by the opening of eight instrumented steam relief valves on the secondary side, triggered by the simultaneous occurrence of low HT pressure and high reactor building pressure (CD2).

(c)   Automatic startup of the high pressure and low pressure emergency coolant injection (ECI) pumps, connected in a series arrangement, and automatic opening of the injection valves between the ECI systems and the HT system (HPI), and

(d)   Manually-initiated low pressure recovery in the long term (LPR).

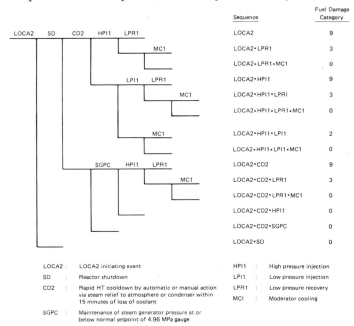

FIGURE 1
Event Tree For Loss of Coolant LOCA 2 Initiating Event

Next, the failure of each one of these functions is postulated, in turn, starting from the right-most function, and the sequences carried on until there are no other systems available to control the accident sequence. Finally, the identified sequences are placed in their appropriate consequence categories, as determined by the amount of fuel damage associated with them. Nine such in-plant fuel damage categories, FDC1 to FDC9, were defined, with FDC1 being the most severe, with about 30% of the nominal equilibrium core inventory released into containment. FDC9, although labelled a fuel damage category, does not actually result in fuel damage, but was included in the study since the actuation of the ECI system in a CANDU reactor following a loss of coolant event causes the injection of light water into the core and the potential for significant economic consequences.

Table 1 describes the fuel damage categorization scheme. A tenth category, called FDC0, was also defined, in which were collected all 'severe' accidents that result from failure of all possible mitigating systems. The safety assurance objective then is to show that the frequency of FDC0 is negligibly small, since an analysis of releases into containment and the response of containment to this event was not carried out. Examples of events that were placed in FDC0 are failure to shutdown the reactor when required, failure of both ECI and the moderator heat sink after a loss of coolant, and total loss of core heat removal after a transient initiating event.

Event tree analysis was also carried out for the containment systems, with fuel damage categories FDC1 to FDC8 as the 'initiating events' and various ex-plant release categories (EPRCs) as the end-states of interest. As in the case of the FDCs, a 'severe' ex-plant release category, called EPRC0, was defined to include those sequences for which there was insufficient analytical support to demonstrate that the containment structure would remain intact. Again, the objective of the safety assessment here was to show that the probability of such events is negligibly small.

TABLE 1
Fuel Damage Category Descriptions

FDC	Release Magnitude[1] BE[2]	PM[3]	Description
0			Loss of core structural integrity.
1	15	30	Large LOCA, total and indefinite loss of ECI injection.
2	5	10	As above, but for a small break or equivalent.
3	2	3	Fuel cooling lost at least one hour after reactor shutdown. Typical event is failure of emergency coolant recirculation.
4	2	4	Large LOCA with near-instantaneous release due to early flow stagnation.
5	1	2	Large LOCA but with potential for delayed release after steam blowdown.
6	0.2	1	Single channel event. End fitting failure with fuel ejection to reactor vault.
7	0.001	1	Single channel event. In-core break with fuel ejection to moderator.
8	0.0001	0.4	Loss of cooling to irradiated fuel in the fuelling machine.
9	0	0	Small LOCA without significant additional fuel failures.

Notes:
1. Approximate release of long-lived alkali metals expressed as a percentage of nominal, equilibrium core inventory.
2. Best estimate.
3. Probable maximum.

5.0   Fault Tree Analysis

Fault trees were developed for all systems whose failure could affect the reliability of the mitigating functions identified in the plant event trees, the supporting high level logic and the containment event tree. A list of the systems analyzed by fault trees is shown in Table 2.

The fault tree analysis was the primary mechanism by which the fundamental objective of the DPSE study, viz., a thorough design review of the station, was expected to be met. Therefore, considerable attention was devoted to this aspect of the study.

The fault trees were constructed in a step-by-step manner so as to promote scrutability and ease of review by others. As well, the step-by-step process provides the capability of carrying out a comprehensive system analysis and the identification of failure modes that may turn out to be significant, although not obvious at first. This method of fault tree development does, however, lead to the generation of fairly large fault trees.

For each mitigating system failure mode identified a single fault tree was constructed, with any boundary conditions and sequence dependencies directly incorporated into the fault tree. This was preferred over the alternative method of generating different fault trees for the same failure modes but for different initiating events or other system failures, as it was felt to provide efficiency and flexibility in the logic model development.

Special care was taken in the fault tree modelling to identify dependencies between systems. Both the so-called shared-equipment and functional dependencies (Reference 2) between systems were explicitly included in the fault trees. Also included were the possibilities that unqualified equipment might fail when exposed to the harsh environment resulting from high energy pipe breaks in the turbine hall or the auxiliary reactor building. Support system failures that might affect a front-line system were included in the front-line system's fault tree as primary, or so-called developed events.

As Table 2 shows, among the systems for which fault trees were developed were the control computer system, and the micro-processor based programmable controllers used in place of conventional relay logic. To obtain logic models for postulated failures of the numerous analog and digital outputs a representative output of each type was first analyzed in detail. Subsequently, the generic models thus developed were used as the basis for the logic development of other outputs. The reliability data for the quantification of component failure probability were obtained either from MIL-HDBK 217D (Reference 3) or from the manufacturer. Further details of programmable controller fault tree models may be found in Reference 4.

Human interactions were modelled in the fault trees at both the component and system levels. The various human errors considered were: operators inadvertently disabling equipment during testing or maintenance, failing to detect that component failure had occurred, or failing to take appropriate corrective action after the occurrence of an initiating event. Generic models of these were developed for use in preliminary quantification (Reference 9). Final quantification of some significant human interactions was based on the results of a "Paired Comparisons" exercise (Reference 6) that involved 12 members of the Darlington Operations staff with a wide background of experience in reactor operations.

Each system fault tree was solved for its minimal cutsets by means of the SETS code (Reference 7). To minimize computing costs, the fault tree was first reduced in size by collapsing into a single event, or module, all the non-replicated (i.e., appearing only once in the fault tree) events below a gate event that were connected through OR gates. The fault tree modularization was carried out automatically by means of a computer code developed within Ontario Hydro. Details of the fault tree evaluation procedure have previously been reported in Reference 5.

TABLE 2
List of Systems Analysed by Detailed Fault Tree Analysis

1	Heat transport, pressure and inventory control, storage, transfer, and recovery systems	16	Class I power system
		17	Emergency power system
2	Heat transport pump gland seal and heat transport circulation systems	18	Standby generator system
		19	Emergency power generator system
3	Shutdown cooling system	20	Low pressure service water (open) system
4	Fuelling machine system		
5	Moderator system	21	Recirculated cooling water system
6	End shield cooling system	22	Powerhouse upper level service water system
7	Boiler feedwater system		
8	Condensate system	23	Emergency service water system
9	Steam generator emergency cooling system	24	Unit instrument air system
		25	Common instrument air system
10	Steam relief and bypass systems	26	Reactivity control systems
11	Unit control computer system	27	Shutdown system No. 1
12	Programmable controller	28	Shutdown system No. 2
13	Class IV power system	29	Emergency coolant injection system
14	Class III power system	30	Containment system
15	Class II power system	31	Airlocks and transfer chamber systems

6.0   Event Tree/Fault Tree Integration

The integration of the event trees and the fault trees is the final step in the calculation of the frequencies of occurrence of the various fuel damage and ex-plant release categories. Each of these categories, typically, represents the simultaneous failure following an initiating event of a number of front line systems for each of which a minimal cutset equation has been obtained in terms of component failures, initiating events and developed (i.e., support system failure) events. Thus, to calculate the frequencies of the FDCs and the EPRCs one must integrate the minimal cutsets of the front-line systems and the support systems as dictated by the logic of the accident sequence. It is the integration (or linking) process by which the impact of dependencies between systems can be assessed.

The integration of fault trees can become computationally impractical unless care is taken to optimize the process. The following were some of the steps taken to make this task manageable.

(a)   The various fault trees that needed to be merged in a given accident sequence were first examined by a computer code to identify any events that appeared in more than one fault tree. If any of these events had previously been placed in a module, it was extracted from the module and the module re-defined.

(b)   All those minimal cutsets of a system that did not contain either a developed event, an initiating event or a replicated event as a literal were identified by temporarily setting the latter types of events to the null set. These minimal cutsets were replaced by a single event.

(c)   Next, the developed events, the initiating events and the replicated events were temporarily set to probability 1.0, thereby artificially increasing their significance, and the minimal cutset list truncated at the probability of the highest contributor to system failure that only contained events unique to that system. This permitted the extraction and retention of only those minimal cutsets containing initiating events, developed events and replicated events that were significant.

(d)   Where the number of initiating events, replicated events and developed events, and their combinations in a minimal cutset equation was small, the system equation was expressed simply as:

$$
\begin{aligned}
\text{SYSTEM-EQN} = \ &\text{SYSTEM-UNQ} + \\
&\text{DD1} \\
&\text{SY-DD2-UNQ} * \text{DD2} + \\
&\text{SY-DD3-DD4-UNQ} * \text{DD3} * \text{DD4} + \\
&\text{SY-RE1-UNQ} * \text{RE1} \qquad + \\
&\text{SY-IE1-UNQ} * \text{IE1} \\
&\text{etc.}
\end{aligned}
$$

where SYSTEM-UNQ, SY-DD2-UNQ etc. contain component failures that do not appear in any other system fault tree, and hence could be treated as single events. The DDs are the developed events (symbolized by double diamonds), the REs the replicated events and IEs the initiating events.

(e)   The much simpler minimal cutset equation resulting from the application of steps (a) to (d) was then fully expanded and reduced by substituting into it the equations for the various developed events. Finally, the sequence equation was obtained, usually by merging minimal cutset equations for its constituents in a number of smaller steps.

The integration procedure followed is described in more detail in Reference 8.

7.0   Results

The computation of the minimal cutsets for the various fuel damage and ex-plant release categories led to the identification of a number of significant sequences that were either unrecognized previously, or whose frequency of occurrence was relatively 'high'. Among these were the following:

(a)   The occurrence of steam on feed-line breaks and the resulting simultaneous failure of unqualified normal electrical power and instrument air compressors had an adverse impact on the shutdown cooling system, which is one of the systems provided to mitigate secondary system failures. This was because the loss of instrument air led to a number of pneumatic valves failing open, and the loss of normal power led to fewer service water pumps being available. The resulting combination of excessive load and insufficient supply led to failure of the cooling water supply to the shutdown cooling heat exchangers.

(b)   Failure of a 48 V dc control power bus led to loss of half of the unit's power supply distribution system. This caused a significant loss of redundancy in the various process systems and, coupled with the random failure of a single instrument air compressor, led to the simultaneous loss of feedwater to the steam generators and shutdown cooling.

(c)   Loss of service water, and the consequent tripping of instrument air compressors, led to closure of the seal return line from the heat transport pumps, as well as simultaneous loss of pump jacket cooling. This led to loss of all heat transport pump seals and a loss of coolant outside containment.

These and other results of the study are still undergoing further review and scrutiny. The resolution of the issues brought up by the study is expected soon, and hence it would be premature at this time to quote any frequency estimates of the various release categories.

8.0   Insights and Conclusions

There is little doubt in Ontario Hydro's experience that the risk assessment process comprising integrated event tree and fault tree development is highly effective in carrying out a thorough safety assessment of the design of a nuclear power plant. The following are some insights and conclusions that can be drawn from the experience of the DPSE study:

(a)   The risk assessment effort should start when the design is still in the conceptual phase so that the required system design features can be established in terms of their importance to the overall safety of the plant, rather than simply to a particular system, separately deemed to be safety-related.

(b)   The fault tree analysis of a system should commence when the design documentation is issued the first time, even when it is expected that the final design may be different in certain respects. This is because the fault tree analysis provides an effective design review of the system and is capable of finding potential weakness in the design which, at that stage, are inexpensive to correct.

(c)   It is important to carry out detailed fault tree assessments so that the interdependencies between systems can be accurately characterized. Quite often, it is at the lower levels of the failure logic that subtle interactions exist which can not only adversely affect a number of mitigating systems but also possibly lead to the initiation of an event sequence.

(d)   The amount of information about the design of the plant that a risk assessment generates is so vast that better computer-aided methods are needed to handle this. Improvements are felt to be required in the areas of fault tree generation, reliability data assignment and the rapid solution of fault trees at the sequence level such that the impact of intended design or operational changes can be easily assessed.

Ontario Hydro is currently investigating the application of the risk assessment process described above to its operating reactors.

9.0   References

1.   F.K. King, V.M. Raina, K.S. Dinnie, "The Darlington Probabilistic Safety Evaluation - A CANDU Risk Assessment", paper presented at Canadian Nuclear Society 8th Annual Conference, June 14-17, 1987, Saint John, New Brunswick, Canada.

2.   "PRA Procedure Guide", US NRC, NUREG/CR-2300, Washington D.C., January 1983.

3.   US Department of Defense, Military Standardization Handbook: Reliability Prediction of Electronic Equipment, MIL-HDBK-217D, January 1982.

4.   V.M. Raina, P.V. Castaldo, "Programmable Controller Fault Tree Models for Use in Nuclear Power Plant Risk Assessments", Proceedings of Third Electronic Systems Safety Symposium, Guernsey, U.K., May 1986.

5.   P.C. Chow et al, "An Integrated Approach to Fault Tree Evaluation in Probabilistic Safety Studies", paper presented at the International ANS/ENS Topical Meeting on Probabilistic Safety Methods and Applications, San Fransico, February 1985.

6.   M.K. Comer et al., "Generating Human Reliability Estimates Using Expert Judgement", US NRC, NUREG/CR-3688, Washington, D.C., November, 1984.

7.   R.B. Worrell, "SETS Reference Manual", US NRC NUREG/CR-4213, Washington, D.C., May 1985.

8.   E.M. Chan, P.C. Chow, V.M. Raina, "A Procedure for Integration of System Failure Logic Models in Probabilistic Safety Studies", paper presented at 14th Inter-RAM Conference, Toronto, Canada, May 1987.

9.   K.M. Iwasa-Madge, J.D. Beattie, "Preliminary Quantification for Human Reliability Analysis", paper presented at the International ANS/ENS Topical Meeting on Probabilistic Safety Methods and Applications, San Francisco, February 1985.

IMPROVED RELIABILITY OF RESIDUAL HEAT REMOVAL CAPABILITY IN PRESSURIZED WATER REACTORS*

Tsong-Lun Chu,† Robert Fitzpatrick,† and Won Hyo Yoon††
(†Brookhaven National Laboratory, Upton, New York, USA, ††Visiting from the Korean Advanced Energy Research Institute under International Atomic Energy Agency Fellowship)

Keywords: Shutdown Risk, Residual Heat Removal System, Auto-closure Interlock

The work presented in this paper was performed by Brookhaven National Laboratory (BNL) in supporting Nuclear Regulatory Commission's (NRC) effort towards the resolution of Generic Issue 99 "Reactor Coolant System (RCS)/Residual Heat Removal (RHR) Suction Line Interlocks on Pressurized Water Reactors (PWRs)." Operational experience[1-3] of U.S. PWRs indicates that numerous loss of RHR events have occurred during plant shutdown. Of particular significance is the loss of RHR suction due to the inadvertent closure of the RHR suction/isolation valves or an excess lowering of the water level in the reactor vessel. In the absence of prompt mitigative action by the operator, the core may become uncovered. Various design/operational changes have been proposed.[1-3] The objective of this paper is to estimate the improvement in the RHR reliability and the risk reduction potential provided by those proposed RHR design/operational changes.[4] The benefits of those changes are expressed in terms of the reduction in the frequency of loss-of-cooling events and the frequency of core damage.

The Nuclear Safety Analysis Center (NSAC) performed a study NSAC-84,[3] on the risk of a plant during shutdown. BNL was able to draw on this study when developing the BNL shutdown model. The BNL shutdown risk model was applied to a generic plant whose frontline systems and support systems were assumed to be similar to those of Zion, so that the system models of NSAC-84 could be used. The analysis was called "generic" mainly because generic component failure data was used and the frequencies of the initiating events were estimated using the operational experience of the PWR population.

In NSAC-84, three types of outages were considered, namely, refueling, drained maintenance, and nondrained maintenance. NSAC-84 developed six procedural event trees representing six different phases of an outage, and three accident event trees. Different types of outages go through different numbers of procedural event trees. The end states of the procedural event trees were three types of initiating events, loss of cooling, loss of coolant accident (LOCA), and low temperature overpressurization (LTOP). The end states become input to the accident event trees. The estimated durations of the phases (mission times for the RHR system) and the assumption that a large fraction of the time at shutdown the plant is in the partially drained condition were two conservatisms in NSAC-84. BNL used the frequency of the three types of outages estimated in NSAC-84 and redefined the phases of the three types of outages, namely 4 phases for a refueling outage, 3 phases for a drained maintenance outage, and a single phase for a nondrained maintenance. Realistic estimates of the duration of the phases and the durations that a plant stays in a partially drained condition were used in the BNL analysis. Instead of the procedural event trees used in NSAC-84, a fault tree for the operating train of the RHR system was developed to determine the conditional probabil-

---

*This work was performed under the auspices of the U.S. Nuclear Regulatory Commission. Views expressed in this paper do not necessarily represent those of the U.S. Nuclear Regulatory Commission.

ity of a loss-of-cooling event in a given phase of an outage. The failure modes
of the operating train include hardware failure of the components, spurious closure of suction valves, overdraining while the RCS is partially drained, inadvertent diversion of reactor coolant flow, etc. In evaluating the frequency of loss-
of-cooling events, any interruption of flow was considered to be such an event.
The fact that a standby train may be available was covered in the loss-of-cooling
event trees. This was modelled in this fashion because it requires operator action to recognize the need for and initiate the standby train. The fault trees
for different phases of an outage were different because the durations of the
phases were different, and some failure modes were only applicable to some specific phases, e.g., overdraining can occur only if the reactor coolant system is
drained.

Three unique failure modes of the RHR system were modelled in the BNL analysis,
i.e., spurious isolation of the RHR suction valves, overdraining in a draindown
operation, and failure to maintain vessel level when the RCS is partially
drained. The failure rates and failure probability of these failure modes were
estimated using operational experience. For example, in the survey of operational
experience for PWRs, 64 events of spurious isolation of RHR suction were identified in 1.79×10^6 hours of RHR system operation. Therefore, the generic frequency
of spurious isolation of RHR suction valves is $64/1.79 \times 10^6 = 3.58 \times 10^{-6}$ per hour.
The data for the period from 1976 to 1981 were taken from NSAC-52.[2] The data for
the period 1982 to 1983 were taken from an AEOD (Office for Analysis and Evaluation of Operational Data) report.[1] BNL performed a licensee event report (LER)
search for the period from 1984 to 1986. These sources of data were also used to
estimate the frequency of two types of LOCAs, i.e., LOCAs such as that caused by a
stuck open RHR relief valve, and LOCAs caused by inadvertent opening a containment
spray recirculation valve. LOCA event trees were developed to model the mitigation of LOCAs that may occur in different phases of an outage.

The NSAC-84 analysis considered the service water system (SWS) and the component
cooling water system (CCWS) as support systems for the RHR system. The dependence
of the charging system and the auxiliary feedwater system on these support systems
was not modelled. In addition, initiating events caused by loss of such support
systems were not considered in NSAC-84. BNL modelled SWS and CCWS as support systems for all systems that may be used to mitigate the postulated accidents. Loss
of these systems as an initiating event was also modelled.

The loss of cooling event trees are quantified using the large fault tree approach.[5] System information and component maintenance unavailability data are
based on the Zion Final Safety Analysis Report, Zion Probabilistic Safety Study
(ZPSS),[6] and NSAC-84. Component failure data was taken from the generic data of
the Oconee PRA.[7] Figure 1 is the loss-of-cooling event tree for phase 2 of a
drained maintenance outage. It was derived from the NSAC-84 loss-of-cooling event
tree by adding the safety injection system as an additional top event. The safety
injection system is made inoperable to avoid LTOP during an outage. However, a
lot of time would be available for the operators to make the system operable. In
phase 2 of a drained maintenance outage, the RCS would be drained to the hotleg
mid-plane to accommodate maintenance that requires draining of the RCS. Therefore, steam generator cooling would not be available. Sequence 5 of the event
tree represents a sequence in which RHR, charging, and safety injection systems
become unavailable due to hardware failure or component maintenance unavailability. The probability, 1.84×10^{-7}, under the top event SI actually represents the
unavailability of all systems in the sequence. It was obtained by linking the

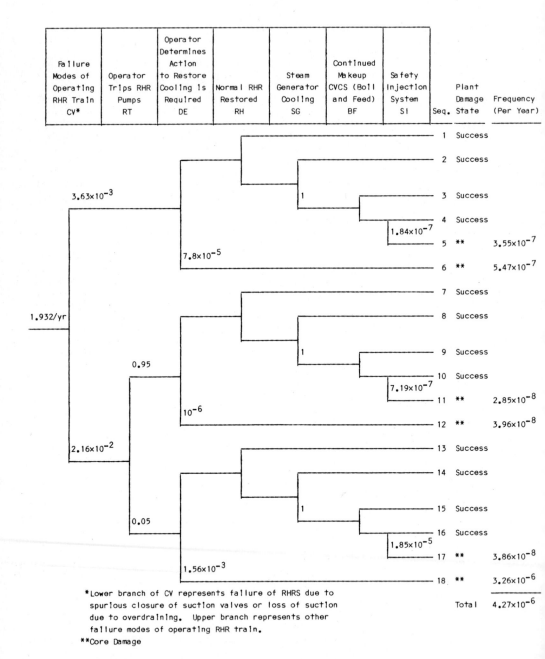

Figure 1: Loss-of-cooling event tree for phase 2 of a drained maintenance outage.

fault trees for the systems. Sequence 6 is a sequence in which the operating train fails and the operators fail to recognize that restoring cooling is needed. Its frequency is simply the product of the frequency of the outage, 1.932 per year, and the probabilities of the failure events that define the sequence. The lower branch of top event CV represents loss-of-cooling due to loss of RHR pump suction, e.g., spurious closure of a suction valve or overdraining. In sequence 11, the operator successfully trips the RHR pump, and subsequent hardware failures of the safety systems cause the core damage to occur. In sequence 12, the operator successfully trips the RHR pump, but fails to recognize the need to restore cooling. Sequences 17 and 18 are similar to sequences 11 and 12, except that the operators fail to trip the RHR pump and the pump is assumed to be unavailable due to cavitation. In NSAC-84, the same human error probability was used for the DE events in the loss of cooling event trees for each of the different phases of the outages. In the BNL model, a simple thermal model[4] was developed to determine the time to core uncovery as a function of time following shutdown, given that a loss of cooling occurs with the RCS partially drained. These core uncovery times were used in a human cognitive reliability model[8] to determine a realistic human error probability for each of the different phases.

Table 1 summarizes the results of the BNL model. Loss of offsite power was analyzed using the ac power recovery model developed in the accident sequence evaluation program (ASEP)[9] for Zion and the simple thermal model that determines the core uncovery time given a loss of decay heat removal as a function of time following shutdown. Loss of CCW or SW was analyzed using a model which was developed during the Sandia Review[10] of ZPSS. Since NSAC-84 did not consider loss of CCW or SW, it is reasonable to compare the BNL core damage frequency 1.64×10^{-5} per year, due to loss of cooling, LOCA, and loss of offsite power with that of NSAC-84. As explained above, the BNL model was developed by making many changes to the NSAC-84 model. The fact that the results are close should not be interpreted that the two models are the same. Also listed are the results of three possible design improvements:

Initiating Events	Core Damage Frequency (Per Year)			
	Base Case	I1	I2	I3
Loss of Cooling	8.48×10^{-6}	3.60×10^{-6}	5.41×10^{-6}	7.28×10^{-6}
LOCA	2.61×10^{-6}	2.44×10^{-6}	2.61×10^{-6}	2.61×10^{-6}
Loss of Offsite Power	5.31×10^{-6}	5.08×10^{-6}	5.31×10^{-6}	5.31×10^{-6}
Loss of CCWS	2.34×10^{-5}	2.34×10^{-5}	2.34×10^{-5}	2.34×10^{-5}
Loss of SWS	4.04×10^{-6}	4.04×10^{-6}	4.04×10^{-6}	4.04×10^{-6}
Total	4.38×10^{-5}	3.86×10^{-5}	4.08×10^{-5}	4.26×10^{-5}
NSAC-84	1.80×10^{-5}			

I1 = Upgraded instrumentation for RHR pumps and availability of emergency procedures.
I2 = Upgraded vessel level indication.
I3 = Removal of auto-closure interlock.

Table 1: Summary of Core Damage Frequency Results for a Generic Plant at Shutdown

1. Availability of an alarm trend recorder for monitoring RHR pump conditions (flow, discharge pressure, motor current), in order to provide the operator with early warning of a potential loss of shutdown cooling and to allow for prompt implementation of emergency procedures (assumed available) for restoration of DHR capability (e.g., RHR pump recovery).

2. Availability of highly reliable, redundant instrumentation, with control room readout and alarm, for monitoring the water level and temperature within the reactor vessel during drained RCS operations, in order to provide the operator with early warning of a potential loss of RHR suction from the hotleg, as well as provide information for determining the time margin to boiling or core uncovery in the event of an extended loss of shutdown cooling capability.

3. Removal of the RHR suction line auto-closure interlock (ACI) to preclude inadvertent closures of the RHR suction valves. The removal of the auto-closure feature may increase the frequency of an interfacing systems LOCA. It is assumed that some features are used to replace ACI such that no significant increase in the frequency of interfacing LOCA is expected.

With the upgraded instrumentation for the RHR system and available emergency procedures, it was assumed that the operators would respond to loss-of-cooling events. The upgraded vessel level indication reduces the frequency of the overdraining events. The removal of ACI reduces the frequency of spurious isolation of the suction valves. Table 2 summarizes the benefits of the proposed design improvements. It can be seen from Table 2 (first line) that each of the three proposed changes have an impact on the reduction in core damage frequency due to loss-of-cooling initiating events. Obviously, upgraded instrumentation for the RHR pumps does not reduce the frequency of the initiating event, but it is most effective in reducing core damage frequency. Both upgraded vessel level instrumentation and removal of ACI reduce the frequency of the initiating events. Removal of ACI is very effective in reducing the frequency of loss of cooling, but its reduction in core damage frequency is smaller than that for upgraded vessel level instrumentation, because the spurious isolation of an RHR suction valve may occur any time during a shutdown while overdraining only occurs when the RCS is partially drained. This is an important distinction because interruption of the RHR system during most of the time over a given shutdown yields ample time for operator recovery; whereas, loss of level instrumentation during a partially drained condition represents a much more vulnerable scenario.

	Base Case	I1	I2	I3
f(LC) (per year)	3.21×10^{-1}	3.21×10^{-1}	2.49×10^{-1}	1.71×10^{-1}
Δf(LC) (per year)	N.A.	0	7.20×10^{-2}	1.19×10^{-1}
CDF (per year)	4.38×10^{-5}	3.86×10^{-5}	4.08×10^{-5}	4.26×10^{-5}
ΔCDF (per year)	N.A.	5.20×10^{-6}	3.00×10^{-6}	1.20×10^{-6}

I1 = Upgraded instrumentation for RHR pumps and availability of emergency procedures.
I2 = Upgraded vessel level indication.
I3 = Removal of auto-closure interlock.
f(LC) = Frequency of loss of cooling.
CDF = Core damage frequency.

Table 2: Summary of Benefits of the Possible Improvements for a Generic Plant

495

In summary, the results of this study indicate that the estimated core damage frequency of a PWR at shutdown is not much lower than when the plant is operating. Each of the three possible design improvements leads to significant reduction in core damage frequency due to loss-of-cooling events.

References

1. H. Ornstein, "Decay Heat Removal Problems at U.S. Pressurized Water Reactors," Case Study Report, Office for Analysis and Evaluation of Operational Data, U.S. NRC, December 1985.
2. Nuclear Safety Analysis Center/Electric Power Research Institute, "Residual Heat Removal Experience, Review and Safety Analysis, Pressurized Water Reactors," NSAC-52, January 1983.
3. Nuclear Safety Analysis Center/Electric Power Research Institute, "Zion Nuclear Plant Residual Heat Removal PRA," NSAC-84, July 1985.
4. T. Chu, W. H. Yoon, A. Tingle, and R. Fitzpatrick, "Improved Reliability of Residual Heat Removal Capability in PWRs," to be published as NUREG/CR.
5. R. A. Bari et al., "Probabilistic Safety Analysis Procedures Guide," NUREG/CR-2815, August 1985.
6. "Zion Probabilistic Safety Study," Commonwealth Edison Company, September 1981.
7. "A Probabilistic Risk Assessment of Oconee Unit 3," NSAC/60, June 1984.
8. G. W. Hannaman, A. J. Spurgin, and Y. Lukic, "A Model for Assessing Human Cognitive Reliability Analysis in PRA Studies," Conference Record for 1985 IEEE Third Conference on Human Factors and Nuclear Safety, June 1985, Monterey, California.
9. T. A. Wheeler, "Analysis of Core Damage Frequency From Internal Events: Zion Unit 1," NUREG/CR-4550, Volume 7, October 1986.
10. "Review and Evaluation of Zion Probabilistic Safety Study," NUREG/CR-3300, Volume 1, May 1984.

MODELLING OF REACTOR COOLANT PUMP SEAL LOCA FOLLOWING LOSS OF EMERGENCY SERVICE WATER

S. K. Cheng, J. S. Wu, Y. H. Yang, and D. Y. Hsia
(Atomic Energy Council, Taipei, Taiwan, Republic of China)

M. G. K. Evans
(NUS Corporation, Gaithersburg, United States of America)

Abstract

A model for the potential reactor coolant pump seal LOCA in a Westinghouse pressurized-water reactor following loss of cooling water (loss of component cooling water system or emergency service water system) is developed based on state-of-the-art knowledge. The core melt frequency is evaluated by constructing an event tree which includes the potential operator actions in coping with this event. The various potential core melt sequences are evaluated, and the interpretation of the results identifies the relationships between mechanical failures, the operator actions and the potential impact of good emergency operating procedures.

1. Introduction

In a Westinghouse-designed pressurized-water reactor (PWR), the reactor coolant pump (RCP) seal is cooled by seal injection, which is usually provided by high-head injection pumps, and/or a thermal barrier cooler, which is cooled by the component cooling water (CCW) system. If both seal cooling systems are lost, the seal is subjected to the reactor coolant system (RCS) temperature and pressure (550·F, 2250 psia). This adverse environment might lead to RCP seal degradation or failure, resulting in a loss-of-coolant accident (LOCA), namely, seal LOCA.

Complete loss of seal cooling can happen following two initiating events: station blackout or loss of component cooling water system as the result of either CCW system failure or loss of its heat exchanger cooling due to loss of nuclear service cooling water (NSCW) system. In the event of loss of CCW, the high-head pump can probably operate for a short period of time before it fails due to loss of CCW cooling to its motor and lube-oil cooler. The subsequent seal LOCA exacerbates these events and contributes the dominant core melt sequences in recent probabilistic risk assessment (PRA) studies[1].

Although it is the dominant contributor to core melt frequency, no conclusion has yet been reached on the various factors involved in seal LOCA, such as time at which failure occurs, the rate of leakage over time following failure, and the potential for catastrophic failure under loss of all cooling condition. However, recent experiments in Atomic Energy of Canada Limited (AECL) Research Company[2] and the French Utility, Electricite de France (EDF)[3], have provided some valuable information concerning the possibility and timing of seal failure.

Since the initiating event frequency of loss of cooling water (CCW or NSCW) in certain Westinghouse PWR from some PRA studies could be as high as 10^{-4} per reactor year, analysis regarding the occurrence of a seal LOCA and the potential mitigation is necessary. It is the objective of this paper to examine the information presently available in order to realistically model the occurrence of seal LOCA and identify the actions the operator might take to mitigate these events. This study is performed based on a 3-loop Westinghouse PWR (referenced plant: Maanshan Nuclear Power Station), in which the (three) high-head centrifugal charging pumps (CCP), (two) low-head residual heat removal (RHR) pumps, and (two) containment spray pumps are cooled by the CCW system. The insights gained from this study can be used as a basis for defining the emergency operating procedures (EOP) to be followed in the event of loss of cooling water.

2. Seal LOCA Model

The Westinghouse-designed RCP shaft seal section consists of three seals, namely, the No. 1 controlled leakage, film-riding face seal and the No. 2 and No. 3 rubbing face seals. Sealing at the interface between two components of the RCP seal system is provided by secondary sealing elastomers (O-ring). Under loss of all seal cooling situation, two possible seal failure modes are identified:

1. Binding failure of the RCP seal ring: the seal surface poping open and no longer responding to the hydraulic forces.

2. Extrusion failure of O-ring: the secondary sealing elastomers extrude and fail to prevent secondary leakage.

Analytical and experimental studies have been conducted to investigate RCP seal behavior in loss-of-cooling scenarios. Westinghouse Electric Corporation has completed a thorough study on the leakage rates for various failure modes. Energy Technology Engineering Center has performed an independent analysis using computer code to determine the seal leakage rate[4]. Testing performed by AECL shows that typical O-ring elastomer materials extrude into the gap[2]. French test, however, indicates that the hydrostatic seals do not fail under conditions of a total loss of cooling for 20 hr[3]. Other tests by AECL indicate that certain alternative elastomer materials can tolerate the high temperature environment without failure for 18 hr[5].

Although the binding failure is not supported by the loss-of-seal cooling experience or the test evidence, it is the only mechanism which can cause a seal LOCA of a leakage rate higher than 300 gpm/RCP. In this study, a mean value of failure probability will be assigned to this failure mechanism which is assumed to occur about 30 minutes after loss of all seal cooling. The previous station blackout experiences indicate that there are six pumps which have experienced loss of all seal cooling longer than 30 minutes. No binding failure was found in these six pumps. The French test adds one more data point. Based on engineering judgement, the prior is assumed to be a beta distribution with 0.001-0.1 per demand as 5-95 percentiles. Using the method recommended by Mosleh and Apostolakis[6], the two parameters for the beta distribution are found to be 0.84 and 25.9. From the Baysian updating of the evidence that no failure in seven demands, the mean failure probability is estimated to be 2.5×10^{-2} per demand. The 5% and 95% points are 8×10^{-4} and 8×10^{-2}, respectively. If binding failure occurs, all three seal surfaces are assumed to pop open simultaneously and lead to a leakage rate of 450 gpm/RCP.

The O-ring extrusion failure data obtained in AECL are used to establish a model for this failure mode. For the typical unqualified (for high temperature performance) O-ring (Parker E515-80), the data in Table 1 of Reference 2 show that only half of the O-rings fail after the 20 hr test period. For those which extruded, the blowout time is always before 6 hr. Assuming the Weibull distribution is applicable, these data are fitted to give a shape parameter of 2.2 and a scale parameter (characteristic life) of 3.5 (hr). The delay time is assumed to be 0.5 hr after loss of all seal cooling. Given the O-ring extruded, the leakage rate is assumed to be 150 gpm/RCP.

3. Operator Response Following Loss of Cooling Water

In most previous PRAs for PWRs designed similar to MNPS, it was assumed that a complete loss of CCW (or NSCW) leads directly to core melt. That assumption was based on the postulation of a seal LOCA, exacerbated by failure of the emergency core-cooling system (ECCS) pumps due to loss of CCW cooling, and hence eventual uncovering of the core. It is our judgement that this assumption is too conservative and that injection can be achieved by intermittent use of the low-head RHR pumps even without cooling (to its motor and seal coolers) if the RCS pressure is reduced to a level lower than their shutoff head (about 150 psig). Because of their high design flow rate (3000 gpm per pump), the RHR pumps are only required to operate for a very short time (roughly 5 to 10 minutes) to refill the RCS. Since the leakage rate is quite low at this pressure, it takes more than 1 hr for the core inventory to reach a level lower than that of the cold leg. Thus each RHR pump has about 2 hr to cool down between each 5 to 10 minutes operation. The operator, however, must fully understand the situation and manipulate these pumps carefully.

The abnormal operating procedures require the operators to trip the RCPs following loss of CCW and then check into the cause of CCW failure. There is no specific EOP applicable to this situation. If the seal LOCA occurs, the resulting falling pressure would lead to a safety injection (SI) signal and prompt the operator to enter (SI) EOP. No further instructions are otherwise available except the operating restriction specified by Technical Specification. However, if CCW cannot be restored in 30 minutes, the operator is likely to cool down the RCS toward a cold shutdown.

To provide seal injection, the CCP must operate continuously until the temperatures in bearing or motor stator reach the limit values. In the bounding case all (three) pumps could be inoperable within 30 minutes which is the assumption made in this analysis. Therefore, if auxiliary feedwater (AFW) system or secondary steam relief (SSR) is not available, core melt is inevitable. Although temporary cooling for ECCS pumps can be provided by feed and bleed operation of CCW system (under loss of NSCW situation) or alternative cooling water from CST (which requires hookup of some pipings), no credit is taken for these recovery actions in this study.

Since all RCPs are stopped, plant cooldown can only be achieved by natural circulation or steam refluxing. Once natural circulation is lost due to leakage, controlled cooldown is no longer possible, although cooldown might continue due to the refluxing. To maintain controlled conditions the operator should cool down and depressurize the RCS to the point where accumulators can inject before sufficient leakage has occurred. This will considerably extend the time to core uncovery and the time available to achieve plant conditions at which the RHR pumps can be used to maintain inventory. The core uncovery times for different leakage rates, with and without secondary depressurization, have been calculated by Westinghouse[7]. The results are summarized in the following table. As no information was available for the purposes of the initial model, cessation of natural circulation has been taken to be half the time to core uncovery.

Case	Leakage rate (gpm/RCP)	Natural circulation cessation (hr) without/with cooldown	Core uncovery time (hr) Without cooldown	Core uncovery time (hr) With cooldown
No failure	20	7/10	14	> 20
Extrusion	150	2/3	4	6
Binding	450	1/1.5	2	3

In order to be able to use the RHR pumps, RCS pressure must be reduced below their shutoff head, i.e., 150 psig (saturation temperature 360°F). At a cooldown rate of 100°F/hr, it takes at least 2 hr to achieve this condition. Therefore, for the highest leak rate (450 gpm/RCP) it is unlikely that this can be accomplished in a controlled manner before cessation of natural circulation.

If the operator does not achieve the RHR operating condition in a controlled manner prior to loss of natural circulation, then the inadequate core cooling (ICC) symptoms as specified in EOP will occur at some late time. At this point the EOPs detail the specific actions which can be taken to achieve core cooling recovery as the result of rapid depressurization and injection from the accumulators and RHR pumps[8].

When the RCS pressure is below 150 psig, the low-head RHR pumps can be operated as required for inventory control. The operator must realize that there is no CCW cooling and thus cycle the pumps to prevent damage. If they are started at any time by the SI signal, they should be stopped as soon as possible.

Even if the operator succeeds in maintaining RCS inventory and secondary cooling, he may still have to confront problems associated with the ultimate heat sink. Although most of the decay heat is removed by the steam generators, some is dumped into the containment from the leakage flow. The temperature of the containment inventory increases, hence the containment pressure increases gradually. Calculation by MARCH code shows that for a one-inch break (equivalent to an initaial leakage of 450 gpm/RCP) and successful cooldown in the first few hours, the containment pressure reaches 60 psig about 10 days into the event. It is assumed that the probability of failure to restore systems within this time scale is negligible.

4. Event Tree and Quantification

Following the discussion in the last two sections, an event tree is constructed to model the sequences of event for loss of CCW (or NSCW) as shown in Figure 1. The three headings which are strongly dependent on operator response are discussed below:

Operator Controlled Cooldown (X). The operator controls cooldown to reduce the RCS pressure below the low-head shutoff head before cessation of natural circulation. The systems required for this function are the steam dump facility or steam generator power operated relief valves (PORVs). Failure of the operator to perform these actions depends on time available, i.e., the time when seal LOCA occurs. For seal binding failure, this function is not applicable since the time available is too short. Using the extrusion failure model, the probability of seal LOCA (150 gpm/RCP) can be discretized as shown in the table below and the failure probabilities of this operator action assigned as shown.

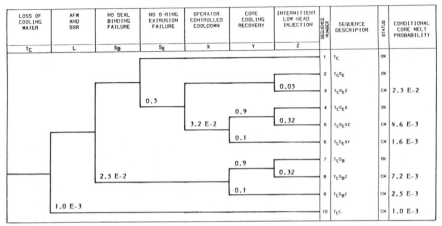

Figure 1. Event Tree for Loss of Cooling Water

Time (hr)	O-ring failure probability	Conditional operator failure probability	Failure probability
1 (0.5-1.5)	0.06	0.3	1.8×10^{-3}
2 (1.5-2.5)	0.19	0.1	1.9×10^{-2}
3 (2.5-3.5)	0.26	0.03	7.8×10^{-3}
4 (3.5-4.5)	0.23	0.01	2.3×10^{-3}
5 (4.5-5.5)	0.15	0.003	4.5×10^{-4}
6 (>5.5)	0.11	0.001	1.1×10^{-4}

The probability that the operator fails to achieve controlled cooldown is given by the sum of the final column, i.e., 3.2×10^{-2}.

Core-Cooling Recovery (Y). If a catastrophic seal failure occurs shortly into the event or the operator fails to perform cooldown in time, symptoms of ICC should prompt him to perform the necessary core-cooling recovery actions. The time available for operator response is about 30 minutes for the largest seal leakage rate[8]. The human error probability (HEP) in performing this action is estimated to be 0.1.

Intermittent Low-Head Injection (Z). After cooldown and depressurization the accumulators inject water into the RCS and the low-head pumps should be cycled to give intermittent injection. The operator should isolate the accumulators when they are about to empty to prevent nitrogen gas injection and carefully manipulate low-head RHR pumps. The failure probability of operator actions in this event depends on whether he is in control of the situation. If controlled cooldown is successful, a operator failure probability of 0.03 is assumed. If operator must perform core-cooling recovery, the stress is high so that a one order higher failure probability, 0.3, is assumed. The system failure probability (of either accumulator isolation valve to close or RHR pump to start) is estimated to be 2.0×10^{-2}.

The core melt sequence conditional probabilities are shown in Figure 1. The total conditional core melt probability following loss of CCW is estimated to be 4.2×10^{-2}. If it is assumed that no seal failure occurs within 20 hr, then the conditional core melt probability is 1.0×10^{-3} (determined by failure of the auxiliary feedwater system), and if catastrophic failure occurs at 0.5 hr the conditional core melt probability would be 0.4.

Folloiwng complete loss of NSCW the compressed air system is also lost leading to loss of the steam dump facility and the inability to effect core-cooling recovery. This gives a guaranteed failure of event Y, and the total conditional core melt probability becomes 6.7×10^{-2}.

5. Conclusions and Recommendations

Investigation and modelling of potential operator actions following failure of CCW or NSCW systems and the development of a seal LOCA model based on state-of-the-art knowledge have been incorporated into an event tree to determine the conditional core melt probability following the loss of cooling water events. The HEP used in this study have been based on generic values for the type of action involved, the availability of procedures, and stress level. It is clear that the operator plays a key role, and therefore more detailed analysis is required in this area. The conditional core melt probability is estimated to be 4.2×10^{-2} for loss of CCW event (6.7×10^{-2} for loss of NSCW), and is bounded by 1.0×10^{-3} and 0.4 based on extreme seal LOCA assumptions.

It is clear that the core melt probability is totally dominated by the three operator actions identified above, particularly, cycling the low-head pumps to prevent their damage due to no cooling. If there is clear procedure regarding these operations under these events, the HEP could be much lower. In addition, in the worst situation the pump being used for accumulators inventory makeup (positive displacement hydrostatic test pump, 25 gpm) could be used for limited injection through accumulators to the RCS. Although the flow rate is small, it might prevent severe core damage. Therefore, it is recommended that the development of EOP for mitigating these events be investigated. The procedure should instruct the operator to cool down the RCS as soon as possible, to prevent damage of all high-head pumps, to carefully manipulate (cycle) low-head pumps for inventory makeup, and in the worst case to use hydrostatic test pump to inject water.

In this study, the low-head RHR pumps are assumed to be operable for about 10 minutes between each two-hour cycle. The soundness of this assumption might need further investigation to justify the basis of the analysis. In any case, the severity of these initiating events comes from the common mode failure of all ECCS pumps due to loss of cooling. Therefore, the diverse design of cooling support, e.g., add a small emergency seal injection or cooling system, could dramatically reduce the core melt risk from these initiators. In particular for the referenced plant (MNPS), with minor modification emergency seal injection could be provided by the hydrostatic test pump. A small diesel can be employed to drive or supply power to this pump for providing seal injection even in the station blackout situation.

Reference

1. NRC (U.S. Nuclear Regulatory Commission). 1987. Reactor Risk Reference Documnet. NUREG-1150, Draft report, Washington, DC.

2. NRC (U.S. Nuclear Regulatory Commission). 1985. Reactor Coolant Pump Shaft Seal Behavior During Station Blackout. NUREG/CR-4077, Washington, DC.

3. Kappler, F., L. Mougey, and R. Simon. 1985. "Primary-System Integrity of French Pressurized-Water Reactors During Station Blackout." Nuclear Safety, Vol. 26, No. 4, pp. 427-437.

4. Jackson, J., G. Bagchi, and V. S. Noonan. 1985. "Failure of Reactor Coolant Pump Seals," In Proceedings of 8th International Conference on Structure Mechanics in Reactor Technology. Paper D55, Brussels, Belgium.

5. Hill R. C. 1986. "Behavior of Primary Coolant Pump Shaft Seals During Station Blackout Conditions." Paper presented at the International ANS/ENS Topical Meeting on Operability of Nuclear Power Systems in Normal and Adverse Environment, Albuquerque, N. Mex.

6. Mosleh A. and G. Apostolakis. 1982. "Some Properties of Distributions Useful in the Study of Rare Events." IEEE Transactions on Reliability, vol. R. 31, No. 1, pp. 87-94.

7. Westinghouse Electric Corporation. 1983. Background Information for Westinghouse Owners Group Emergency Response Guideline. ECA-0.0, Response to Loss of All AC Power, HP-Rev. 1, Pittsburgh, Penn.

8. Westinghouse Electric Corporation. 1980. Inadequate Core Cooling Studies of Scenarios with FW Available, Using NOTRUMP Computer Code. WCAP-9754, Pittsburgh, Penn.

REALISTIC ASSESSMENT OF INTERFACING SYSTEMS LOCA SCENARIOS IN PWR PLANTS

Karl N. Fleming[1], R. Kenneth Deremer[2], and James H. Moody[3]
[1--Pickard, Lowe and Garrick, Inc., Newport Beach, California, USA]
[2--GA Technologies, San Diego, California, USA]
[3--New Hampshire Yankee, Seabrook, New Hampshire, USA]

Abstract

A common thread in the results of many published probabilistic risk assessments (PRA) is the apparent importance of loss of coolant accidents (LOCA) of interfacing systems. Although the published PRAs that have included this event all agree that this event is very unlikely, it has often appeared as a dominant contributor to the frequency of early release and the risk of early health effects. As part of an ongoing risk management program at Seabrook Station, a number of conservative assumptions normally made in the risk analysis of this event were identified and reviewed. This resulted in a reassessment of this event in which the conservative assumptions were replaced by more realistic models and data. The current estimate of the frequency of a large, early containment bypass and release resulting from this event is now estimated to be more than an order of magnitude less than previously estimated in the Seabrook Station probabilistic safety assessment (PSA). Many of the insights and results obtained about this event for Seabrook Station would be applicable to other plants.

Introduction

An interfacing systems LOCA is a leak in the reactor coolant system (RCS) pressure boundary at the interface with systems that communicate with the RCS through a series of check valves and/or isolation valves. Because some of these interfacing systems are not designed to full RCS pressure and because these systems are partially located outside the containment building, there is a concern that leaks or ruptures of the valves at this interface may result in a containment bypass. In addition, such a leak may result in an adverse systems interaction in which a need for RCS makeup is realized by the same event that fails or degrades the operation of the emergency core cooling system (ECCS).

Previous Analysis

Although the potential consequences of an interfacing system LOCA have often been assumed to be severe, published estimates of their frequency indicate they are very unlikely events. This stems from the fact that there are usually two or more normally closed valves at the interfaces in question and from the fact that, at most interfaces, a passive failure, such as a severe disk rupture, must be postulated to result in a significant concern for containment bypass. In some boiling water reactor (BWR) plants, a combination of check valve leakage and inadvertent actuation of a testable redundant check valve has resulted in overpressurizing interfacing systems on a number of occasions (Reference 1). There have also been reports of significant leakage in interfacing check valves at pressurized water reactor (PWR) plants. However, there has never been a disk rupture in more than 10^4 valve-years of experience with check valves at the interface between the RCS and the ECCS at PWR plants, with a similar level of experience BWR plants.

The interfacing system LOCA scenario was first identified as "event V" in the Reactor Safety Study (RSS, Reference 2). In that study, it was found to be a dominant contributor to early release frequency and to the risk of early health effects. The approach to modeling event V in the RSS set the stage for subsequent PRAs on PWRs through the one on Seabrook Station (Reference 3), which adopted a similar approach. This "traditional" approach to modeling event V is characterized by the following steps and assumptions.

1. Interfacing system drawings are reviewed to identify significant interfacing system leak paths. Normally selected are low pressure injection or residual heat removal (RHR) system interfaces at the cold legs and hot legs of the RCS.

2. An initiating event frequency is estimated, based on combinations of valve failure modes, the different leak paths, and highly uncertain failure rates.

3. The initiating event is assumed to result in a LOCA, ECCS failure, and containment bypass with a large early release. In the RSS, the event was assigned directly to release category PWR-2. Typically, no credit is taken for operator actions to mitigate the consequences of the event.

Seabrook Station Analysis

A comparison of the results of "V-sequence" analyses from selected PRAs on PWR plants is presented in Table 1. The initiating event results span about 2 orders of magnitude. The differences in initiating events are due to different assumptions regarding testing intervals, different numbers of analyzed leak paths, different numbers of valves per path (normally two or three valves per path), different types of valves, and, finally, different valve failure rates. In all cases except in the Seabrook PSA update results, the frequency of the initiating event is equated with the frequency of a large, early release.

PSA	Number of Leak Paths	Event "V" Mean Frequency (events per reactor-year)	
		Initiating Event	Large, Early Release
• Surry (WASH-1400) - 5-Year Test - Annual	3	1.1-5* 1.9-6*	1.1-5 1.9-6
• Indian Point 2	5	4.6-7	4.6-7
• Oconee (NSAC-60)	4	1.4-7	1.4-7
• Seabrook Station - Original PSA (PLG-0300) - PSA Update (PLG-0432)	6	1.8-6 6.5-6	1.8-6 3.4-8

*Calculated from reported medians and lognormal range factors.

NOTE: Exponential notation is indicated in abbreviated form; i.e., 1.1-5 = 1.1 x 10^{-5}.

Table 1: Comparison of Event "V" Frequencies from Selected PSAs

The updated results for Seabrook Station made use of the following insights and enhancements (Reference 3).

- Initiating Event Analysis. The initiating event model was expanded to include demand failures of the second valve in a path at the time the first valve leaks or ruptures. Data were analyzed to support the development of a relationship between check valve failure rate and leak size, as illustrated in Figure 1.

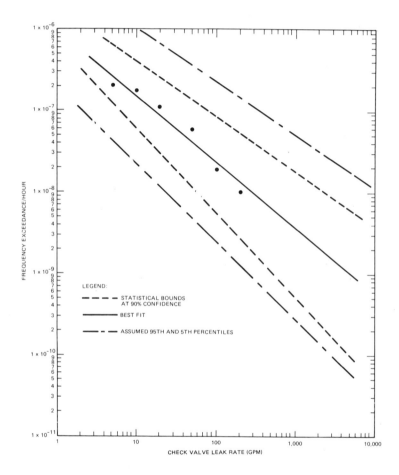

Figure 1: Frequency of Check Valve Leakage Events

- Event Tree Analyses. Instead of simply assuming the consequences of the initiating event, an event tree analysis was performed to identify different sequences that could follow it. Important in this regard is the response of the RHR relief valves to limit the degree of RHR system depressurization, operator actions to terminate and mitigate the leak, and the ability of the plant hardware to cope with these events.

- RHR Piping Integrity. Rather than assume that RHR overpressurization would result in piping failure, a piping fragility evaluation was conducted. A piping fragility curve was developed, based on the yield and ultimate strengths of the piping material and on a consideration of preexisting design flaws. This curve, which is illustrated in Figure 2, was then compared to hoop stresses calculated for RHR piping and heat exchanger tubes. The probability of unfilled piping was shown to be bounded by this curve. Use was made of insight from the Industry Degraded Core Rulemaking Program that the peak dynamic pressure in the RHR system would be no greater than the initial RCS pressure. This pressure would result in hoop stresses in the RHR piping somewhat less than the yield stress of the material. The most likely failure mode of the RHR pressure boundary due to overpressure is failure of the RHR pump seals.

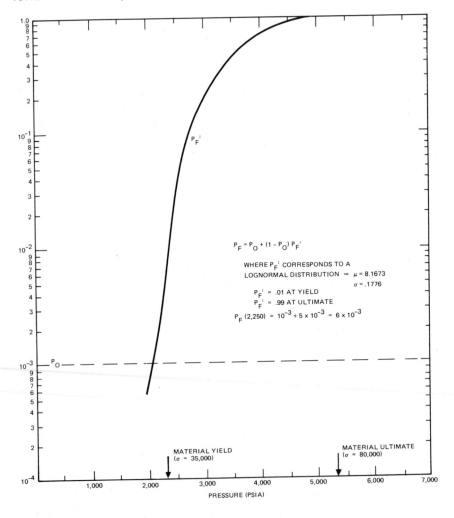

$$P_F = P_O + (1 - P_O) P_F^{\,i}$$

WHERE $P_F^{\,i}$ CORRESPONDS TO A
LOGNORMAL DISTRIBUTION $\Rightarrow \mu = 8.1673$
$\sigma = .1776$

$P_F^{\,i} = .01$ AT YIELD
$P_F^{\,i} = .99$ AT ULTIMATE
$P_F (2,250) = 10^{-3} + 5 \times 10^{-3} = 6 \times 10^{-3}$

MATERIAL YIELD
$(\sigma = 35,000)$

MATERIAL ULTIMATE
$(\sigma = 80,000)$

PRESSURE (PSIA)

Figure 2:   Probability of Pipe Failure

Conclusions

Although the frequency of an interfacing LOCA is now estimated to be somewhat more likely than estimated previously for Seabrook Station, the likelihood of a large, early release from this event is between 1 to 2 orders of magnitude less than estimated previously. In addition to this reduction in frequency, the consequences of the most probable early release are also much less because the release path in this case is through failed RHR pump seals that are submerged under about 10 meters of water. This water provides a significant reduction in the source term for the event.

References

1. U.S. Nuclear Regulatory Commission, "Preliminary Case Study Report, Overpressurization of Emergency Cooling System in Boiling Water Reactors," February 1985.

2. U.S. Nuclear Regulatory Commission, "Reactor Safety Study: An Assessment of Accident Risks in U.S. Commercial Nuclear Power Plants," WASH-1400, NUREG-75/104, October 1975.

3. Pickard, Lowe and Garrick, Inc., "Seabrook Station Risk Management and Emergency Planning Study," prepared for New Hampshire Yankee Division of Public Service Company of New Hampshire, PLG-0432, December 1985.

INTERFACING SYSTEMS LOCAs AT BOILING WATER REACTORS*

Tsong-Lun Chu,† Robert Fitzpatrick,† and Stoyan Stoyanov††
(†Brookhaven National Laboratory, Upton, New York, USA, ††Visiting from the Bulgarian ENERGOPROEKT under International Atomic Energy Agency Fellowship)

Keywords: Interfacing LOCA, Boiling Water Reactor, Overpressurization

The work presented in this paper was performed by Brookhaven National Laboratory (BNL) in support of Nuclear Regulatory Commission's (NRC) effort towards the resolution of Generic Issue 105 "Interfacing System Loss of Coolant Accidents (LOCAs) at Boiling Water Reactors (BWRs)." The Reactor Safety Study[1] identified an interfacing system LOCA in a pressurized water reactor (PWR) as a significant contributor to risk from accidents that result in severe core damage. For BWRs, interfacing LOCA have typically either not been considered in probabilistic risk analyses, or if considered, were judged to contribute little to the risk estimates because of their perceived low frequency of occurrence. However, recent operating experience indicates that the pressure isolation valves (PIVs) in BWRs may not adequately protect against overpressurization of low pressure systems.[2] In fact, four events of overpressurization of low pressure systems have already occurred at BWRs. The objective of this paper is to present the results of a study[3] which analyzed interfacing system LOCA at several BWRs. The BWRs were selected to best represent a spectrum of BWRs in service using industry operating event experience and plant-specific information/configurations. The results presented here include some possible changes in test requirements/practices as well as an evaluation of their reduction potential in terms of core damage frequency (CDF).

All lines penetrating the containment for each of the selected plants were identified using the tables of the containment isolation valves listed in the Final Safety Analysis Reports. Screening criteria were used to eliminate those lines that are not interfacing lines, or those lines that are interfacing lines but for which the frequency/risk of an interfacing LOCA was judged to be low compared to the obvious lines (e.g., residual heat removal (RHR) suction) that were considered in detail. The lines that were analyzed in this study were the emergency core cooling system (ECCS) injection lines, the feedwater lines, the decay heat removal suction and return lines, and the steam condensing lines to the RHR heat exchangers. In particular, the feedwater line had not been recognized as a possible interfacing line in past PRAs as the system was considered to always be operating at pressures above the primary system. The discharge side of the feedwater pump is connected to the reactor coolant system, however, the suction side is of low pressure design. If a feedwater pump trip occurs and the check valves in the discharge piping fail open, an interfacing LOCA may occur. Reference 4 provided an analysis of such a scenario using the experience of the San Onofre event[5] as evidence of common cause failure of the feedwater check valves.

For each of the lines identified, the PIVs were identified. Typically, for the plants analyzed, the ECCS injection lines have one air-operated check (AOC) valve inside the containment and one or two motor operated valves (MOVs) outside the containment, the steam condensing lines and the RHR suction lines have two MOVs in series. The MOVs, except those in the high pressure injection systems, are

*This work was performed under the auspices of the U.S. Nuclear Regulatory Commission. Views expressed in this paper do not necessarily represent those of the U.S. Nuclear Regulatory Commission.

equipped with interlocks that prohibit valve opening if the system pressure is too high. Since the experienced overpressurization events are related to test or maintenance activities, the surveillance requirements for the PIVs and the associated systems were identified and the test procedures were collected and reviewed. The tests included local leak rate tests (LLRT) for containment isolation values, leak rate tests for PIVs, operability tests, auto actuation tests, etc. All interfacing lines identified for the selected plants penetrate the containment, and some of the PIVs are also containment isolation valves. Containment isolation valves are subject to 10CFR50 Appendix J requirements, namely, leak testing once per refueling and after maintenance. Also identified were the potential alarms or indications of overpressurization or interfacing LOCA.

Surveys of operational event experience were performed using the RECON[6] data base to identify check valve failure events in BWR ECCS discharge lines, feedwater lines, and ECCS injection valve failures. The operating event experience was used to determine the failure modes and the failure rates. Whether or not a failure mode is applicable to a valve in a specific line of a specific plant is determined by the plant-specific surveillance requirements, the plant-specific test procedures and the plant-specific configuration. For example, in the Browns Ferry-1 incident[7] on August 14, 1984, the testable check valve was held open by its air operator, and the injection valve was opened due to human error during a logic system functional test. Such inadvertent opening of the injection valve is of concern only if a plant performs such testing when the reactor is at power. One of the plants analyzed performs such tests at power while the others do not. Therefore, the Browns Ferry scenario was found to be applicable to only one of the plants selected but not the others. If a failure mode was considered credible for a PIV, and no relevant failure was found in the licensee event report search,[6] then generic valve failure data were used, e.g., Probabilistic Safety Analysis Procedures Guide.[8]

The frequency of overpressurization in an interfacing line was calculated as the sum of the frequencies of different combinations of the failure modes of the PIVs in the line. Table 1 shows the summary of calculations for the low pressure coolant injection (LPCI) line of one of the selected plants. Nine failures of the air-operated check valves were reported in 1361 valve years. They were grouped into five groups according to the causes of failure, which are listed in the first column of Table 1. The frequency of each failure cause was estimated as the number of failure events divided by 1361 valve years, and is shown in the second column. The third column lists the failure modes and the conditional failure probabilities for the MOVs. A MOV may fail to reclose after being cycled. The probability of this failure mode was estimated by considering the frequency of valve operability testing and the specifics of the test procedure used. For such MOV failure modes, it was assumed that the size of the opening would be small and only a small LOCA would result. The MOV rupture rate of 1.2×10^{-3} per year was estimated using the evidence collected in an LER search in which five events of disk separation from the stem were found in 4173 valve years. The MOV may be opened inadvertently during the logic system functional test. The probability of such human error was taken from the Handbook[9] of Human Reliability Analysis. The MOV may be opened spuriously due to failure of hardware such as valve control circuits and power supplies. A generic failure rate of 8.1×10^{-4} per year was used for this failure mode. By reviewing the related test procedures, the Browns Ferry scenario was judged to be credible for the LPCI lines of one of the selected plants as indicated above. The Browns Ferry event was then used to estimate the frequency of

Experience	AOV	MOV	f(OP)	P(Rupture)	S$_2$	A*
Browns Ferry-1 Hatch-2 (Reverse Air)	1.47E-03	1.93E-06 Failure to Reclose	2.83E-09	0.00E+00 0.00E+00 0.00E+00	2.83E-11 2.83E-11 2.83E-11	0.00E+00 0.00E+00 0.00E+00
		6.00E-04 Rupture	8.82E-07	1.00E-01 1.00E-03 3.00E-05	8.81E-09 8.82E-09 8.82E-09	8.82E-10 8.82E-12 2.65E-13
		3.00E-03 Inadvertent Opening	4.41E-06	1.00E-01 1.00E-03 3.00E-05	4.40E-08 4.41E-08 4.41E-08	4.41E-09 4.41E-11 1.32E-12
		4.05E-04 Transfer Open	5.95E-07	1.00E-01 1.00E-03 3.00E-05	5.95E-09 5.95E-09 5.95E-09	5.95E-10 5.95E-12 1.79E-13
Browns Ferry Scenario (Reverse Air, Inadvertent Opened)			7.35E-04	1.00E-01 1.00E-03 3.00E-05	7.34E-06 7.35E-06 7.35E-06	7.35E-07 7.35E-09 2.20E-10
Cooper (Foreign Material)	7.35E-04	1.93E-06 Failure to Reclose	1.42E-09	0.00E+00 0.00E+00 0.00E+00	1.42E-11 1.42E-11 1.42E-11	0.00E+00 0.00E+00 0.00E+00
		6.00E-04 Rupture	4.41E-07	1.00E-01 1.00E-03 3.00E-05	3.97E-09 4.40E-09 4.41E-09	4.41E-08 4.41E-10 1.32E-11
		3.00E-03 Inadvertent Opening	2.20E-06	1.00E-01 1.00E-03 3.00E-05	1.98E-08 2.20E-08 2.20E-08	2.20E-07 2.20E-09 6.61E-11
		4.05E-04 Transfer Open	2.98E-07	1.00E-01 1.00E-03 3.00E-05	2.68E-09 2.97E-09 2.98E-09	2.98E-08 2.98E-10 8.93E-12
Pilgrim-1 Sept. 29, 1983 (Rusted Linkage)	7.35E-04	1.93E-06 Failure to Reclose	1.42E-09	0.00E+00 0.00E+00 0.00E+00	1.42E-11 1.42E-11 1.42E-11	0.00E+00 0.00E+00 0.00E+00
		6.00E-04 Rupture	4.41E-07	1.00E-01 1.00E-03 3.00E-05	4.40E-09 4.41E-09 4.41E-09	4.41E-10 4.41E-12 1.32E-13
		3.00E-03 Inadvertent Opening	2.20E-06	1.00E-01 1.00E-03 3.00E-05	2.20E-08 2.20E-08 2.20E-08	2.20E-09 2.20E-11 6.61E-13
		4.05E-04 Transfer Open	2.98E-07	1.00E-01 1.00E-03 3.00E-05	2.97E-09 2.98E-09 2.98E-09	2.98E-10 2.98E-12 8.93E-14

Table 1: Summary of Calculations for LPCI Line of One of the Selected Plants (Page 1 of 2)

Experience	AOV	MOV	f(OP)	P(Rupture)	S_2	A*
LaSalle-1 Sept. 14, 1983 (Misalignment of Gears)	7.35E-04	1.93E-06 Failure to Reclose	1.42E-09	0.00E+00 0.00E+00 0.00E+00	1.42E-11 1.42E-11 1.42E-11	0.00E+00 0.00E+00 0.00E+00
		6.00E-04 Rupture	4.41E-07	1.00E-01 1.00E-03 3.00E-05	3.97E-09 4.40E-09 4.41E-09	4.41E-08 4.41E-10 1.32E-11
		3.00E-03 Inadvertent Opening	2.20E-06	1.00E-01 1.00E-03 3.00E-05	1.98E-08 2.20E-08 2.20E-08	2.20E-07 2.20E-09 6.61E-11
		4.05E-04 Transfer Open	2.98E-07	1.00E-01 1.00E-03 3.00E-05	2.68E-09 2.97E-09 2.98E-09	2.98E-08 2.98E-10 8.93E-12
Four Remaining Incidents (Leakage)	2.94E-03	1.93E-06 Failure to Reclose	5.66E-09	0.00E+00 0.00E+00 0.00E+00	5.66E-11 5.66E-11 5.66E-11	0.00E+00 0.00E+00 0.00E+00
		6.00E-04 Rupture	1.76E-06	0.00E+00 0.00E+00 0.00E+00	1.76E-08 1.76E-08 1.76E-08	0.00E+00 0.00E+00 0.00E+00
		3.00E-03 Inadvertent Opening	8.82E-06	0.00E+00 0.00E+00 0.00E+00	8.82E-08 8.82E-08 8.82E-08	0.00E+00 0.00E+00 0.00E+00
		4.05E-04 Transfer Open	1.19E-06	0.00E+00 0.00E+00 0.00E+00	1.19E-08 1.19E-08 1.19E-08	0.00E+00 0.00E+00 0.00E+00

Notes: $f(\dot{OP})$ = Frequency of Overpressurization (/ry).
P(Rupture) = Probability of Major Pipe Rupture.
S_2 = Frequency of Unisolated Small LOCA (/ry).
A = Frequency of Large LOCA (/ry).
AOV = Failure Rate of Air Operated Check Valve (/ry).
MOV = Probability of MOV Failure.
CDF = Core Damage Frequency (/ry).
AOC = Air-Operated Check Valve
*Zero in this column means that the PIV failure mode limits the LOCA to a small LOCA.

Table 1: Summary of Calculations for LPCI Line of One of the Selected Plants (Page 2 of 2)

overpressurization due to such scenarios for this plant. This turned out to be the dominant cause of overpressurization determined by this study.

Given an overpressurization event, sensitivity calculations were performed on the probability of low pressure system rupture. The BWR Owner's Group[10] estimated the probability of rupture, given an overpressurization, to be approximately $3x10^{-5}$. This was used as one of the values for the probability of rupture. The other two valves were chosen such that a wide range is covered. In particular, the value of 0.1 is believed to be conservative. If rupture did not occur from the overpressurization event, a small LOCA was assumed to occur due to open relief valves or possible failures of gaskets and seals. The possibility that the operator isolates the small LOCA was also considered. A small LOCA event tree was used to analyze the ECCS systems that may be available and the operator actions that would be needed to prevent core damage. If a rupture occurs from an overpressurization event a large LOCA is assumed to occur with a probability of one unless there may be a check valve in the line that may close on high back flow and terminate the large LOCA; in that case, a small LOCA is assumed as per the above. If an unisolated large LOCA occurs in the ECCS, it has been assumed that core damage will result from flooding, structural failure, or possibly draining of the suppression pool.

Table 2 summarizes the core damage frequency results for the reference plants. Also shown in the table are the results of some possible corrective actions. BNL has been made aware of the fact that some of the possible corrective actions have been independently identified by the plants operators and are already being implemented. It is noted that the possible corrective actions are basically procedural in nature and that significant reductions in core damage frequency can be attained from their implementation. For example, from Table 2 it can be seen that not opening some MOVs at plant 2 while at power gives almost two orders of magnitude reduction in CDF across all three postulated pipe rupture probabilities. As a follow-on to these results BNL is currently assessing the pipe rupture probabilities given an overpressurization event and the potential offsite consequences of the core damage scenarios.

In summary, the core damage frequency due to interfacing systems LOCA has been assessed (conditional on the chosen values for the probability of low pressure system rupture) for the selected BWRs. Some possible corrective actions were identified and their benefits were assessed in terms of the reductions in the frequency of overpressurization and the frequency of core damage.

References

1. "Reactor Safety Study - An Assessment of Accident Risks in U.S. Commercial Nuclear Power Plants," WASH-1400 (NUREG-75/014), USNRC, October 1975.
2. P. Lam, "Overpressurization of Emergency Core Cooling Systems in Boiling Water Reactors," Office for the Analysis and Evaluation of Operating Data, USNRC, February 1985.
3. T-L. Chu and S. Stoyanov, "Interfacing LOCA at BWRs," Draft Letter Report submitted to NRC, Brookhaven National Laboratory, November 1986.
4. T-L. Chu and S. Stoyanov, "A New Scenario for Intersystem LOCAs in BWRs," Transactions of American Nuclear Society, 1986 Winter Meeting, Washington, DC, November 16-20, 1986.

Case		f(OP)	P(Rupture)	S2	A	CDF
Plant 1	Base Case	9.01E-03	1.00E-01	3.11E-05	1.05E-04	5.49E-06
			1.00E-03	3.12E-05	1.05E-06	1.98E-07
			3.00E-05	3.12E-05	3.16E-08	1.46E-07
	Leak Test AOC After Maintenance	4.34E-03	1.00E-01	1.43E-06	1.01E-04	9.74E-07
			1.00E-03	1.46E-06	1.01E-06	1.65E-08
			3.00E-05	1.46E-06	3.03E-08	7.08E-09
	Logic System Functional Test Only at Shutdown	1.36E-03	1.00E-01	1.04E-06	1.01E-04	6.64E-07
			1.00E-03	1.07E-06	1.01E-06	1.15E-08
			3.00E-05	1.07E-06	3.02E-08	5.15E-09
	Leak Test AOC in HPCI and RCIC	8.49E-03	1.00E-01	3.11E-05	1.05E-04	5.33E-06
			1.00E-03	3.12E-05	1.05E-06	1.97E-07
			3.00E-05	3.12E-05	3.15E-08	1.46E-07
	All Corrective Actions	1.03E-03	1.00E-01	9.50E-07	1.00E-04	2.96E-07
			1.00E-03	9.79E-07	1.00E-06	7.46E-09
			3.00E-05	9.79E-07	3.01E-08	4.63E-09
Plant 2	Base Case	9.93E-03	1.00E-01	3.37E-05	3.23E-04	2.23E-04
			1.00E-03	3.44E-05	3.23E-06	2.23E-06
			3.00E-05	3.44E-05	9.68E-08	7.14E-08
	Do Not Cycle Valves F052 and F218 at Power	3.45E-03	1.00E-01	2.11E-05	1.61E-04	6.09E-05
			1.00E-03	2.14E-05	1.61E-06	6.12E-07
			3.00E-05	2.15E-05	4.82E-08	2.13E-08
	Do Not Cycle Valve F087 at Power	7.53E-03	1.00E-01	2.90E-05	2.63E-04	1.63E-04
			1.00E-03	2.96E-05	2.63E-06	1.63E-06
			3.00E-05	2.96E-05	7.88E-08	5.28E-08
	Both Corrective Actions	1.05E-03	1.00E-01	1.64E-05	1.01E-04	9.14E-07
			1.00E-03	1.67E-05	1.01E-06	1.17E-08
			3.00E-05	1.67E-05	3.02E-08	2.83E-09
Plant 3	Base Case	6.89E-03	1.00E-01	4.15E-05	1.09E-04	9.59E-06
			1.00E-03	4.16E-05	1.09E-06	3.17E-07
			3.00E-05	4.16E-05	3.28E-08	2.26E-07
	Leak Test AOC in ECCS	5.54E-03	1.00E-01	3.13E-05	1.01E-04	1.36E-06
			1.00E-03	3.13E-05	1.01E-06	1.80E-07
			3.00E-05	3.14E-05	3.03E-08	1.68E-07
	Leak Test AOC After Maintenance	6.28E-03	1.00E-01	3.75E-05	1.03E-04	3.51E-06
			1.00E-03	3.76E-05	1.03E-06	2.35E-07
			3.00E-05	3.76E-05	3.10E-08	2.03E-07
	Both Corrective Actions	5.49E-03	1.00E-01	3.09E-05	1.00E-04	7.54E-07
			1.00E-03	3.09E-05	1.00E-06	1.72E-07
			3.00E-05	3.09E-05	3.01E-08	1.66E-07

Notes: See Table 1.

Table 2: Summary of Results

5. Loss of Power and Water Hammer Event at San Onofre, Unit 1, on November 21, 1985," NUREG-1190, USNRC, January 1986.
6. DOE/RECON, Nuclear Safety Information Center (NSIC), File 8, 1963 to present.
7. "Trip to Browns Ferry Unit 1 Regarding Potential Core Spray Overpressuriza-tion," NRC Memorandum from Scott Newberry to Barry Holahan, Operating Reactors Assessment Branch, Office of NRR, USNRC, September 29, 1984.
8. R. A. Bari et al., "Probabilistic Safety Analysis Procedures Guide," NUREG/CR-2815, July 1985.
9. A. D. Swain and H. E. Guttman, "Handbook of Human Reliability Analysis with Emphasis on Nuclear Power Plant Applications," NUREG/CR-1278, August 1983.
10. H. S. Mehta and R. W. Howard, "BWR Owner's Group Assessment of Emergency Core Cooling System Pressurization in Boiling Water Reactors," Draft Report, June 30, 1986.

DIFFERENCES IN CORE DAMAGE RISK FOR YOUNGER AND OLDER REACTOR PLANTS BASED ON ACCIDENT SEQUENCE PRECURSOR PROGRAM DATA

Joseph W. Minarick
(Science Applications International Corporation, Oak Ridge, Tennessee, USA 37831)

Existing Accident Sequence Precursor data and models were utilized to develop an estimate of the increased core damage risk associated with plants during the first two years of operation compared to later operation. Plant risk during the first two years of operation appears to be from six to ten times greater than that for later operation, depending on industry-wide improvements following the Three Mile Island 2 accident, the Browns Ferry Fire and the 1978 Rancho Seco non-nuclear instrumentation failure.

Keywords: Operational Event, Licensee Event Report, Severe Core Damage Accident, Core Damage Frequency, Precursor.

Introduction

The Accident Sequence Precursor (ASP) program identifies and probabilistically ranks more serious operational events which have occurred at U.S. light-water power reactors. The ASP program, begun at Oak Ridge National Laboratory in 1979, is sponsored by the U.S. Nuclear Regulatory Commission. An event is documented as a precursor if it meets one of the following criteria:

1. the event involved the failure of at least one system required to mitigate a loss of feedwater (LOFW), loss of offsite power (LOOP), small-break loss of coolant accident (LOCA) or steam-line break;

2. the event involved the degradation of more than one system required to mitigate one of the above initiating events; or

3. the event involved an actual initiating event which required safety system response.

Initiating event frequency and system failure probability estimates are used, in conjunction with core damage event trees, to estimate a conditional probability associated with each precursor. This probability is an estimate of the chance of severe core damage, given that the precursor event occurred in the manner it did, and can be considered a measure of the residual protection available during the event.

Retrospective industry-average core damage frequency estimates for 1969-79 and 1980-81 were developed in the ASP program from precursor conditional probabilities based on an approach described in the 1969-79 and 1980-81 precursor reports (1,2). In this approach, an estimate of core damage frequency $<\lambda>$ is given by:

$$<\lambda> = \sum_i p_i/T$$

where p_i is the conditional probability for precursor i and T is the observation period. Precautions concerning the use of this method are discussed in Ref. 2. As described in Ref. 2, only precursors involving initiators occurring or potentially occurring at power are used to estimate $<\lambda>$. To approximate the impact of core-damage related initiators not selected as precursors, a frequency for core damage due to losses of feedwater was added to $<\lambda>$. Losses of feedwater were the most significant events not reportable under the pre-1984 U.S. Licensee Event Report (LER) system.

Analysis

This analysis uses precursors identified in the ASP program to estimate the difference in core damage frequency between younger and older light water reactors. For the purpose of this analysis, younger plants are defined as those less than two years from initial criticality. The analysis takes advantage of improvements in both modeling in the ASP program and documentation of reactor trip events reported in the LER system. Event sequence models currently employed in the ASP program recognize differences in response to initiators for different classes of plants listed in Table 1. Use of these revised event sequence models is described in Ref. 3 and summarized in Ref. 4. The revised LER reporting requirements, which went into effect in 1984, require the detailed reporting of all reactor trip-related events. Detailed documentation of reactor trips permits the core damage impact of actual LOFWs and reactor trips with main feedwater operability to be directly addressed.

Table 1. Accident Sequence Precursor Program Plant Categorizations

Class	Plants in Class
PWR Class A	Westinghouse plants which utilize containment spray recirculation for post-LOCA cooling (e.g., Surry, Beaver Valley, and North Anna)
PWR Classes B, C, E and F	The majority of other Westinghouse plants plus Davis-Besse (because of the need to open the PORV for bleed and feed) and Maine Yankee (because of its similarity to other Class B plants)
PWR Class D	Babcock & Wilcox plants (except Davis-Besse)
PWR Class G	Combustion Engineering plants (except Maine Yankee)
BWR Class A	Early BWRs, which utilize feedwater coolant injection
BWR Class B	Dresden 2, 3
BWR Class C	Remaining General Electric plants

Conditional probabilities for precursors identified in 1985, LOFWs and reactor trips with main feedwater operability were calculated using the newer plant-class specific event sequence models. Conditional probabilities associated with 1969-81 precursors were not recalculated using the new models for the estimate described herein. (Precursor conditional probabilities initially estimated for 1969-79 had been revised in 1984-85 based on comments on the first report and for consistency with the approach used to address 1980-81 events (5)). Because of the small number of precursors and because many precursors can be associated with a number of plant classes, the fact that conditional probabilities for earlier events were not recalculated based on the revised plant-class specific models is not expected to substantially impact the results of this assessment.

Branch probabilities used in the event sequence models were not revised to reflect differences in plant age at the time of the event. In so far as the reliability of many systems appear to improve as plants age (at least for the fraction of plant lifetime which has been observed), the risk differences calculated in this analysis may underestimate the actual difference in risk between the two plant age groups.

Core damage frequency estimates based on precursors alone for plants less than and greater than two years old are:

	Plant age ≤ 2 yrs	Plant age age > 2 yrs
BWRs, including the Browns Ferry fire precursor	2.6E-3/RY	5.0E-5/RY
BWRs, excluding the Browns Ferry fire precursor	1.3E-5/RY	5.0E-5/RY
PWRs, including the Three Mile Island 2 and 1978 Rancho Seco non-nuclear instrumentation (NNI) precursors	5.4E-3/RY	6.8E-4/RY
PWRs, excluding the Three Mile Island 2 and 1978 Rancho Seco NNI precursors	9.6E-4/RY	1.4E-4/RY

The core damage frequency impact of reactor trips with feedwater operability and LOFWs for plants less than and greater than two years old was developed based on LERs for trips at 15 percent power or greater occuring during 1984-1985. Trips from the following set of plants were used to estimate frequencies for these intitiators for plants less than two years old: Shoreham; Limerick 1; McGuire 2; Waterford 3; St. Lucie 2; Catawba 1, 2; Perry 1; River Bend 1; and Callaway 1.

Trips and losses of feedwater associated with all other plants were used to estimate frequencies for plants older than two years. Initiator frequencies developed using these two plant sets are listed on a plant-class basis in Table 2. Table 3 lists associated conditional probabilities of core damage estimated in the ASP program. These probabilities were combined with the initiator frequencies listed in Table 2 and normalized based on reactor years for each plant class within the observation period to estimate the core damage frequency contribution for non-precursor events:

	Plant age ≤ 2 yrs	Plant age age > 2 yrs
BWR LOFW and reactor trip (main feedwater operability)	1.8E-4/RY	4.0E-5/RY
PWR LOFW and reactor trip (main feedwater operability)	1.6E-5/RY	4.3E-6/RY

Table 2. Reactor Trip (Main Feedwater Operable) and LOFW Frequencies

Plant Class	Reactor trip frequency (age<2 yr)	Reactor trip frequency (age>2 yr)	LOFW frequency (age< 2 yr)	LOFW frequency (age> 2 yr)
PWR Class A	*	3.0	*	0.40
PWR Class B, C, E, F	10.4	3.7	1.5	0.31
PWR Class D*	*	2.8	*	0.48
PWR Class G*	8.6	2.8	1.7	0.17
BWR Class A	*	1.8	*	0.13
BWR Class B	*	2.0	*	0.25
BWR Class C	6.1	3.1	1.1	0.38

* no plants less than two years old exist in these classes.

Table 3. Reactor Trip (Main Feedwater Operable) and LOFW Conditional Probabilities

Plant Class (Plant Used in Calculation)	RT (Main Feedwater Operable)	LOFW
PWR Class A (Beaver Valley)	2.2E-6	3.2E-6
PWR Class B, C, E, F (Farley 1)	1.1E-6	2.2E-6
PWR Class D (Oconee 1)	1.1E-6	2.1E-6
PWR Class G (Calvert Cliffs)*	5.0E-8	6.8E-7
PWR Class G (Waterford)*	3.0E-8	1.2E-5
BWR Class A (Oyster Creek)	6.0E-7	3.5E-6
BWR Class B (Dresden 2)	3.4E-8	5.8E-7
BWR Class C (Browns Ferry 1)	9.8E-6	5.8E-5

*Two plant models were utilized for Combustion Engineering plants to reflect the lack of a PORV on later plants.

Results

The combined core damage frequency estimates from precursors, LOFWs and reactor trips with main feedwater operability are:

	Plant age $\leq$ 2 yrs	Plant age age > 2 yrs
Estimate including TMI-2 accident, Browns Ferry fire, and Rancho Seco NNI precursors	4.4E-3/RY	4.5E-4/RY
Estimate without above three events	6.6E-4/RY	1.2E-4/RY

The relative difference between the two plant periods is therefore a factor of ~10 if three major early precursors - the Three Mile Island 2 accident, the Browns Ferry fire and the 1978 Rancho Seco NNI failure are included, and a factor of ~6 if these events are excluded. Since work has occurred to implement lessons learned from the three events, the actual ratio would be expected to be somewhere between the two estimates.

Differences in risk (factors) between the two age groups were also estimated for three plant classes with plants in the younger plant population:

	Factor
PWR Class B, C, E, and F (without Davis-Besse, Maine Yankee)	9
PWR Class G	5
BWR Class C (without Browns Ferry fire precursor)	2

For the two PWR groups, the risk due to both precursors and trips (with and without feedwater operability) was greater for plants less than two years old than for older plants. For BWR Class C plants (excluding the Browns Ferry fire precursor), however, the increased younger plant risk was the result of a greater number of trips in that period. The risk due to precursors was less for younger plants of this class than for older plants.

Precursors from 1969-81 and 1985 with conditional probabilities of 1E-3 or greater were qualitatively reviewed to identify differences in precursors which occurred within the two age groups. Failures in electrical, main and auxiliary feedwater, and instrumentation systems predominate both age groups for the more serious precursors which were reviewed. Improvement with plant age was observed for PWR auxiliary feedwater and BWR high pressure coolant injection systems; problems involving electrical systems (other than the diesel generators) appear to increase with plant age. Maintenance and operator errors play a significant role in higher ranked precursors in both age groups, although a decrease in these types of contributors is noted as plants age. Mechanical failures appear to occur at the same rate in both age groups.

Many precursors which occurred in the first two years exhibit similar characteristics to events which occur later in plant life. However, it appeared events occuring early in life included more:

o problems in communication between members of the operating crew.

o construction, equipment manufacture and procedural errors discovered during anticipated transients (for example, during AFW system demands and LOOPs) and during environmental conditions different from conditions at startup testing and calibration.

One would expect these events to occur more frequently during early plant operation. It is possible that more carefully designed startup test procedures, which address a wider range of operating conditions, could reduce the number of events seen following anticipated transients early in plant life.

References

1. J.W. Minarick and C.A. Kukielka, Precursors to Potential Severe Core Damage Accidents: 1969-1979, A Status Report, NUREG/CR-2497, June 1982.

2. W.B. Cottrell, J.W. Minarick, P.N. Austin, E.W. Hagen and J.D. Harris, Precursors to Potential Severe Core Damage Accidents: 1980-1981, A Status Report, NUREG/CR-3591, July 1984.

3. J.W. Minarick, J.D. Harris, P.N. Austin, J.W. Cletcher, and E.W. Hagen, Precursors to Potential Severe Core Damage Accidents: 1985, A Status Report, NUREG/CR-4674, Vol. 1, December 1986.

4. J.W. Minarick, F.M. Manning, and J.D. Harris, The Accident Sequence Precursor Program: Methods Improvements and Current Results, this conference.

5. D.L. Phung, J.W. Minarick, and J.D. Harris, A Review of Comments on the 1969-79 Accident Sequence Precursor Report: NUREG/CR-2497, ORNL/NRC/LTR-85/14, June 1985.

PRESSURE-TUBE FAILURE PROBABILITY ASSESSMENT FOR A PRESSURE-TUBE NUCLEAR REACTOR

M.G. Stamatelatos, A.W. Barsell and C.F. Dahms
[GA Technologies Inc., San Diego, CA - USA]
K.V. Scott
[UNC Nuclear Industries, Inc., Richland, WA - USA]

ABSTRACT

A probabilistic model based on linear elastic fracture mechanics has been developed and applied to the N Reactor pressure tubes. The model tracks, as a function of time, the probability of wall penetration due to crack growth, the probability of brittle fracture (fracture toughness exceeded), and the probability of exceeding ASME Section XI code safety margins. Both normal operation and selected accidents (safe shutdown earthquake andpressure tube rupture event) were analyzed. Results help to define the future surveillance program for the pressure tubes.

1   INTRODUCTION

The Hanford N Reactor is a graphite-moderated, pressurized light water reactor operated for the U.S. Department of Energy (DOE) for dual purposes of economic and efficient production of special nuclear materials, and electricity generation. It contains 1003 horizontal fuel channels and has operated since 1964 at an average thermal power of 3450 MW. The channels consist of cold-worked Zircaloy-2 pressure tubes inside a graphite moderator matrix. The pressure tubes are in contact with the moderator only at the trunnions which are spaced 0.8 m apart.

Graphite distortion, due to irradiation, affects the pressure tube safety margins against brittle fracture. This growth imposes distortion forces on tubes which, coupled with the internal pressure of 12 MPa, can magnify stresses in the pressure tubes. The cyclic nature of the combined normal operation stresses during reactor shutdown can promote fatigue crack growth. Another possible growth mechanism, delayed hydrogen cracking (DHC), is caused by temperature cycling in the presence of high stress loading and hydrogen concentration in the Zircaloy-2 tubes. Although no pressure tube failure has occurred (leak or rupture), the concern relates to future operation where fluence and hydrogen embrittlement could degrade the fracture toughness. The purpose of this study is to address these concerns from a probabilistic standpoint to supplement other conservative deterministic assessments.

2   METHODOLOGY AND DATA

2.1 Flaw Initiation or Existence

Multiple sources of data consistently indicate a frequency of existence of around 10^{-1} per pressure tube for a significant base metal or weld crack or flaw (deeper than 0.25 mm). These sources include:

1. Preservice inspection of the tubes (100% ultrasonic testing, radiography, etc.).

2. Eddy current testing of spare tubes.

3. Destructive examination of nine tubes which have been removed from the core periodically since initial reactor startup.

4. Incore surveillance examination using eddy current and ultrasonic testing methods.

Early in the study, it was determined that the potential for crack initiation in a scratch or groove due to creep-fatigue damage or DHC is negligible because the stress concentrations are too small. The existence of a crack is therefore assumed to be a prerequisite for potential growth/failure in the model.

2.2 Fatigue Growth

The internal pressure stresses and graphite distortion loadings on the pressure tubes during plant operation are relatively invariant with power level until near shutdown conditions. However, the transition from operation to shutdown creates a cycling in both hoop and axial stresses. This stress cycling creates a change in stress intensity factor, ΔK_I, from steady state to shutdown conditions. Laboratory experimental data (Refs. 1 and 2) on fatigue crack growth in Zircaloy-2 were fitted to a power function of ΔK_I,

$$da/DN = C \, (\Delta K_I)^{2.6} \tag{1}$$

The coefficient C was found to be a weak function of cyclic frequency. A statistical fit to over 200 data points yielded a median value for C of 2.3×10^{-3} if the growth rate da/dN has units of microns/cycle and the stress intensity is in the MPa $\sqrt{m}$. The parameter C was taken to be lognormally distributed with an uncertainty factor of 2.42 (ratio of 95th to 50th percentile values) from the statistical analysis. This growth rate for fatigue was used in the model with no limiting conditions. The integrated fatigue growth considers the number of cycles which have occurred in previous plant operation and the probabilistic number of cycles projected for the future.

2.3 Delayed Hydrogen Cracking

DHC growth is an observed failure mechanism for Zircaloy-2 and Zr-2.5% Nb tubes in the CANDU reactors, due to local cold spots on the tube and high residual stresses. Although no evidence of DHC growth in N Reactor tubes has been uncovered, it has been postulated as a hypothetical growth mechanism in view of increasing hydrogen concentrations in the N Reactor tubes.

Three conditions appear to be essential for DHC growth (Ref. 3): high hydrogen concentrations, temperature conditions resulting in exceedance of hydride solubility limits and a stress intensity, K_I, exceeding the threshold stress intensity, K_{IH}. When these conditions are met, the DHC growth rate is described by a temperature sensitive Arrhenius rate equation

$$da/dt = 0.0532 \exp (-8039/T) \qquad\qquad (2)$$

where da/dt is the rate of change of crack depth a with time t in units of m/s and T is the temperature, K. In the equation, the constants are median values from a statistical analysis of data for Zircaloy-2. This growth rate was taken to be lognormally distributed with an uncertainty factor, from the statistical analysis, of 1.73.

The theory of DHC is basically that dissolved hydrogen (in solid solution in the zirconium alloy matrix) migrates at high temperatures (during steady state operation) to locations of high tensile stress, such as a crack tip. During cooldown, the temperature falls below the solubility limit and local hydride platelets can be formed. If the stress is high enough (i.e., $K_I > K_{IH}$), the hydride can crack.

The DHC growth equation was applied to a typical shutdown temperature transient (T vs t) to calculate the integrated growth over a single cycle. The median cumulative growth over the cooldown period (0 to 7h) was calculated to be 2×10^{-4} mm. This occurs only if the H_2 concentration exceeds the solubility limit and if K_I exceeds K_{IH}. Time and location dependent H_2 concentration equations and temperature dependent H_2 solubility limits were derived from test data and used in the analysis to test whether DHC growth conditions are present. The DHC growth during heatup was calculated to be negligibly small.

2.4 Stress Analysis

Best estimate and uncertainties of bending and membrane stresses due to graphite-induced bowing and ovalization, internal pressure and tube-to-shield interface forces were derived for normal operation based on parametric analyses performed in previous studies. Both steady state and shutdown conditions were considered for different core locations and circumferential and through-wall variations.

The stresses are expressed in terms of the fundamental parameters causing the stresses. Best estimates and uncertainties for these parameters were derived and used to formulate the stress algorithm incorporated in the probabilistic model. Table 1 presents the best estimate stresses, taken to be median values for lognormally distributed stresses. The uncertainty factors are derived from propagation of uncertainties in the parameter distributions.

TABLE 1. BEST ESTIMATE MIDPOINT STRESSES

		STRESSES (MPa)		
Stress Type	Tube Surface	Fringe Tube	Spike Tube	Central Tube
Axial Stress - Steady State	Inner	69	48	38
	Outer	51	29	23
- Shutdown	Inner	59	23	7
	Outer	77	52	33
Hoop Stress - Steady State	Inner	112	112	103
	Outer	16	20	27
- Shutdown	Inner	12	14	12
	Outer	0	3	3

2.5 Fracture Toughness

An algorithm for fracture toughness, K_{IC}, was derived from a statistical analysis of 128 data points for Zircaloy-2. This algorithm is a function of temperature, neutron fluence and crack orientation. Both best estimate values and uncertainties were derived for use in the probabilistic model.

2.6 Probability Model

The approach is to generate probability distributions for the calculated
crack depth, stress intensity factors and corresponding fracture toughness
values simultaneously at selected points in time. Then, by comparing the
crack depth distribution with the wall thickness, and comparing the stress
intensity distribution with the fracture toughness distribution (with and
without the ASME code safety factor of $\sqrt{10}$), the probabilities of failure
for the three modes of failure are calculated using the standard
interference or overlap method. The tool for doing this is the STADIC-2
Monte Carlo computer program (Ref. 4).

The stress intensity solutions, functions of stresses and crack depth and
length, are based on standard linear elastic fracture mechanics (LEFM)
equations for a semi-elliptical surface flaw subjected to perpendicular
membrane and bending loads (Refs. 5-7). These equations are programmed in
a user-provided subroutine of STADIC-2 and they provide the relationship
between the input distributions and distributed output functions.
Distributed input variables include initial flaw size, crack growth rate
parameters, stress parameters, number of cycles in future operation and
fracture toughness. These distributions were sampled from two to ten
thousand times in a Monte Carlo procedure to derive the output functions at
selected times. These functions include distributions of a/h (ratio of
crack depth to wall thickness) and K_I/K_{IC}. Failure probability is
indicated when these distributions exceed unity. Also, the relative number
of times in the sampling when K_I exceeds $K_{IC}/\sqrt{10}$ is tracked as a measure of
ASME code margin exceedance.

3   RESULTS AND CONCLUSIONS

Table 1 presents typical results from the probabilistic analysis. These
pertain to a fringe area tube in year 1995 at the worst circumferential
location, namely at the top of the tube. Both axial base metal and
circumferential weld cracks on the inside surface are included. Three
axial locations along the fringe tube are included: inlet quarterpoint
(QP), midpoint, and outlet QP. Results for other tubes are similar or
lower.

TABLE 2. CALCULATED FAILURE PROBABILITIES (FRINGE TUBE)

Crack Orientation/Location	1995 PROBABILITIES	
	Wall Penetration	Brittle Fracture*
Axial Crack - Inlet QP	1×10^{-3}	$< 10^{-7}$
- Midpoint	3×10^{-3}	$< 10^{-7}$
- Outlet QP	1×10^{-3}	$< 10^{-7}$
Weld Crack - Inlet QP	2×10^{-4}	2×10^{-4}
- Midpoint	1×10^{-3}	2×10^{-6}
- Outlet QP	1.5×10^{-4}	8×10^{-6}

*during shutdown

The results show that wall penetration probabilities are generally orders of magnitude higher than brittle fracture probabilities, supporting the contention that leak before break is the dominant failure mode. DHC is the dominant crack growth mechanism at high stress locations. Midpoint locations were critical for crack growth due to the greater stresses there. Inlet locations were more critical for brittle fracture because of lower fracture toughness at the lower temperatures. For the same reason, brittle fracture during plant operation was found to be less likely than during shutdown.

Probabilities of brittle fracture due to accident condition loading during a safe shutdown earthquake or a pressure tube rupture event are low relative to normal operation, considering their occurrence frequencies.

Surveillance program recommendations include eddy current and ultrasonic testing for inside surface flaws, especially around tube midpoints and inlets and removal of tubes with crack indications in order to examine for evidence of DHC growth. Also, laboratory measurements of the DHC growth threshold and the fracture toughness at high fluence values can reduce key uncertainties in the analysis.

REFERENCES

1. Picker, C. and Pickles, B.W., "The Enhancement of Fatigue Crack Growth Rates in Zirconium Alloys in a Reactor Environment," Proc. Conf. on Dimensional Stability and Mechanical Behavior of Irradiated Metals and Alloys, British Nuclear Energy Society, London, UK, 1983.

2. Pickles, B.W. and Picker, C., "The Effects of Environment and Neutron Irradiation on the Fatigue Crack Growth Behavior of Zircaloy-2," Transactions of the 6th International Conference on Structural Mechanics in Reactor Technology, Paris, France, 1981, paper F 6/4.

3. Coleman, C.E., "Effect of Texture on Hydride Reorientation and Delayed Hydrogen Cracking in Cold-Worked Zr-2.5 Nb," Zirconium in the Nuclear Industry; Fifth Conference, ASTM STP 754, 1982, pp. 393-411.

4. Koch, P.N., and St. John, H.E., "STADIC-2, A Computer Program for Combining Probability Distributions," GA Technologies Report GA-A16227, July 1983.

5. Raju, I.S., and Newman, J.C., "Stress-Intensity Factors for Internal and External Surface Cracks in Cylindrical Vessels," Journal of Pressure Vessel Technology, Vol. 104, No. 4, 1982, pp. 293-298.

6. Raju, I.S., and Newman, J.C., "Stress-Intensity Factors for Circumferential Surface Cracks in Pipes and Rods Under Tension and Bending Loads," NASA Technical Memorandum 87594, August 1985.

7. Erdogan, F., "Circumferentially Cracked Cylinders Under Tension or Bending," Appendix D of Theoretical and Experimental Study of Fracture in Pipelines Containing Circumferential Flaws, Report DOT-RSPA-DMA 50/83/3, U.S. Department of Transportation, September 1982.

CONVERSION OF THE PUN PROBABILISTIC SAFETY STUDY INTO A LIVING PRA
FORMAT

Dr S. Serra
ENEL-DCO, Rome, ITALY

Dr. S. Sancaktar and Dr. D. R. Sharp
Westinghouse Electric Corporation
Pittsburgh, U.S.A.

1. INTRODUCTION

The 1981 Italian Energy Plan recommended that a number of nuclear
power plants of 1000 MWe be built and operated in Italy on the basis
of a reference design, Progetto Unificato Nucleare (PUN) PWR type,
which is a standard plant design for all future nuclear power
stations. A further requirement of the energy plan is that an
evaluation of safety be performed for the entire Nuclear Power
Reference Design. A Probabilistic Safety Study (PSS) is a part of
this safety evaluation.

The preliminary goal of the PSS was to provide an assessment of core
damage frequency for the PUN design. For this purpose, a level 1 PRA
was performed by ENEL, ANSALDO and Westinghouse and was completed in
1984. (ref 1). The PUN-PSS has been revised by the Italian Safety
Authority, which pointed out that the model gives a measure of the
core damage probability that is representative of the safety level of
the standard plant. Furthermore, the Italian Safety Authority
required that PUN-PSS shall be interactive with the design (Living
PRA). Therefore a second goal is to provide a Living PRA model which
can be used during the plants' design and operation to optimize
design considerations (ref. 2).

The conversion of the PUN-PSS into a Living PRA is been carried out
by Westinghouse for ENEL. The objective of this paper is to
summarize the work done, present some results and the experience
gained during this job, showing an example where, through this tool,
indication to the risk management can be given.

2. PUN LIVING PRA MODEL

The PUN Living PRA Model was built and quantified on an IBM-AT micro
computer based engineering workstation. The model consists of fault
trees and event trees, supported by data banks. Two Westinghouse
proprietary codes that run on the IBM-AT are used to perform fault
tree, event tree and plant coremelt analysis. Every aspect of the
model exists on the micro computer. One exception is that it is
convenient to print large fault tree pictures on a CALCOMP printer
driven by a micro computer.

Tests on other microcomputer have been performed, that is Olivetti M24, Sperry IT and portable Toshiba. A micro computer workstation can accommodate up to four PRA studies for different plants, which may be BWR as well as PWR. The code systems are generic PRA codes that can be used not only to requantify the present PUN Living PRA model, but they can also be used to make new PRA models for other nuclear plants, or be used for plant system reliability analysis studies.

Initially, the PUN model existed in and was quantified by a main frame. The basis for this model on micro computer was taken from PUN Probabilistic Safety Study carried out by ENEL, Westinghouse and ANSALDO. The same model is placed and can be completely quantified on an IBM-AT with the implementation of the Living PRA capabilities. No approximations were done in the fault tree and event tree models. The results of the event tree and fault tree models in the present study match the corresponding results in the base PUN-PSS (see table 1).

The two menu driven code system used to make and quantify the model are named GRAFTER and SUPER. GRAFTER is an all-purpose fault tree analysis code system. It can be used to create, modify, print, and quantify fault trees. The code system interacts with a master data bank to quantify basic event probabilities for a large number of fault trees, automatically. The large number of fault trees that exist for the PUN model can be quantified in a batch mode, without user interaction. Also the probabilities in all fault trees can be automatically updated, once the master data bank is modified.

The SUPER code system is used to make, print and quantify event trees. It also uses a master data bank to place system and operator action failure probabilities in all the event trees, automatically.

The above characteristics of the codes enable the user to make and automatically document sensitivity calculations, as well as modify any part of the fault tree and event tree models in a very short time.

The model has been delivered to ENEL in May 1987 for in-house use. The ENEL engineers have been trained in use of the model by active participation in its construction and by a week-training for experts on micro computer and reliability analysis.

During its construction, the PUN-PSS provided valuable insights into the plant design, and affected the final form of the design. Now in a Living PRA format, it can be a valuable tool during the detailed design construction, licensing and operation phases of a power plant.

In the base scope of this project, no attempt was made to rigorously recreate the complicated support state model (ref. 3)of the original PUN-PSS. A support state model was included to quantify the support state probabilities of the transient, LOCA and loss of offsite power. To make PUN-PSS a practical tool for analysis and sensitivity studies, the original support state model needs to be restructured.

The present model goes beyond the original PUN-PSS model in three areas:

1. The capability to evaluate the plant risk curves is obtained through the SUPER code System. Example containment and site matrices are provided to obtain the plant risk curves. This enables the ENEL analysts to compare the PUN plant design on a different site with a different containment.

2. The capability to automatically identify dominant accident sequences and to calculate the importance of the event tree nodes (plant systems and operator actions) is provided by the code system.

3. The fault tree and event tree analyses are run in batch modes using master data banks to provide the analysis results in the shortest possible time with a single command given by the user.

2.1 Fault tree model.

The fault tree model converted in the micro computer is basically constituted by 160 fault trees, that represents either the front line systems or the support systems. Beyond the easy way to build fault trees, they can be quantified in different ways, depending on the needs of the user:

a. single case, as is
b. single case, after updating the basic event frequencies
c. fault trees for a given plant system for all cases after updating the basic event frequencies
d. all fault trees for all plant systems.

The batch quantification of all fault trees takes about 6 hrs. The results in terms of availabilities of the systems obtained via micro computer were compared with those calculated by main frame using the WAM and SALP series of codes and showed a perfect agreement; where some differences exist they can be justified.

2.2 Event tree model and Core Damage Frequency

The event tree model converted in the micro computer has been represented by 35 event trees, 24 of which are initiating events and 11 consequential events.
The event tree code can be used to analyze the result of the event tree analysis to:

a. calculate the plant core damage frequency;

b. to identify and rank the dominant accident sequences;

c. to sort the contributors to the plant core damage frequency by plant coremelt states, by initiating events, and by support states;

d.   to calculate the importance of the event tree nodes
(systems and operator actions).

The major differences between the micro computer model and the
previous model are in the presentation of the event tree analysis.
Namely, the event tree coupling (looping function) in the PUN-PSS is
removed and the consequential events are modeled by individual event
trees.

Table 1 shows the results of the core damage frequency for the base
case (ref. 1) and for the sensitivity case (ref. 2) compared with
the calculation made through the Living PRA; this comparison shows a
good agreement.

Also the distribution of the various contributions to the core damage
frequency among support states, initiating events and damage states,
as well as the rank of dominant sequences complies with the previous
calculation.

3.   AN EXAMPLE OF SENSITIVITY ANALYSIS.

From the importance analysis results described in ref. 4 it was
choosen a simple example where a single sensitivity analysis can be
done in short time. The human operator errors in the sensitivity
case of table 1 are among the less significant contributors to the
core damage frequency (less than 5%) in terms of Fussel-Vesely
importance.

The model by micro computer has been run with an hypothetical
situation where the operator makes errors, except on the manual scram
and on the long term action (RHR intervention).

The results show that the core damage frequency will increase and the
main initiating event contributor changes to Steam Generator Tube
Rupture and ATWS. Table 2 shows the contribution to the core damage
frequency of these events, in the two situations: the sensitivity
case with actual human error probabilities and the hypothetical
unreliable operator. So it is necessary that during the operator's
training a clear understanding of these two events from both the
points of view of diagnosis and emergency procedures, and operation
during shutdown after these events shall be stressed.

4.   CONCLUSION

Living PRA can be realistically developed only if the tool has the
capability to answer quickly to the designer in terms of input-output
presentation and the code system described offers it. As a matter of
fact modifications of the PUN design made from July 83 to July 87
will be incorporated to formulate a new base case using the "living
PRA" tool.

REFERENCES

1. D.C. Richardson, G. Russino, V. Valentini "Use of a Probabilistic Safety Study in the Design of the Italian Reference PWR" International ANS/ENS Topical Meeting on Probabilistic Safety Methods and Applications, San Francisco, California, USA, February 1985

2. V. Cavicchia, M.Nobile, S. Serra "Overview of the Probabilistic Safety Studies for Nuclear Power Plants in Italy - Points of view and Prospects for the utilization of the Probabilistic Methodology". Workshop: Probabilistic Safety Assessment as an Aid to Nuclear Plant Management Brighton - England May 20-23rd 1986.

3. A.M. Amendola, M. Genco, P. Moretti, W.E. Shopsky "Support State Modeling of Intersystem Dependence in the Probabilistic Safety Study for Italian ENEL PWR Nuclear Standard Power Stations" International ANS/ENS Topical Meeting on Probabilistic Safety Methods and Applications, San Francisco, California, USA, February 1985

4. A.M. Amendola, G. Genco, S. Serra "System Importance Analysis in the Probabilistic Safety Study on the Italian Reference PWR" International Topical Conference on "Probabilistic Safety Assessment and Risk Management" Zurich, Switzerland, Aug. 30-Sept. 4, 1987.

TABLE 1

COMPARISON OF CORE DAMAGE FREQUENCY
BETWEEN MAIN FRAME AND MICRO COMPUTER ANALYSIS

	MAIN FRAME	MICRO COMPUTER
BASE CASE	4.39E-05	4.38E-05
SENSITIVITY CASE(*)	8.10E-06	8.05E-06

(*) related to a set of modifications described in ref. 2, and
recommended to the designer.

534

TABLE 2

COMPARISON OF THE CONTRIBUTORS TO CORE DAMAGE FREQUENCY
IN THE SENSITIVITY CASE AND IN THE HYPOTHETICAL UNRELIABLE OPERATOR

	SENSITIVITY CASE % core damage frequency	UNRELIABLE OPERATOR % core damage frequency
- LOCAs & Steam Line Break	27.8	8.4
- Steam Generator Tube Rupture	2.3	45.6
- Loss of Main Feedwater	2.4	4.8
- Secondary to Primary Power Mismatch	6.0	11.3
- Turbine or Reactor Trip	2.1	8.1
- Other transients	3.9	0.9
- Loss of Offsite Power	12.3	1.8
- Station Black-out	1.6	0.9
- ATWS	3.0	14.2
- Loss of Service and Component Cooling Water	4.0	1.2
- Loss of vital buses	8.7	0.3
- Consequential Events	20.5	2.0
- Other (ISL,RVR)	5.2	0.2

APPLICATION OF INDIVIDUAL PLANT EVALUATION METHODOLOGY TO THE GRAND GULF
NUCLEAR STATION

S. Visweswaran, G. W. Smith
[General Electric Company, San Jose, CA, USA; Systems Energy Resources, Inc.
Jackson, MS, USA]

Abstract

This paper describes the application of IDCOR Individual Plant Evaluation (IPE)
methodology to the Grand Gulf Nuclear Station (GGNS) - a single unit 1250 MW(e)
power plant with a General Electric BWR6 Boiling Water Reactor (BWR), located in
Claiborne County, Mississippi, USA. The first objective of the GGNS IPE was to
determine if any GGNS plant design features or procedures are vulnerable to severe
accidents involving core damage. A second objective of the GGNS IPE was to test
the specific applicability of the IPE methodology to BWR6 plants.

1.   Introduction

This paper describes the application of IDCOR Individual Plant Evaluation (IPE)
methodology (Reference 1) to the Grand Gulf Nuclear Station (GGNS) - a single unit
1250 MW(e) power plant with a General Electric BWR6 Boiling Water Reactor (BWR),
located in Claiborne County, Mississippi, USA. The first objective of the GGNS
IPE was to determine if any GGNS plant design features or procedures are
vulnerable to severe accidents involving core damage. A second objective of the
GGNS IPE was to test the specific applicability of the generic IPE methodology to
BWR6 plants.

The Industry Degraded Core Rule Making (IDCOR) Program, after reviewing a number
of Boiling Water Reactor probabilistic risk assessments (PRA) and consolidating
and applying the results to representative BWR surrogate plants, concluded that
the BWR core damage frequency is very low. In order to determine if this general
conclusion is applicable to specific BWR plants, and to identify any plant-unique
core damage vulnerability that may exist, IDCOR has developed an Individual Plant
Evaluation methodology. The IPE methodology provides a focused plant-specific
evaluation of severe accident scenarios and core damage prevention and mitigation
capability through a study of plant systems, operational and maintenance
procedures and plant operating history.

As part of their severe accident policy statement, the United States Nuclear
Regulatory Commission (USNRC) is expected to require some type of individual plant
examination for all operating nuclear power plants. In order to facilitate the
USNRC review of plant submittals, the IPE methodology was developed and tested on
four BWR plants, which included GGNS as the lead plant representing BWR6 plants.
The NRC has reviewed the basic IDCOR IPE methodology and has established
guidelines for its use.

The GGNS IPE was conducted over a period of approximately six months by a team of
engineers from the four US BWR6 utilities and General Electric Company.

2. Methodology

The IPE methodology (IPEM) uses a "differencing approach" by which plant-unique features and conditions are compared to the bases of the IDCOR surrogate plant analysis to provide an assessment of plant-specific applicability of the IDCOR conclusions, and to identify any plant-unique core damage vulnerability that may exist. In order to test the methodology, fault trees and event trees were constructed and evaluated in much the same manner as in a PRA, and the results compared to IDCOR/IPE results.

3. Results of the Evaluation

3.1 Core Damage Frequency

The total expected core damage frequency (CDF) at GGNS due to internally initiated events is determined to be 3.9E-6 per reactor-year. The contribution of the various accident initiators to the plant CDF is given in Table 1.

Accident Initiator	CDF (per reactor-year)	Percentage of Total CDF
Loss of Offsite Power (LOOP)/Station Blackout (SBO)	3.4E-6	85.3
Transients (Except LOOP)	4.8E-7	12.0
Loss of Coolant Accidents	7.0E-8	1.8
Anticipated Transient Without Scram	3.4E-8	0.9
Special Initiators	8.2E-11	~0
	3.9E-6	100%

Table 1. CDF Contribution of GGNS Accident Initiators

A comparison of these results with those from other BWR6 studies shows that the GGNS IPE core damage frequency of 3.9E-6 is in the same range as CDFs predicted by other studies. The GGNS IPE CDF is essentially the same as that for the General Electric Standard BWR6 plant documented in the GESSAR II PRA (Reference 2) and a factor of two smaller than the GGNS results in the basic IDCOR analysis (Reference 3). It is also within the range of the CDFs calculated in the recently published "Reactor Risk Reference Document" NUREG-1150 (Reference 4).

The dominant contributor to the core damage frequency was determined to be the station blackout (SBO) event, which is a subset of the loss of offsite power event. SBO was found to be the predominant contributor in both the GESSAR II and

NUREG-1150 studies also. However, in the IDCOR analysis, CDF for the SBO event was determined to be a factor of six lower than for the GGNS IPE attributed mainly to 1) the use of a lower value for the initiating event frequency, and 2) modeling differences which predict a lower unavailability for the Reactor Core Isolation Cooling (RCIC) System. RCIC is the only system available during an SBO event for reactor coolant make up.

The basic IDCOR study and the IPE methodology identify ATWS as a dominant contributor to plant CDF, whereas the GGNS IPE (and other BWR6 studies) found ATWS to be a negligible (or very small) contributor. The IDCOR results are dominated by the use of a conservative value of 3.0E-5 for the probability of scram failure upon demand based on NRC estimates given in 1978 in NUREG-0460 (Reference 5). The corresponding GGNS IPE value is 1.0E-6 per demand based on the GESSAR II PRA and a more recent detailed evaluation by the BWR Owners Group (Reference 6) as part of their Technical Specification Improvement Program. In addition, the GGNS IPE took credit for the Alternate Rod Insertion (ARI) system.

The contribution of loss of coolant accidents (LOCA) to the CDF was found to be small in the GGNS IPE as well as in the other BWR6 studies.

No core damage-related plant-unique vulnerability was identified in the GGNS IPE.

3.2 Special Analysis

The IPE methodology recommends that certain plant-unique analyses be performed, one of which is the evaluation of the expected frequency of interfacing system LOCAs. Interfacing LOCAs result from exposure of low-pressure piping and components to reactor pressure. The LOCA may disable the low-pressure safety systems involved. Based on a detailed review of piping arrangement, plant layout, operating and testing procedures, the expected frequency of interfacing system LOCA was determined to be less than 1.0E-7 per reactor-year.

3.3 Source Term Evaluation

A source term evaluation was carried out using the "Approximate Source Term Methodology for Boiling Water Reactors" (Reference 7). The evaluation shows that for all dominant severe accident sequences, the fission products released to the environment consist only of noble gases. The suppression pool effectively removes most volatile and non-volatile gases before containment venting. Containment venting essentially eliminates any chance that the containment would be overpressurized. Assessment of containment structural capability has indicated that containment will not fail until 56 psig, which gives the operators adequate time to implement venting procedures. The low frequency of interfacing system LOCAs discussed before assures that containment bypass is extremely unlikely and can be neglected. In summary, no plant-specific containment related vulnerability was identified.

3.4 Insights Gained from the Study

A number of specific insights were gained from the GGNS IPE study. Examples of the insights gained are as follows:

a) The station blackout event is the largest contributor to core damage frequency at GGNS. Any improvement in system design or operating procedures which would prevent or mitigate the effects of station blackout events should reduce the plant core damage frequency. For instance, in the GGNS IPE, diesel-driven firewater pumps were not considered as a source of low-pressure water injection due to the lack of specific procedures and hardware required to properly align the system. With proper connections and procedures, firewater pumps could be used to further mitigate effects of the the station blackout event.

b) It was noted that the plant Instrument Air and Service Air Systems have considerable redundancy due to the availability of Unit 2 compressors.

c) It was noted that installation of the Alternate Rod Insertion (ARI) system significantly reduced the risk related to ATWS events.

d) Venting plays a significant role in reducing the core damage frequency associated with accident sequences involving failure of the containment heat removal systems.

4. Applicability of IPE Methodology to BWR6 Plants

The BWR6 IPE Methodology was developed based on the results of a BWR5 surrogate plant analysis. As part of the GGNS IPE, additional analyses were carried out to test the applicability of the IPE Methodology to BWR6 plants. Most significant tests involved calculating the system unavailabilities based on detailed GGNS (BWR6) fault trees and then comparing the results to values obtained by application of the IPE methodology. The results are documented in Table 2.

System/Function	Initiating Event	System Unavailability (Per Demand)	
		IPE Methodology	GGNS System Fault Trees
Alternate Rod Insertion	All	1.0E-2	2.3E-2
Recirculation Pump Trip	ATWS	1.0E-1	5.1E-4
Standby Liquid Control	Turbine Trip	8.5E-2	7.6E-2

TABLE 2.   COMPARISON OF SYSTEM UNAVAILABILITIES

System/Function	Initiating Event	System Unavailability (Per Demand)	
		IPE Methodology	GGNS System Fault Trees
High Pressure Core Spray	All	2.2E-2	8.4E-3
Reactor Core Isolation Cooling	All	1.2E-1	1.9E-1
Automatic Depressurization	All	1.2E-3	3.4E-5
Low Pressure Core Cooling	All Transient	1.0E-5	8.2E-8
Containment Heat Removal	Non-Isolation	2.2E-8	1.0E-8

TABLE 2.   COMPARISON OF SYSTEM UNAVAILABILITIES (continued)

In most cases, the unavailability values using the IPE methodology were within a factor of three of the values obtained from the fault tree analyses. The exceptions are as follows:

a)   The IPE methodology value for the Recirculation Pump Trip unavailability is a factor of 200 higher than the fault tree value of 5.1E-4 per demand. The basis for the IPE methodology value is not provided.

b)   The IPE methodology value for the Low Pressure Core Cooling function is a factor of 120 higher than the fault tree value of 8.2E-8 per demand. The IPE methodology value is higher because of a common-cause failure value assigned to an operator action that has the potential to disable the entire low pressure core cooling function. The value recommended by the methodology is believed to be highly conservative.

c)   The IPE methodology value for Automatic Depressurization function is a factor of 35 higher than the fault tree value of 3.4E-5 per demand. The IPE methodology value is high because of a value of 5.4E-4 assigned to common-cause failure of all safety/relief valves. This value is believed to be highly conservative.

In summary, the IPE methodology values are generally found to applicable to a BWR6 plant. However, for certain systems, use of the IPE-recommended values result in very conservative unavailability estimates.

5. Conclusions

The primary objectives of the GGNS IPE were met. The core damage frequency was
found to be small and no GGNS plant design features or procedures were found to be
vulnerable to severe accidents involving core damage. The IPE methodology, while
predicting very conservative estimates of system unavailabilities for some
systems, was generally found to be applicable for use on BWR6 plants.

6. References

1. "BWR Individual Plant Evaluation Methodology", Delian Corporation,
    March 1986.

2. "GESSAR II BWR/6 Standard Plant PRA, Appendix 15D", NEDO-22A7007, General
    Electric Company, 1986.

3. "IDCOR Technical Report 21.1 Risk Reduction Potential", IDCOR, June 1985.

4. "Reactor Risk Reference Document," (Draft), USNRC Report NUREG-1150,
    February 1987.

5. "Anticipated Transients Without Scram for Light Water Reactors," USNRC
    Report NUREG-0460, December 1978.

6. "Technical Specification Improvement Analyses for BWR Reactor Protection
    System," NEDC-30851P, General Electric Co., May 1985.

7. "Approximate Source Term Methodology for Boiling Water Reactors," (Draft),
    FAI/86-1, Fauske and Associates, Inc., January 1986.

A PROBABILISTIC SAFETY ASSESSMENT OF THE CIRENE PLANT

P. Gumley
(Atomic Energy of Canada Limited - CANDU Operations)
F. Cipiranni and G. Locchi
(Ente Nazionale per L'Energia Electtrica - ENEL)

ABSTRACT

The CIRENE reactor is a demonstration heavy water moderated and light water
cooled reactor under construction at the Lattina site near Rome. This paper
describes an independent event sequence review undertaken by Atomic Energy of
Canada Limited (AECL) on behalf of Ente Nazionale per L'Energia Electtrica
(ENEL), the owner and operator of the station. The methods and the selection of
the initiating events are discussed. Some of the more important findings from
the review are described. The paper concludes with the results of a sensitivity
analysis intended to focus attention to the significant contributors to the plant
system unreliability estimates.

1. Introduction

The CIRENE reactor is a demonstration heavy water moderated and light water
cooled boiling reactor being constructed at the Lattina site near Rome. Ente
Nazionale per L'Energia Elettrica (ENEL), the owner and operator of this station,
requested an independent event sequence review of the CIRENE design as part of a
general systematic safety review.

This independent event sequence review was undertaken by Atomic Energy of Canada
Limited (AECL) and was based on AECL practice for these type of studies and
described in Reference 1. The analyses are probabilistic and based on fault tree
and event sequence analyses techniques. These studies, completed during the
detailed design and construction phases, have the advantage of providing early
feedback to designers of the adequacy of the safety design.

This review was performed for a selected number of initiating events, grouped
into the following tasks:

1) Review of Expected Operating Transients
2) Review of Design Basis Event Transients
3) Review of Service Support Systems.

The subdivision of the review into these tasks, although not essential, does
offer some organizational advantages. The expected operating transients are
higher frequency events and can be expected to be dominated by operator actions
rather than the automatic actions of the safety systems following design basis
events. The separate grouping of the service support systems, i.e. instrument
air, service water, and the electrical power distribution was made on the basis
of previous AECL experience. The potential for service system failures to cross
link systems used for accident mitigation is always present and can produce very
complex event sequences unless adequate precautions are taken in the design.

Only accidents starting from normal plant operating conditions were considered.
In these event sequence reviews, since the objective is to retain as much realism
in these analyses as possible, only best estimate conditions were considered in
the supporting studies associated with plant or system behaviour. This paper

summarizes the more important findings of the task reports and gives the general
overview perspective.

2. Event Sequence Review Methods

A list of initiating events was prepared following a systematic review of the
plant design. The completeness of this list is a critical assessment item and is
very plant specific. As is usual with these studies certain failure modes only
become apparent as each study progresses and the CIRENE evaluation was no
exception in this respect. The selection of the initiating events for this
limited review is based on a critical appraisal of the design and on CANDU
experience with similar systems.

Fault trees were developed to establish the initiating event frequencies and the
unreliabilities of the mitigating systems. A data table was prepared giving the
assigned reliability data and the source of that data respectively for all basic
and undeveloped events in these fault trees. This information together with a
unique labeling scheme enabled the fault trees to be reviewed for potential cross
linked failure modes within each event sequence.

In preparing the event sequences every effort was made to retain the event
chronology. Whenever possible a timescale of the events was included to give
credence to the chronology and assigned operator unreliabilities.

2.1 Operator Model

Operator errors in the developing event sequences are shown explicitly. The
analysis of operator errors is difficult and the probabilistic evaluation of
these errors even more so because of the many influencing factors involved.
Although considerable progress has been made recently in the analysis of human
factors it is customary in these types of scoping studies to define an 'operator
model' based on certain assumptions and easily definable parameters.

The parameters used for the AECL operator model are: time from the first alarm
signals of the initiating event and operator stress. Operator stress does not
have a universally accepted quantitative definition. For these analyses, low
stress conditions are usually claimed where the alarms initiated give a clear and
concise indication of the failure modes and sufficient time is available to the
operator to take corrective actions.

Assigning operator unreliability and explicitly including the operator actions in
the event sequences gives a very useful input to the Abnormal Incidents Manuals
for the station.

2.2 Acceptance Criteria

Each event sequence was developed by considering the necessary mitigating systems
and operator actions until one of the three following plant states was achieved.

1) Stable plant condition from which a normal plant recovery can start.
    Recovery actions, however, were not included in the analysis.

2) The event sequence end frequency becomes less than 10^{-7} events per year.

3) The event sequences were terminated at credible frequencies (greater than 10^{-7} events per year) where no further mitigating systems were available and stable plant conditions were not achieved. These sequences were critical and additional analyses and/or plant changes were generally required.

Each event sequence is considered in isolation against the acceptance criteria stated and no attempt is made in this review to evaluate risk to the public from radio nuclide releases.

This represents a major departure from most probabilistic safety assessment studies and demonstrates the thrust of these studies as a design assist activity during the construction stages of a reactor plant.

3. Selection of Initiating Events

The guidelines followed for selecting the initiating events for this probabilistic review were based on CANDU experience. In general, three types of initiating event were identified in order of priority as follows;

1) Initiating events at high frequencies, placing significant demand on timely operator actions and/or process system/safety system mitigating actions.

2) Low frequency initiating events which have the potential for failing consequentially safety or safety support mitigating systems.

3) Initiating events which give rise to unknown plant conditions or behaviour having the potential for fuel damage or fission product releases.

3.1 Operating Transients

The initiating events selected for review and grouped under operating transients include:

1) Events causing primary circuit pressure increases
2) Events causing primary circuit flow loss
3) Events causing primary circuit inventory reductions
4) Moderator system failures
5) Shield cooling system failures
6) Events leading to positive reactivity insertion.

Moderator and shield cooling system failures were selected as separate subtasks in this review. For CANDU, a loss of cooling or a loss of inventory from the moderator or end shield requires that the reactor is shutdown and the primary circuit cooled down within a specified time period to prevent unacceptable calandria vessel damage.

3.2 Design Basis Transients

The specific classes of loss of coolant accidents, examined in this task, were:

1) Steam line breaks inside containment
2) Steam line breaks outside containment
3) Water line breaks inside containment
4) Water line breaks outside containment
5) Breaks affecting a single channel

6) Fuelling machine loss of coolant, and
7) Spurious initiation of containment isolation.

The ability of the automatic systems provided to respond to the break sizes was used as the basis for the categorization of the loss of coolant accidents into leaks and small, intermediate and large breaks. The break location is only of importance when it affects the ability of the sensors to detect the loss of coolant and this in turn dictates the sequence of events that is to be expected for each break size.

3.3 Service System Failures

The initiating events included under service system failures and covering electrical power failures were:

1) Total loss of station A.C. electric power supplies
2) Loss of one A.C. essential safety bus.

In selecting the initiating event resulting from a total loss of electrical supplies, adequacy of the automatic actions (i.e. starting and loading sequence for the standby diesel generators) and the required operator actions were reviewed.

There are five service water systems provided in the CIRENE design and failures causing total and partial loss of flow for each of the systems were included. Partial failures can become important and unless care is taken in the design of say the load reduction logic, a partial loss of flow can result in a complete loss of cooling to other users where one system automatically takes all available supplies. This effect has to be allowed for in developing the event sequences.

In the case of instrument air failures, the system design dictates the selection of initiating events. Local air tanks are provided to essential short-term safety support systems and the operator is required in the longer term to stabilize the plant conditions before the tanks become depleted. In the CIRENE review two initiating events were examined:

1) Total loss of instrument air supplies

2) Spurious isolation of the preferential instrument air supply to the reactor building with the remaining air supplies intact (partial instrument air loss).

4. Some of the More Important Findings of the Review

The main contribution to the loss of feedwater flow frequency (λ = 4.5 x 10^{-1} events per year) is the tripping of the normally operating feedwater or condensate extraction pumps. This high failure frequency has a direct effect on plant availability and places unacceptable demands on the operator.

In reviewing moderator system failures, two common mode failures were identified which could incapacitate both the main and shutdown moderator cooling circuits. The frequency of this initiating event is 3.4 x 10^{-3} events per year. The potential cross linked failure modes in the main moderator cooling circuit are:

1) Both main moderator circulation pumps are supplied from the same bus supply.

2) The main moderator heat exchangers service water control valve is common to both heat exchangers and fails closed on loss of instrument air.

3) System redundancy in the moderator system is compromised by one manual valve in the main component cooling system. This valve is normally closed and requires operator action in the field to open it. This may be acceptable if adequate operator alarms/indicators and available action time is demonstrated.

In reviewing loss of coolant accidents, several sequences were found to terminate in no-heat-sink conditions at frequencies greater than 10^{-6} events per year. A large steam line break inside containment and an unavailability of two trains of the residual heat removal system gave rise to 'no heat sink' conditions at a frequency of 1.8×10^{-6} events per year. Similarly if one residual heat removal train is unavailable following a large steam line break in containment it is also credible that the remaining train will experience a running failure within a three month mission period.

A non isolable break in the conditioning and pressurization circuit was found to cause a draining of the fuelling machine charging and discharging vessel with fuel becoming exposed and overheating in about an half hour. The operator is expected to transfer fuel from the charge/discharge machine to the transit pool within this time period to prevent fuel failures and release to containment.

A single check valve in the shield cooling system is provided to act as a siphon breaker and prevents a draining of the end shields in the event of a loss of shield coolant. There are two failure modes of significance associated with this valve;

1) If it fails to reclose on say a pump interchange it provides a bypass flow for the shield coolant. This bypass flow causes the operating pump to run out on its characteristic and trip.

2) If it fails closed in the event of a shield coolant loss resulting from a pipe break it will cause the end shields to drain with the reactor remaining at power.

Two recirculating pumps are provided in the shield cooling system but no automatic standby control is provided. A failure of one pump requires that the operator start the second pump to protect the structural integrity of the vessel. The adequacy of this arrangement was solely a function of the time available for corrective operator action.

A review of the CIRENE design and the role of the operator in accident mitigation, identified in these studies, is on-going.

5. Sensitivity Analysis of Critical Sequences

To complete this event sequence review at the design state it was necessary to introduce undeveloped events into the fault trees due to lack of system design information at the level of equipment control. It was necessary to assign best estimates for the failure data of these events based one engineering judgement. A review of the sensitivity of the critical event sequence end conditions to the failure frequency/unreliability estimates assigned to the undeveloped events was undertaken.

The sensitivity analyses consisted of the following steps:

1) Identify all the undeveloped events in the fault trees for the initiating events and mitigating systems in each critical event sequence.

2) Decrease the failure frequency/unreliability estimates within each sequence above by a factor of 5 from the assigned value.

3) Recalculate the effects on the initiating event, mitigating systems and the event sequence end points.

4) Identify the most significant undeveloped event contributors to the change in each event sequence end point frequency.

This sensitivity analysis was intended to focus attention to the significant contributors to system unreliability in this event sequence review. This review showed that only ten of all the critical event sequences identified, had the initiating event as the main contributor to the end point frequency. The extent by which the critical event sequences are principally affected by changes to mitigating systems are shown in the following Table 1.

Mitigating Systems	Number of Critical Event Sequences Affected
Moderator Dump	1
H.P. Make Up	3
Emergency Condenser	1
Residual Heat Removal System	25
Emergency Injection	2
Feedwater	1
Containment Isolation	2
Auto Depressurization	1
Total	36

Table 1: Critical Event Sequences Affected by Underdeveloped Events
In The Mitigating System Fault Trees

The mitigating system which appeared most frequently in this sensitivity review was the Residual Heat Removal System. A review of the fault trees for this system showed that the decrease in the unavailability is most sensitive to the reliability of the control systems for the containment bottom valves. These valves must open to provide the cooling and recirculation flow. If the electrical interlocks provided fail, these valves close and the residual heat removal system becomes unavailable.

This analysis of the sensitivity of the critical event sequences to the undeveloped events assumed in the supporting fault tree logic gives an important insight to designers responsible for developing the control logic details.

6. References

Ref. 1. Comparison between Canadian Probabilistic Safety Assessment Methods Formulated by AECL and Probabilistic Risk Assessment Methods. H. Shapiro and J. Smith Paper presented at the PSA Conference, Zurich, 1987.

Pra related to multiple ruptures of steam generator tubes

M. Bloch, D. Dussarte, JL. Pierrey
(CEA IPSN, BP n° 6 - 92265 Fontenay-aux-Roses Cedex - France)

Abstract

Reactor safety could be impaired if some systems or components have their designed useful lifetimes shorten because of design or construction errors or phenomena not taken into account.

This paper presents a methodology which can treat the non-simultaneous aspect of
the successive failures which can lead to a hazard.

As an illustration the safety problems related to the multiple ruptures of steam-
generator tubes in normal operation of the plant is presented.

1 - Introduction

Data from the operating experience of french PWR have indicated that the steam-
generator tubes are submitted to a number of aggressions which can shorten their
lifetimes. Among these, the phenomena of stress corrosion for inconel 600, the
tube's material, can lead to damages which could be described as a premature
ageing for part of the heat exchange tubes. Stress corrosion cracking leads mostly to small leaks without consequence on plant safety. However, one can expect
occasionally that some cases of cracking can lead to rupture for the affected
tubes.

It is considered important for safety analysis to be able to have a quantitative
assessment concerning the risks associated with the ruptures of several tubes
from the common cause of stress corrosion in order to check the relevance of the
hypothesis made in the design studies and to reevaluate these studies if necessary.

The assessment of risks related to multiple ruptures either in normal operating
condition or in accidental condition (secondary circuit depressurization) requires the development of a probabilistic tool which can take into account the time
dependency inherent to stress corrosion damages.

Classical methods which make the hypothesis of a constant failure rate are not
applicable and use of a time dependent rate (Weibull law for instance) requires a
large effort of development.

2 - Methodology

2.1 - General description

The methodology used in this paper has been developed in order to evaluate the probability of loss of a safety function secured from use of redundant systems when the lifetimes of these systems are shortened unexpectedly for instance by not taking properly into account some physical phenomena at the design stage. The lifetimes can be treated as random variables with a given probability distribution generally taken as an uniform distribution in a time interval Δ or a normal distribution of standard deviation σ.

From the lifetime distribution one can deduce the probability laws for the time intervals elapsing from the failure of the first system and the second one, the third... and the last which leads to the loss of the function.

These laws can then be used to evaluate the risk of severe consequence to the reactor taking into account the possibility to put the reactor in a safe state before a critical time θ after detection of the first failure.

The methodology takes into account directly this critical time, the width of the lifetime distribution and the order of the redundancy.
If $\tau_n = t_n - t_1$ is the time elapsed from the first failure and the one of order n, then the probability densities $f(\tau_n)$ can be obtained in general through a simple Monte-Carlo method. However, in the case of an uniform distribution of width Δ an analytic form can be obtained. For instance :

$$f(\tau_2) = N/\Delta^N (\Delta - \tau_2)^{N-1}$$

$$f(\tau_3) = N (N-1)/\Delta^N \tau_3 (\Delta - \tau_3)^{N-2}$$

$$f(\tau_N) = N (N-1)/\Delta^N \tau_N^{N-2} (\Delta - \tau_N)$$

The probability of loss of the safety function seemed by N redundant systems before reaching a safe state for the reactor is then

$$P(\theta) = \int_0^\theta f(\tau_N) \, d\tau_N = N (\theta/\Delta)^{N-1} - (N-1) (\theta/\Delta)^N$$

2.2 - Application to multiple ruptures

In the case of the risk assessment related to multiple ruptures of steam-generator tubes, the large population of tubes has to be taken into account. Only the first ruptures lead to a safety problem. They occur in the forward tail of the lifetime distribution, typically more than three standard deviations before the mean value for a normal distribution. Modelization of the problem with an uniform law is consequently not appropriate. A normal law has been chosen, this law being in good agreement with different tests for stress-corrosion in several couples alloy - aggressive medium [1].

A very simple Monte-Carlo computer code is used to get the distributions for time-intervals τ_2, τ_3 up to τ_6 - In order to save computer time only the first 30 lifetimes are drawn according to the forward part of the gaussian law. The resulting statistical error has been checked to be negligible.

2.3 - Input parameters selection

The lifetime t of a tube can be written $t = t_i + t_p$ where t_i is the initiation time for cracks and t_p is the propagation time to the mechanical rupture.

From experimental observations made on inconel 600 samples, it is reasonable to suppose that for the phenomena of stress-corrosion, the crack growth rate is constant from the initiation up to the failure [2]. In this study, the propagation time t_p is identical for all the tubes. This hypothesis can be considered as pessimistic.

The standard deviation σ of the lifetime distribution is then given approximately by the standard deviation of the t_i distribution. The value of σ can be estimated from the results of periodic controls which can detect cracks at an early stage.

The other parameters needed in the study are :
N_c : number of tubes sensitive to stress corrosion and which are liable to break during the life of the plant.
n   : number of consecutive ruptures taken into account.

It should be noted that if all the components have been started at the same time, the results concerning the probability densities for the time-intervals $f(\tau_i)$ are not dependent on the mean value of the component lifetime. These densities $f(\tau_i)$ are obtained from the Monte-Carlo computation described above (10.000 draws).

3 - **Multiple ruptures during normal plant operation**

From the knowledge of the probability densities $f(\tau_n)$ and their computed dependence on the parameters σ, N_c, n, a number of problems related to safety analysis can be studied.

In order to illustrate the methodology, the risk assessment related to multiple ruptures occuring in a state of normal operation of the reactor has been chosen because of its importance in nuclear safety analysis.

The rupture of one tube is taken into account in the operating rules and requires a time Θ to bring the plant into a safe state. Ruptures of one or more extra tubes in a time less than Θ represents the risk to be evaluated. It will turn out that the risk is significant only for n = 2 and 3. The corresponding probabilities $P_i(\Theta) = \int_0^\Theta f(\tau_i)\, d\tau_i$ (i = 2,3) can be expressed, regardless of the value N_c of the tube population sensitive to the stress-corrosion effects by :

$P_2(\theta) = a\ \theta$

$P_3(\theta) = 1/2\ b\ \theta^2$

This form is similar to the analytical formulas obtained in paragraph 2 in the case of an uniform distribution.

The values of the coefficients a and b are shown in the following table, for N_c values corresponding to 100 %, 10 %, 1 % of the total number of tubes N_t (about 3.400) present in a french 900 MWe PWR steam-generator. These values are obtained from a fit applied to 10.000 draws. The statistical error depends on the number of draws and is here about 10 %.

Nc/Nt	100 %	10 %	1 %
a (h^{-1})	$3.0/\sigma$	$2.5/\sigma$	$2.0/\sigma$
b (h^{-2})	$17.0/\sigma^2$	$12.0/\sigma^2$	$7.2/\sigma^2$

From that table, the weak dependence of a and b on N_c is apparent and consequently the results for the case $N_c/N_t = 100$ % although slightly pessimistic can be considered as a realistic assessment.

This result is quite different from the one obtained in the uniform distribution case ($f(\tau_2)$ and $f(\tau_3)$ respectively proportional to N and N(N-1)). This is due to two opposite effects. On the one hand, the time-intervals decrease with the population increases ; on the other hand, the first ruptures occur at times more and more remote from the mean value in regions of weak statistical weights.

Sensitivity to the parameter σ is expressed functionally in the table ($a \sim 1/\sigma$, $b \sim 1/\sigma^2$).

Numerical values have to be given to the parameters θ and σ in order to achieve a quantitative assessment of the risk. The following values have been chosen : $\theta = 0,25$ h which corresponds to the time required for operator's action in such an accident.

$\sigma = 15.000$ h which results from a study based on findings of periodic tests on the tubes. This value has been taken from the worst generated observed. In that case and for $N_c/N_t = 100$ %, one gets :

$P\ (\tau_2 < \theta) \sim 10^{-4}$

$P\ (\tau_3 < \theta) < 10^{-8}$

These results indicate that the probability that the two first ruptures occur in a short time-interval is weak. The occurrence of a third one inside the same interval is highly improbable.

4 - Other applications

The same methodology has been used to evaluate :

- the probability of multiple ruptures of steam-generator tubes in accidental situation (accident of depressurization in secondary circuits).

- the probability of loss of a safety function when the redundant systems which secure it suffer from a premature wear. Two safety analysis have been performed on some accidental sequences for decay heat removal with an evaluation of the gain which could be achieved by heat exchangers diversification.

5 - Conclusions

Systems or components failures resulting from a premature wear are not simultaneous and the methodology presented in this paper allows an evaluation of probability densities related to the time-intervals between the first failure, the second, the third and, in general, the failure of order n.

From these laws, it is then possible to evaluate the probability of severe accidents taking into account corrective actions which can be implemented by the plant operators to bring the reactor into a safe state in a characteristic time θ.

To illustrate the methodology, the case of multiple ruptures of steam-generator tubes in normal plant operation caused by stress corrosion phenomena has been presented.

For that accidental situation, the results show that the probability that the first two ruptures will occur in a short time-interval ($\theta. \sim 0,25$ h) is about 10^{-4}. This event has a low probability but should be taken into account in safety analysis.

In the same time interval, a third rupture seems to be highly improbable (probability less than 10^{-8}).

However, it should be stressed that this study is related to only one possible mode of tube rupture. Safety analysis has to take into account other modes such as ruptures caused on a tube by another tube breaking (tube whipping, jet phenomena... etc).

6 - **References**

[1] : F.F. BOOT H and G.E.G. TUCKER
Statistical Distribution of Endurance In Electrochemical Stress-Corrosion
Tests.
(Corrosion - National association of corrosion engineers - volume 21 mai
1965)

[2] : PH. BERGE, J.R. DONATI
Materiels Requirements For Pressurized Water Reactor Steam-Generator
Tubing.
(Nuclear technology - volume 55 - octobre 1981).

PROBABILISTIC SAFETY ASSESSMENT OF THE INCLINED FUEL TRANSFER SYSTEM

A. Ruggaber, N. Dobrosavljevic and A. Jacobi Jr.,
(Electrowatt Engineering Services Ltd., CH-8022 Zurich, Switzerland)

Risk assessment, probabilty, nuclear power plants

1.   INTRODUCTION

The Inclined Fuel Transfer System (IFTS) at the Leibstadt Nuclear Power Station (KKL) is used either to transfer two fuel elements or one control rod or other small items between the reactor containment and the fuel building pools without compromising the barrier function of the containment.

Figure 1 shows a schematic arrangement of the IFTS.

Accidents caused by failure of this system have been analysed by Electrowatt using probabilistic safety assessment methods. Such accidents have not been considered in the initial Safety Analysis Report (SAR) of KKL. Only the drop of a single fuel element and its consequential damage was considered earlier and thought to cover sufficiently the radiological consequences of all other possible fuel handling accidents.

2.   EVENT SEQUENCES LEADING TO RELEASES

Damage of irradiated fuel elements during their transport from the containment to the fuel building can have significant radiological consequences. Main causes for a fuel damage could be:

- mechanical causes, for example due to a runaway of the transfer carriage

- thermal causes, for example due to insufficient cooling of the fuel elements within the IFTS.

The second accident causes can lead to overheating of both fuel elements, followed by high radioactive releases for an extended time, and, hence, to more important radiological consequences than the fuel handling accident analysed so far in the SAR (characterized by short duration release from a single fuel element).

Initiating events for such accidents are human errors, multiple failure of the control system or failures of mechanical components of the IFTS. For these possible initiating events accident scenarios have been developed and then put in form of event trees.

The following scenarios have been analysed explicitly:

1) Fuel and carriage are mechanically damaged due to incorrect tilting operation. This event sequence is shown in the event tree in Fig. 2.

554

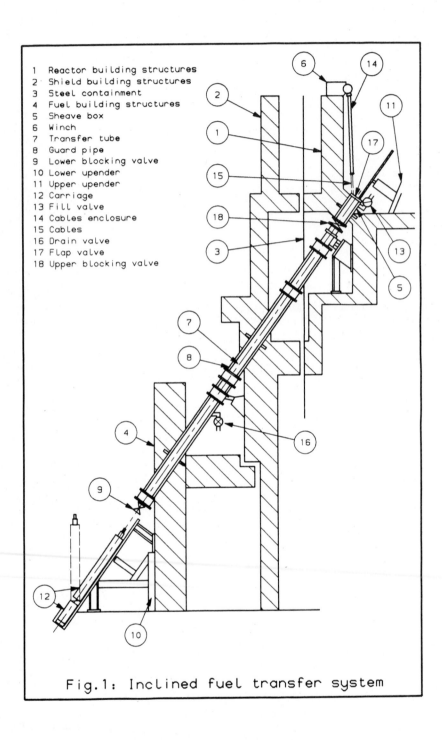

1 Reactor building structures
2 Shield building structures
3 Steel containment
4 Fuel building structures
5 Sheave box
6 Winch
7 Transfer tube
8 Guard pipe
9 Lower blocking valve
10 Lower upender
11 Upper upender
12 Carriage
13 Fill valve
14 Cables enclosure
15 Cables
16 Drain valve
17 Flap valve
18 Upper blocking valve

Fig.1: Inclined fuel transfer system

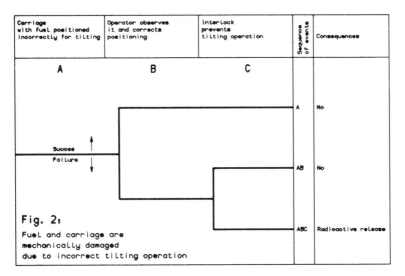

Fig. 2:

Fuel and carriage are
mechanically damaged
due to incorrect tilting operation

2) Runaway of the carriage loaded with fuel elements in the transfer tube. This can happen e.g. due to a winch failure combined with a failure of both safety brakes.

3) Carriage with fuel is blocked in the lower part of the transfer tube. It is assumed that water level in the tube is lowered to the water level of the spent fuel pool in accordance with the operational instructions. Blockage occurs either due to lower blocking valve failure or due to a loss of electric power. Decay heat of fuel elements heats up the water in the tube and subsequently the latter boils. Eventually the fuel becomes uncovered and damaged due to overheating. The corresponding event sequences are shown in Fig. 3.

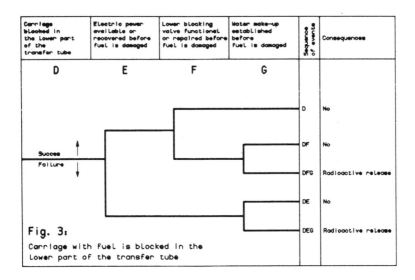

Fig. 3:

Carriage with fuel is blocked in the
lower part of the transfer tube

4) Carriage with fuel is uncovered in the upper part of the transfer tube. This scenario could be caused by a malfunction of the ITFS control logic not preventing loss of water from the inclined tube before the fuel-loaded carriage has reached the appropriate "low" position. This event sequence is shown in Fig. 4.

5) Opening of either the lower blocking valve or of the drain valve, during the operational sequence when the upper blocking valve is open for fuel transfer operations, causes an inadvertent draining of the transfer tube. Operator can reclose the corresponding valve or move the carriage with the fuel to the lower part of the transfer tube which is permanently filled with water to improve the situation. This event sequence is shown in Fig. 5.

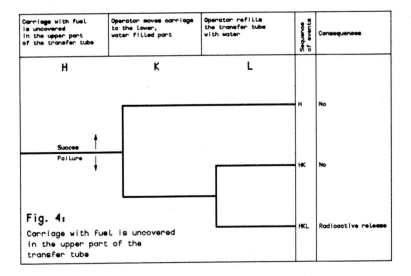

Fig. 4:
Carriage with fuel is uncovered
in the upper part of the
transfer tube

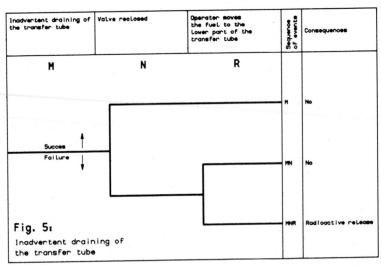

Fig. 5:
Inadvertent draining of
the transfer tube

Other possible accident scenarios involving the IFTS have been judged to have a too low probability of occurrence or too unimportant consquences to justify a detailed analysis.

3.   PROBABILISTIC ANALYSIS

3.1   Probability of Event Occurence

The probability of an event occurence was assessed, where appropriate, using fault tree methodology.

Following fault trees have been developed:

-   Lower blocking valve does not open on demand (Fig. 6).

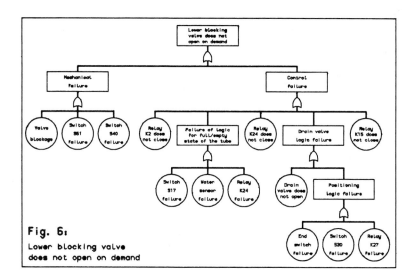

Fig. 6:
Lower blocking valve
does not open on demand

-   Carriage with fuel uncovered in the upper part of the transfer tube (Fig. 7)

-   Winch failure (Fig. 8)

Component failure data were in most cases taken from the relevant open litera-ture (Ref. 1 - 5). In case that applicable component failure data have not been found, an engineering judgement has been made. Experience at KKL with the IFTS was so far trouble free; hence, no true reliability data could be derived for individual components of the operating unit.

Results of the estimation of event occurence probability (individual event or, if applicable, fault tree top event) are shown in Table 1.

558

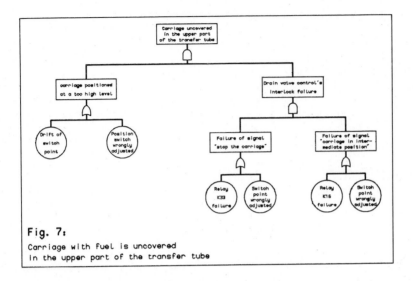

Fig. 7:
Carriage with fuel is uncovered
in the upper part of the transfer tube

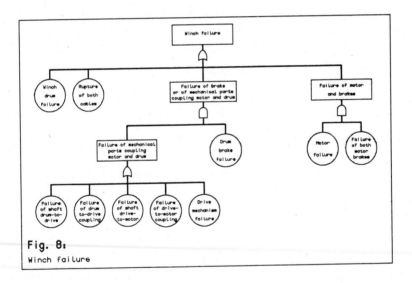

Fig. 8:
Winch failure

Event	Event label	Probability (p.d.= per demand p.h.= per hour
Carriage with fuel is incorrectly positioned for tilting	A	1.0 E - 2 p.d.
Operator does not recognise the incorrect position	B	5.0 E - 1 p.d.
Interlock does not prevent tilting while carriage is in wrong position	C	6.7 E - 7 p.d.
Lower blocking valve does not open due to loss of power	D1	8.1 E - 8 p.d.
Lower blocking valve fails to open	D2	2.3 E - 2 p.d.
Electric power supply is not reestablished during the available intervention time (16 hours)	E	1.0 E - 4 p.d.
Lower blocking valve is not repaired during the available intervention time (16 hours)	F	9.16E - 1 p.d.
Water make-up is not established during the available intervention time (16 hours)	G	9.1 E - 3 p.d.
Carriage with fuel is uncovered in the upper part of transfer tube	H	1.7 E - 9 p.d.
Operator does not move the carriage to the "low" (water filled) part of the transfer tube	K	1.0 E - 3 p.d.
Operator does not refill the transfer tube with water	L	3.0 E - 1 p.d.
Inadvertent opening of the lower blocking valve (M1) or the drain valve (M2)	M (M1) (M2)	2.9 E - 6 p.h. (2.0 E - 6) (9.0 E - 7)
Valve not reclosed in time	N	1.0 E - 1 p.d.
Operator does not move the carriage with fuel to the lower part of the tube	R	1.0 E - 1 p.d.
Winch failure to hold carriage	-	3.1 E - 9 p.h.

Table 1: Event occurrence probabilities

3.2 Event Sequence Probabilities

Based on the operating time period of IFTS components or on the number of demands per year for certain functions, the probabilities of event sequences leading to fuel failure and consequently to radioactive releases have been estimated. Results are shown in Table 2.

Event sequence	Probability of occurrence a[1]	Fuel element failure mode
ABC	4.0 E - 7	mechanichal
winch failure	3.7 E - 6	mechanical
DFG	2.1 E - 4	thermal
DEG	9.7 E - 10	thermal
HKL	6.1 E - 11	thermal
MNR	1.2 E - 4 (1.1 E - 4 + 5.4 E - 6)	thermal

Table 3: Occurrence probability of event sequences leading to
radioactive releases

4. ACCIDENT CONSEQUNCES

4.1 Radioactive inventory

Radioavtive inventory of 2 transported fuel elements representing the maximum
inventory, is shown in Table 3.

Nuclide group	Radioactive inventory of 2 spent fuel elements, 24 hours after reactor shutdown (Ci)
Noble gases	7.11 E + 5
Halogenes	5.38 E + 5
Volatile solids	3.17 E + 5
Other solids	6.17 E + 6

Table 3: Radioactive inventory in IFTS

4.2   Radioactive release

The estimated release fraction for radionuclides from damaged fuel rods is shown in Table 4.

Nuclides	Released fraction	
	Mechanical damage	Thermal damage
Noble gases	1.8 %	10 %
Halogens	0.33 %	3.0 %
Volatile solids (Cs, Te)	0.001 %	2.0 %
Other solides	0.0001 %	0.1 %

Table 4: Release fraction for radionuclides

In case of a mechanical damage which occurs in water, 99% of the halogens and 99.9% of solids were assumed to be retained in water.

In case of thermal damage releases, these are directed towards and mixed with the building atmosphere and then removed by the ventilation system.

In case of detection of increased radioactivity in the building atmosphere, the ventilation exhaust flow is diverted over the emergency filters, which are capable to hold 99.8% of the halogenes and 99.9% of other aerosols.

4.3   Radiological Accident Consequences

The radiological consequences of accident sequences identified in Section 2 above, have been calculated at 3 different locations, i.e.:

1) Direct radiation from an uncovered fuel element stuck in the drained containment pool to an operator on the pool's edge;

2) Radiation from gaseous and airborne radioactivity in the containment atmosphere onto an operator immersed in it standing on the containment service floor;

3) Radiation at the "worst" point outside the plant fence due to both the short and long term releases after the surveyed accidents.

Only the doses due to gamma radiation have been assessed at these locations, whereby the gamma source has been divided into 8 energy groups.

5. SUMMARY OF RESULTS

The main results of this assessment are summarized in Table 5.

	Mechanical fuel element damage	Thermal fuel element damage
Probability of occurrence	$< 4.1\ 10^{-6}a^{-1}$	$< 3.3\ 10^{-4}a^{-1}$
Time available for operator intervention (corrective measures)	0 hours	< 2.5 hours
Dose rate on the containment service floor	< 760 mrem/h	< 45 rem/h
Dose to the most exposed person outside the fence	< 0.6 mrem	< 3.5 mrem

Table 5: Summarized assessment results

6. REFERENCES

/1./ Reactor Safety Study: An Assessment of Accident Risk in U.S. Commercial Nuclear Power Plants, WASH-1400/NUREG-75/(014).

/2./ Leibstadt Nuclear Power Station: System Reliability Study, Analysis of ECCS, Electrowatt Internal Report.

/3./ Availability of the Emergency Core Cooling System of a CANDU Pressurized Heavy-Water Reactor Following a Small Loss-of-Coolant Accident, Tawfik A Al Kusayer, Nuc. Techn. Vol. 69, June 1985.

/4./ Reliability Techniques Used in the Assessment of Cranes, Duke A J, UKAEA-Report: NCSR/GR/64, March 1985.

/5./ Deutsche Risikostudie - Kernkraftwerke, Verlag TUeV-Rheinland, Köln 1980.

DETERMINATION OF RELIABILITY CRITERIA FOR STANDBY DIESEL GENERATORS AT A NUCLEAR POWER STATION

M.G.K. Evans
NUS Corporation, Gaithersburg MD. 20878, U.S.A.

The requirement for standby diesel generators at nuclear power stations is developed and a probabilistic approach used to define the reliability parameters. The present criteria used when ordering a diesel generator are compared with the testing required by the regulatory body and the most likely requirement following an accident. The impact of this on the diesels at a particular station and the root cause of failures are discussed.

Introduction

Loss of offsite power has been identified in many Probabilisitic Risk Assessments (PRA) as a significant event leading to core melt. Station blackout, the loss of all offsite power and all onsite ac power sources was identified by the US Nuclear Regulatory Commission (USNRC) as an unresolved safety issue of concern in the operation of both boiling water and pressurized water reactors. As a result of this, it has been studied in depth as part of the Severe Accident Sequence Analysis (SASA) programme(1) funded by USNRC. An important part of the treatment of loss of offsite power in a probabilistic risk assessment is the inclusion of the possibility of timely recovery of the offsite power and repair of the onsite diesel generators, should they fail. In earlier papers(2,3) the author has presented an approach to analyzing the sequence of events following loss of offsite power. This requires explicit information concerning the potential for recovering offsite power at the particular site being analyzed and also detailed information on the reliability and performance of the diesel generators. In this paper we explore the requirements for diesel generator reliability, the testing programme demanded by the licensing authority and the compatibility of this testing programme with actual reliability requirements, and the generator specification submitted by the utility to the diesel generator manufacturer.

The Loss of Offsite Power Event

In this section, we give an example of a logic diagram (Event Tree) developed to model the sequence of events following a loss of offsite power event in a pressurized water reactor (PWR).

In considering the sequence of events following loss of power as depicted in the event tree in Figure 1, the key system is the auxiliary feedwater system. This system for the particular plant being analyzed had one turbine-driven auxiliary feedwater pump, whose performance is modelled in the function L_{TM}, and two motor-driven pumps, whose performance is modelled in the function L_M. The performance of the diesel generators and recovery of offsite power is modelled in the function L_E. The design of the system is such that only dc power is required for the operation of the turbine-driven pump. Therefore, if the turbine-driven pump starts and runs, secondary heat removal will be assured until the dc batteries run out, even in the absence of all ac power. This is represented by the upper branch under the function L_{TM}. Therefore, the timing for recovery of offsite ac power or the starting of the diesel generators is determined by the battery capacity or some other unrelated requirement, such as the provision of seal cooling water to the reactor coolant pump seals. However, if the turbine-driven pump fails to start or is in maintenance at the time of the initiating event, the lower branch for function L_{TM} is followed. In this case, it will be necessary to restore power within 40-60 minutes. This becomes the limiting case for diesel starting starting following the loss of power. The exepcted frequency of loss of offsite power depends on the local grid situation. For many power plants, this is of the order of once every 10 years. For those plants in very exposed sea shore areas it can be higher.

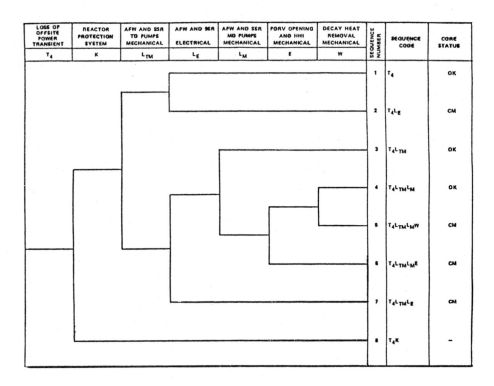

Figure 1 Event tree for loss of offsite power

However, in the United States, the design basis for diesel generator reliability is not based on the required response to this initiating event. The postulated accident which determines the requirement for diesel performance is the large loss of coolant accident coincident with loss of offsite power. In this case, because the injection systems required to mitigate the loss of coolant use motor-driven pumps, the diesels are required to run up and be capable of taking load within 10 seconds of receiving the start signal. Historically, no large loss of coolant has occurred in any light water reactor in approximately 2,000 RY of operation and recent reports from the SMIRT(4) conference indicate that the type of rupture that would lead to such an event is extremely unlikely given the materials used in these reactors. For this event to occur coincident with loss

of power is extremely unlikely, unless as the result of an event such as a severe
earthquake. In this case, the same earthquake is also likely to cause failure of
the diesel generators.

Diesel Generator Performance Requirement

In this section, the diesel generator performance requirements as given to the
manufacturer, and those required by the regulatory body are compared with those
derived from the above probabilistic analysis. The relevant sections of the
manufacturer'g requirements relating to loading and starting are as follows:

Rated Output

Each diesel generator set shall have an IEEE Standard 387-1972 continuous rated
output of 3,600 KV, .8pf 3 phase 60 hertz 4,160 volts, with an availability equal
to or greater than 95 percent. The diesel generator unit shall be capable of
maintaining this output in the service environment for 8,760 hours per year,
including only scheduled outages for maintenance.

Start and Load Time

The unit shall be capable of attaining rated frequency and voltage within 10
seconds of receipt of the start signal which may occur at any time after being
shut down following an 8-hour or longer run at rated temperature and load.

Engine Starting

The engine shall be capable of starting cold solely from the heat of compression
and shall make at least five consecutive automatic starts without external
support or assistance before the automatic feature is blocked, requiring manual
attention. It shall be a design requirement that the unit start and be at rated
frequency and voltage in less than 10 seconds after receipt of the start signal.

The diesel generator performance in standby required by the regulatory body is as
follows.

Periodic testing of the diesel shall be carried out as follows:

1. If the number of failures in the last 100 valid tests is one or zero, the
    test interval should be 31 days

2. If the number of failures in the last 100 valid tests is two, three, or four
    or more, the test interval should be 14, 7 and 3 days, respectively. A
    valid test is one in which the diesel generator is run up to at least 50
    percent load and run for at least one hour. The generator voltage and
    frequency shall be at rated value 10 seconds after start.

In addition to the above periodic testing, it is also required that the diesel
generators be tested if certain other systems fail or are put into maintenance.
However, in these cases the test is not a fast start test, nor is it necessary to
run the diesel at more than 50 percent load for one hour so they are not counted
as "valid" tests. If we look at the data for two diesel generators at one power
station for a period of 2-1/2 years, we will see the following results:

Diesel Generator Unit	Valid Test	Invalid Test	Failed Test	Total Test
1	106	83	5	194
2	101	85	6	192

There is not sufficient space to show the month on month test results, however. If they are examined and only valid tests are counted, Units 1 and 2 would presently be on a 3 day test interval. If all tests were included, Unit 1 would now be on a 14 day test interval and Unit 2 on a 7 day test interval.

Root Cause Analyses of Failures

In order to improve the diesel generator reliability, it is necessary to look at the root causes of the failures. There are two areas of concern. The first is the relationship between standby failures and demand-related failures, and the second the long-term impact on the diesel generator reliability. In any large machine that is on standby, degradation will take place due to such causes as corrosion, lack of lubrication, or build-up of corrosion products in filters in the lubricating system, such that, when the machine is required to operate, it will not run. Typical of this type of failure are dirty contacts which will lead to loss of the starting signal. These are defined as standby stress-related failures. The other type of failure is demand-related and, in this case, the faiure occurs because of the demand placed on the diesel. In this case, given a constant failure rate, the more test demands placed on the generator, the more failures will occur in a period of time and the maintenance outage will be increased. Typical failures of this type are bearing failures due to poor lubrication at the instant of starting. This could be particularly important in the case of the cold start requirement discussed in the previous section.

Both of the above types of failure will always occur, regardless of the testing requirements. But the other concern is that the stringent testing requirement and the fact that the diesel is started many times in excess of the valid test (a factor of 2) will lead to premature aging of the diesel generator and that the random failure rate will increase. This also impacts the running failure rate. The following table lists some of the failures associated with the two diesel generators studied.

Failure Description	Failure Type	
Failed after 10 minutes operation due to turbocharger failure		DEMAND
Failure to start due to lube oil temperature high signal -- loose connection	STANDBY	
Failure to take load - AVR failure	STANDBY	
Tripped due to governor failure	DEMAND	
Failure to start, water penetrated air start motor		STANDBY
Failure to run, high vibration	RUNNING	
Failure to run, high lube oil temperature		RUNNING

However, in addition to these failures, major work was required on the diesel generators to rectify incipient defects which were discovered during routine inspection. A number of these were the direct result of the very high number of cold starts that the diesel generator had to make and the loading this put on certain components. For example, in the case of the turbocharger, the original design did not include lubrication to the turbocharger when the engine was on standby. Over the combined five diesel-years of operation for both diesels, four failures have occurred. A design change has now been made. The nozzle ring impeller has cracked due to overstressing during the fast load-up conditions (three times); problems were encountered with the connecting rods where bolts were found severely bowed; and, finally, piston skirts were found to be cracked. These defects were corrected during refuelling outages and, so, did not contribute directly to diesel generator unavailability. However, if a long period of emergency operation had been required, it is likely that these failures would have been important. To optimize the diesel availability, it is necessary to have a good monitoring programme to identify the root causes of failure and the most appropriate actions to be taken to correct them. The continuing assessment of reliability is discussed in the next section.

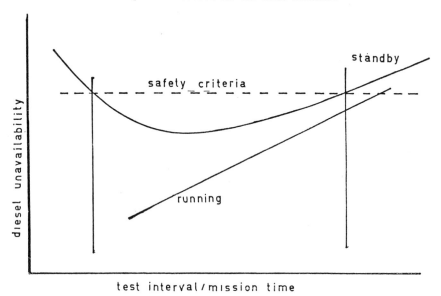

test interval/mission time

Figure   2   Variation of diesel unavailability with
test interval or mission time

Continuing Assessment of Reliability

Provided the root causes of the standby diesel failure can be categorized into the three types of failures discussed above, then it is possiblke to use a sensitivity model to relate the failure rates, repair times and test intervals to a desired availability. The equation relating these variables suggested in the Procedure for Evaluating Technical Specifications (PETS)(5), Generic Issue B-56/6, is:

$$Q_s = f_s \, \tau_s + f_d \, \tau_d/T + 1/2 \, \lambda_s T + q_d \qquad\qquad (1)$$

where Q_s is the unavailability and the remaining terms give the unavailability as the result of maintenance following the two types of failure, and the unvailability arising directly from the failure. It can be seen that this is a qudratic in T, whose two solutions are a minimum and maximum value of T to meet a desired reliability criterion Q_s (see Figure 2). The usefulness of this function depends very much on the ability to identify these failures which are demand-related and those which are time-related. It is clear that the value of Q_s is directly related to q_d so that any change in q_d, the failure rate on demand, will give a directly proportional change in Q_s. One of the concerns with a testing programme which requires frequent testing is that q_d is not independent of the number of tests. Another way of looking at this is to say that aftera run-in period, one would expect that the diesel would have a relatively constant failure rate in time, equivalent to the flat portion of the traditional bathtub curve. However, if the number of test demands is high, wear-out may be reached before a plant refuelling outage, with the opportunity for major overhaul, is reached. The type of testing programme which calls for increased testing as failure rates increase merely exacerbates this situation.

The use of this type of reliability assessment will enable the utility to determine in which areas failures are occurring and to adjust the maintenance/testing programme to optimize diesel availability. In addition to the unavailability during standby, there are also failures which occur during the running of the diesels. In this case, it is necessary to identify two classes of running failures – those which occur during the first hour of the mission and those which occur later. This is because historically it has been observed that diesel failure rates during the first hour are much higher than those in subsequent operating periods. In fact, it may be convenient to include failures which occur in the first hour as starting failures and use the above classification to group these with the other standby failure categories. If this grouping is not adopted, the running failure rates fall into two categories λ_1 (failure rate for the first hour) and λ_t (failure rate in subsequent hour), and the unavailability is given by:

$$Q_r = \lambda_1 + \lambda_t t \tag{2}$$

where t = mission time.

This is also shown in Figure 2. The combined unavailability is then the sum of the standby unavailability plus the running unavailability. The latter will be mission dependent rather than test interval dependent. Once again, the assumption is made that the testing programme does not have a major impact on the value of λ_1 or λ_t. This assumption has not been valid in the past and close monitoring of the values of f_d, f_s, λ_1 and λ_t will indicate deterioration in the diesels' performance.

Conclusion

A deterministic approach to the definition of system requirements for the performance of required emergency functions following an event leading to plant shutdown at a nuclear power plant, although apparently conservative, may actually contribute to an increase in the probability of core melt. In the case of the diesel generators, it appears that the testing requirements, design requirements and actual requirements for the machines are not compatible. In the performance requirements, the derived availability of 95 percent is, by implication, associated with the ability to run continuously for the whole year (8,760 hours). No reference is made to the frequent starting to which the machines are likely to be subjected. The testing regime demands a high reliability to start within 10 seconds and reach 50 percent load very rapidly (less than 1 minute), once again in excess of 95 percent. Analysis of the actual requirements following a range of accidents shows that fast starting is not required to meet the most likely occurring accidents and, therefore, the testing programme should be optimized to allow such actions as prelubrication before starting and the load sequencing adjusted to slow down the rate at which the machine is loaded. It may be that the fast start option is still required, but as the event requiring this response is extremely unlikely to occur ($\triangleq$ 1.0 x 10^{-5}/RY), this test should only be required annually or half-yearly. At the same time, the requirement to operate the diesel generators when unconnected system failures occur should be carefully examined and, if possible, eliminated. Finally, a diesel generator unavailability monitoring programme, along the lines suggested in the previous section, should be adopted to optimize diesel generator availability and provide feedback information on diesel generator performance or design deficiencies.

Symbols Used

f_d = frequency of demand stress-related failures (per demand)

f_s = frequency of standby stress-related failures (per hr)

λ_s = standby stress-related failure hourly rate

λ_1,t   = hourly failure rate when running

Q_r = unavailability due to mission

Q_s = unavailability on standby

q_d = failure rate on demand

T   = Test interval (hr)

τ_d = repair time following demand stress-related failure (hr)

τ_s = repair time following standby stress-related failure (hr)

References

1. Baranowsky, P.W. 1985. NUREG-1032, US Nuclear Regulatory Commission, Washington D.C.

2. Evans, M.G.K. and Parry, G.W. 1983. Reliability Engineering, Vol. 6 43-55.

3. Evans, M.G.K., Parry, G.W. and Wu, J.S. 1986. Proceedings ANS/ENS Topical Meeting on Thermal Reactor Safety, San Diego, Feb. 2-6. VIII.2.

4. Schmidt, T., Schokburg, U. 1985. Reliability of PWR Primary Coolant Pipes, 8th SMIRT Conference, Transaction MIFI 1/2, Brussels, Belgium.

5. Lofgren, E.V. 1985. SAIC Project N° 1-265-00-740-00, Data Analysis of Diesel Generator Failures. SAIC, McLean, Va.

SAFETY AND RELIABILITY ANALYSIS OF THE COOLING SYSTEM OF DRY-STORAGE WELLS FOR IRRADIATED FUEL ASSEMBLIES

ALTIERI.D   SIMONOT.H   MINARINI.C
(CEP, Paris F)   (ANSALDO, Genoa I)   (ENEA, Bologna I)

Abstract

Various tools are in current use for Probalistic Safety Assessment (FMECA, fault trees, cause-consequence diagrams, Markov diagrams...). But in the case of a complex system, presenting various degrees and types of redundancy, none of these tools is sufficient on its own. It is therefore necessary to combine them, in order to reduce the complexity of the problem, first modelizing the different subsystems and then the whole system.

This paper presents the methodology used in a real application : a cooling circuit of the italian fast-breeder reactor PEC (destinated to performing experiments on fuel assemblies), in order to assess the risk of loss of cooling, partial or total, for longer than a given period.

0 - Introduction

The paper presents a probabilistic approach used in assessing the risk of loss or degradation of function, for a complex circuit presenting various degrees of redundancy.

The system involved in this application is a cooling circuit of the italian prototype fast breeder reactor PEC.

The analysis is in keeping with the general framework of safety studies required by ENEA (italian board for nuclear safety) for nuclear plants. The main contractor of the PEC reactor, ANSALDO S.p.A, leant on a consulting company, CEP (Contrôle et Prévention), for technical and methodological support.

1 - Presentation of the system

The PEC reactor (Prova Elementi di Combustibili) is an italian prototype fast breeder reactor, destinated to performing experiments on fuel assemblies.

In this plant, the irradiated fuel assemblies are dry-stored in a number of wells before undergoing their designed experiments. The cooling of these wells is obtained by circulating their nitrogen atmosphere, by means of two redundant circuits.

Principal circuit is normally on, and includes internal redundancies. It is mainly composed of :

  - 3 redundant fans, whith given redundancy management (automatic or manual),
  - 2 redundant heat exchangers, whith given redundancy management (automatic or manual),
  - a part of the circuit, common for all users (wells + other users),
  - a part of the circuit, common for all the wells
  - a specific part for each well.

Power supply of the principal circuit is the plant one, with its own redundancies.

Emergency circuit is normally off, and is switched on by operator on failure of the principal one. It is mainly composed of :

- one fan,
- the heat exchanger system,
- a part of the circuit, common for all users (wells + other users),
- a part of the circuit, common for all the wells,
- a specific part for each well.

Power supply of the secondary circuit is provided by a specific diesel engine.

One part of the cooling system is common to the principal and emergency circuits.

2 - Terms of the problem - First approach

Object of the study was to calculate the probability of loss of cooling, partial or total, for longer than a given period.

The main difficulties of the problem were :

- the various degrees of redundancy (2 redundant circuits, internal redundancy for some subsystems, redundancy in control-command and power supply),
- the various types of redundancy (active/passive),
- redundancy management (automatic/manual),
- very different repairing rates for components or subsystems,
- not totally-defined repairing and testing policy,
- taking into account the acceptable period for loss of cooling.

After a first analysis of the circuit, it can be seen that :

Partial loss of cooling (one well) concerns the components that are specific to each well (some of these are common to normal and emergency circuit ; some others are specific to each circuit).

Total loss of cooling may be due to one of the following sequences :

- normal circuit fails, then emergency one fails to start,
- normal circuit fails, then emergency one starts, but fails before the principal one is reparired,
- normal circuit fails, for a common cause failure (the emergency circuit is inefficient).

Failure of the principal circuit may itself be due to :

- the redundant system of fans,
- the redundant system of heat exchangers,
- non redundant parts of the circuit,
- electrical reasons.

3 - <u>Use of FMEA</u>

After the analysis of the circuit, the first stage of the study was to look up
the failure modes of each component, using FMEA (Failure Modes and Effects
Analysis). Effects of the failure modes included immediate effects and ultimate
effects (after reaction of the system).

The analysis pointed out :

- simple failure points for "loss of cooling of one well" (components
  common to normal and emergency circuit),

- hidden failure points : for example, if regulation of one heat exchanger
  of the normal circuit fails (blocked), then the other one automatically
  compensates the failure, that remains undetected.

4 - <u>Calculation of "partial loss of cooling"</u>

Loss of cooling of one well was modelized using a fault tree. As this tree was
relatively simple, calculation of loss of cooling was made "by hand".

5 - <u>Modelisation of "total loss of cooling"</u>

As seen in the first approach (§2), several sequences can lead to loss of
cooling ; they all refer to three main failures : failure in operation of the
normal circuit, failure in operation of the emergency circuit, failure to start
of the emergency circuit.

But, because of the internal redundancies, the failure of some components of
the principal circuit does not require the intervening of the emergency one. It
is therefore necessary to calculate equivalent failure rates and repairing
rates for redundant subsystems (fans, heat exchangers).

The general modelization of the system is show in fig.1

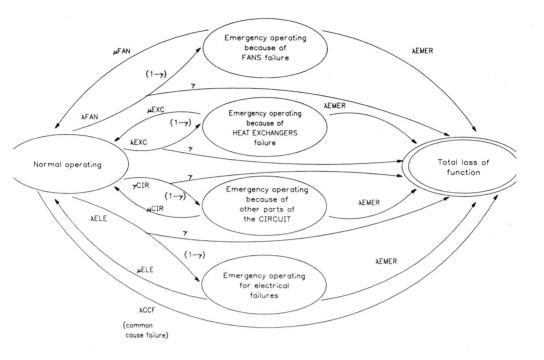

Figure 1 : principle of the modelization with Markov diagram.

5.1 Analysis of the normal circuit.

Object of this stage was to calculate the equivalent failure rates of the fig.1, that represents the frequencies of requesting the emergency circuit.

Each equivalent rate was calculated using combinations of fault trees, cause - consequence diagrams and Markov Diagrams.

For quantitative valuation, the following computer codes were used :

    - DEFAIL 2/FIAB 2 (*) for reduction and calculation of boolean structures,
    - MARK EXD (**) for calculation of Markov Diagrams.

For example, the different phases in modelizing the "frequency of requesting the emergency circuit for fan failure reasons" include :

(*) DEFAIL 2 and FIAB 2 : used and commercialized by CEP under licence of EDF-DER - Validated for french nuclear program and within EEC frame (ISPRA).

(**) MARD EXD : used and commercialized by CEP under license of SNEAP, CFP, IFP. Validated for french nuclear program and oil-producing plants.

- a flow chart representing the assumptions made about redundancy
  management and repairing policy,
- cause/consequence diagrams modelizing the transient phases following the
  failure of a fan, with various operating states obtained,
- a Markov Diagram, carried out from the previous cause/consequence
  diagrams, modelizing the different operating states with the transitions
  between states.

"Failure of the heat exchangers subsystem" was modelized in a similar way,
"Failure of non redundant part of the circuit" was modelized using fault trees,
"Requesting the emergency circuit for electrical" reasons was modelized using a
Markov diagram.

5.2 Analysis of the emergency circuit

Probability of failure to start was modelized using cause/consequence diagrams,
while failure in operation was modelized by a fault tree.

5.3 Probability of "loss of cooling"

At this stage of the study, all the failure rates of the fig.1 were calculated.

Equivalent repairing rates (μ_{eq}) of subsystems were calculated using the
formula :

$$\tau_{eq} = \frac{\Sigma (\lambda_i \tau_i)}{\Sigma \lambda_i}$$

where τ_i is the MTTR of the component , and λ_i its failure rate.

So, the probability of loss of cooling could be calculated, using the same
computer code MARK-EXD.

6 - Taking into account the acceptable period for loss of cooling.

After the cooling system has failed, the irradiated fuel assemblies reach a
critical temperature after a certain time T. This delay can be taken into
account, considering the probability that repairing is not finished when t = T

$$P = 1 - \frac{1}{\theta} \int_0^T e^{-\mu t} \, dt = e^{-\mu T}$$

Where $\mu = \frac{1}{\theta}$ is the repairing rate ($\frac{1}{\theta}$: MTTR)

On the Markov Diagram - simplificated on Fig.1 - the "final state" (total loss
of cooling) has in fact been split into many "final states", in order to
distinguish the different subsystems (failure paths) for which equivalent
repairing rates can be calculated.

For each failure path, the probability of loss of cooling for longer than T is
obtained by multiplicating the probability of the state and the probability
that repairing is not finished when t = T.

The total probability is finally obtained by adding the previous ones.

CONCLUSION

This combination of classical methods used in Probabilistic Safety Assessment
permitted to solve a complex problem, in a real case application.

Some interesting recommandations were pointed out by the analysis, concerning :

- redundancy management (at the various levels of redundancy),
- repairing policy, for redundant or non-redundant subsystems,
- preventive maintenance and testing, and the cost - effective necessity of
  using such a probabilistic approach.

And, beyond the particular results and recommandations, this study also pointed
out the efficiency of a partnership between two complementary kinds of
specialists : specialists of the system, and specialists of the methods. P

EVALUATION OF VERY LOW FREQUENCIES OF ATWS AND PLOHS IN A LOOP-TYPE FBR PLANT BY MAKING USE OF INHERENTLY SAFE FEATURES

K. Sakata, K. Koyama, S. Aoi
(Mitsubishi Atomic Power Industries, Inc., Tokyo, Japan)
R. B. Simonelli, I. T. Wallace
(Westinghouse Electric Corporation, Madison, PA, USA)

Frequencies of ATWS (Anticipated Transient Without Scram) and PLOHS (Protected Loss of Heat Sink) for a large loop-type FBR plant were evaluated by applying PSA methodologies. The frequencies were found to be so low that ATWS and PLOHS could be excluded from candidates of the design basis events. Furthermore, the inherently safe features introduced to the system design were verified to be very effective for reduction of the Probability of CCF (Common Cause Failure), which deteriorates reliability of both the reactor shutdown and the decay heat removal systems.

1. Introduction

HCDA (Hypothetical Core Disruptive Accident) is desired to be excluded from the design basis events from the standpoint of commercialization of FBR plants. In these days, there is a consensus that HCDA can be eliminated from the design basis events if the total frequency of HCDA is less than 10^{-6}/ry. It is crucial to verify that both the frequencies of ATWS and PLOHS are much less than 10^{-6}/ry, since they are typical and dominant initiators of HCDA. Here, ATWS is a whole core damage state resulting from a failure to scram in the case of the anticipated transients such as TOP (Transient Over-Power), LOF (Loss of Flow), and LOHS (Loss of Heat Sink) events. PLOHS is a state without ultimate heat sinks for an extended period, resulting from multiple failures of the DHRS (Decay Heat Removal System) or a complete loss of heat flow path to the ultimate heat sinks after the reactor shutdown.

In the present paper, frequencies of ATWS and PLOHS for a 1000MWe loop-type FBR plant were evaluated by applying PSA methodologies. Furthermore, the effects of inherently safe features were examined on reduction of the CCF that deteriorates system reliability in the reactor shutdown system and the DHRS.

2. Characteristics of the reference system

Characteristics of the reference systems are as follows. The design philosophy of inherent safety has been adopted for each system to reduce the frequency of HCDA.

(1) RSS (Reactor Shutdown System)

The reference plant has two shutdown systems, i.e., the Main and the Backup systems. Each system consists of two parts: PPS (Plant Protection System) which includes instrumentation channels, logic circuits, and trip breakers, and RSS which consists of absorber rods and electromagnets. A two-out-of-four coincidence logic is used in the PPS. The absorber rods of each system are actuated by the PPS signal of the relevant system. Furthermore, the electric power for the electromagnet is supplied from the bus common to main coolant pumps. Solid and articulated type absorber rods are adopted in the Main and Backup systems respectively. A "self-actuation" concept is introduced in the Backup system as an inherently safe feature (1). The Backup system utilizes temperature sensitive electromagnet for self-actuation, as well as the actuation by trip breakers of the PPS. This self-actuation concept, what is called SASS (Self Actuated Shutdown System), is designed to respond to all types of anticipated transients: LOF, TOP, and LOHS. The adoption of different scram parameters, parts, circuitries, and rod types between the two shutdown systems reinforces their independency.

(2) DHRS (Decay Heat Removal System)

The reference plant is equipped with passive DRACS (Direct Reactor Auxiliary Cooling System) which removes decay heat by natural circulation. The DRACS consists of four independent loops, each loop having a 50% decay heat removal capability just after the reactor shutdown. The system is automatically actuated, upon the reactor scram, by opening the dampers of sodium-to-air heat exchangers. The DRACS is a passive system except for the dampers, since it does not need any active component including supporting system during operation. Furthermore, the grace period for opening the dampers makes their unavailability insignificant, since they can also be opened manually.

3. Evaluation of frequencies of ATWS and PLOHS

3.1 Event Tree Analysis

The events of potentially significant contributors to risk were selected and categorized into 12 kinds of initiators, where only plant internal events were considered. Important factors in the reliability analysis of this plant are the number of scram parameters and the availability of NHTS (Normal Heat Transport System) after the reactor shutdown, which are dependent on each initiator.

Accident sequences following the initiators were analyzed by the event tree methodology and the paths to ATWS and PLOHS were identified. A typical event tree is shown in Fig. 1.

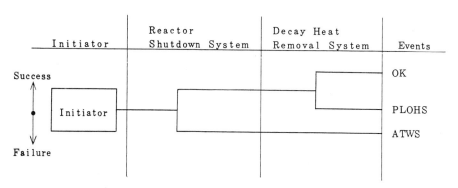

Fig.1   Event Tree

3.2 Fault Tree Analysis

Unavailabilities of the RSS and the DHRS were evaluated by the fault tree methodology. The CCF in this analysis was evaluated by the β-factor method (2), in
which the parameter β has been determined principally by engineering judgement
considering the degree of dependency of components or systems involved. The
failure rates were derived from the documents when appropriate, such as CRBRP-1
(3), WASH-1400 (4), EPRI-NP-2784 (5), and IEEE-STD-1984 (6). The fault tree of
the RSS is shown in Fig. 2.

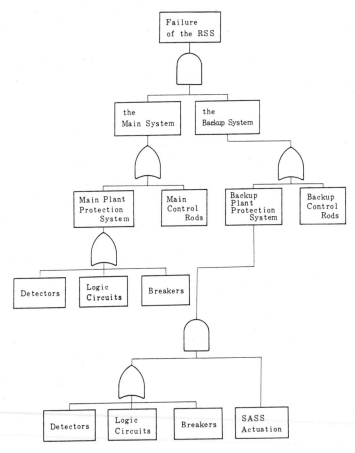

Fig.2 Functional Fault Tree of the RSS

Keys in the fault tree analysis are as follows.

(1) RSS

o Success criteria of the RSS is that either the Main or the Backup system
   succeeds to insert required number of absorber rods. Although the required
   number may be fulfilled by combination of two systems, such a case is conservatively ignored.

o The CCF of intra- and inter-system are considered.
o The PPS is assumed to be tested every 30 days.
o Failure probability of SASS actuation is estimated as 10^{-2}/d.
o Actuation of the RSS due to loss of the power source to the electromagnet is conservatively neglected.

(2) DHRS

o Success criteria of the DHRS is that either the NHTS or at least two DRACSs must be operated for a short period after the reactor scram, and at least one DRACS for an extended period.
o The CCF of only the air cooler dampers and the active components in the NHTS are considered, since passive components are not as sensitive to the CCF.
o Recovery action by operator is taken into account in the case of the damper failure. The failure probability of the recovery action is estimated as 10^{-3}/d.

3.3 Results

The frequencies of ATWS and PLOHS evaluated are:

6.2x10^{-10}/ry for ATWS, and 2.5x10^{-9}/ry for PLOHS.

Both the frequencies are much less than 10^{-6}/ry. The introduction of the SASS and the passive DRACS contributes to high reliability of those systems.

4.   Inherently safe features and reduction of CCF

Sensitivity studies were made to examine the contribution of inherently safe features to system reliability. Reduction of the CCF is an important subject in the system design, since the reliability of a highly redundant system is generally dominated by the CCF.

4.1 RSS

The results of the sensitivity study shown in Table 1 indicates the following.

(1) Introduction of the SASS is most effective for TOP events, since there are fewer scram parameters available for TOP events than for other anticipated transients. Therefore, a SASS which responds only to LOF events is less effective for reliability improvement of the RSS.

(2) The reliability goal could be met even in the RSS design without the SASS, if the parameter β of inter-system CCF of the PPS is less than 10^{-4}. However, introduction of the SASS makes the RSS more tolerable to unidentified CCFs.

(3) If the value is increased of the parameter β between the Main and the Backup systems, CCF between the absorber rods of both systems dominates the reliability of the RSS. Therefore, diversity in the absorber rods is important. Solid and articulated type absorber rods adopted in the reference plant are effective for the introduction of diversity.

(4) The reliability of another RSS design, in which either Main or Backup PPS actuates both of their absorber rods simultaneously, is higher than that of the reference plant. However, such a system may be CCF-prone, since some inter-connection is inevitable between two PPSs.

Table 1   Results of Sensitivity Study for the RSS

(unit:/demand)

Event	Reference System	System without the SASS	Decreased Inter-system Independency	Simultaneous Actuation of Both Rods
T O P	5.49×10^{-10}	1.34×10^{-8}	4.34×10^{-7}	3.00×10^{-10}
L O F	3.17×10^{-10}	8.42×10^{-10}	2.08×10^{-7}	1.11×10^{-10}
L O H S	3.16×10^{-10}	8.09×10^{-10}	2.08×10^{-7}	1.11×10^{-10}

4.2 DHRS

The results of the sensitivity study shown in Table 2 indicates the following.

(1) The passive DRACS has high reliability, since its operation is guaranteed as long as passive components are intact, which are hard to be affected by the CCF.

(2) Even if the capacity of DRACS is doubled (100%x4) by addition of electro-magnetic pumps and air blowers, reliability improvement can not be expected for the cost increase, since the system reliability is dominated by the failure of the reactor and the guard vessels.

(3) The DRACS actuated only by forced convection is orders of magnitude less reliable than the passive DRACS, since it is strongly affected by the CCF of active components. If a system depends on active components, it is necessary to introduce diversity into the system.

Teble 2   Results of Sensitivity Study for the DHRS

(unit:/demand)

Availability of NHTS	Reference System	System added Forced Convection Capability	Active System
Unavailable	1.14×10^{-8}	5.70×10^{-11}	2.89×10^{-4}
Available	2.28×10^{-10}	5.62×10^{-11}	2.17×10^{-4}

5. Conclusions

These studies are very helpful to improve knowledge of the inherently safe features as a measure of the CCF reduction and the reliability improvement.

Both frequencies of ATWS and PLOHS are found to be so low that ATWS and PLOHS can
be excluded from candidates of the design basis events in the reference plant
that utilizes the SASS and the passive DRACS. Although there are some uncertainties especially in estimation of the CCF, this conclusion will not change
because the inherently safe features contribute very much to reduction of CCF.

6. References

(1) Tupper, R. B. et al., Development of a Self-Actuated Shutdown System, Joint
    ASME/IEEE Power Generation Conference, (Oct. 1981).

(2) Fleming, K. N. and Raabe, P. H., A comparison of three methods for the quan-
    titative analysis of common cause failures, in "Probabilistic Analysis of
    Nuclear Reactor Safety," Vol. 3, p. X.3-1. American Nuclear Society,
    LaGrange Park, Illinois, 1978.

(3) Clinch River Breeder Reactor Project, The Clinch River Breeder Reactor Plant
    (CRBRP) Safety Study-Assessment of Accident Risks in CRBR, Report CRBRP-1,
    Vol. 1 and 2, 1977.

(4) Nuclear Regulatory Commission, Reactor Safety Study - An Assessment of Acci-
    dent Risks in U.S. Commercial Nuclear Power Plants, NRC Report WASH-1400
    (NUREG-75/014), NTIS, 1975.

(5) Tzanos, C. P., A Comparison of Selected Risk Contributions of an LMFBR and an
    LWR: phase A, EPRI-NP-2784, (Jan. 1983).

(6) IEEE Guide to the Collection and Presentation of Electrical, Electronic, Sens-
    ing Component, and Mechanical Equipment Reliability Data for Nuclear-Power
    Generating Stations, IEEE Std. 500-1984. Institute of Electrical and Elec-
    tronic Engineers, (Dec. 1983).

SALP-PC, A COMPUTER PROGRAM FOR FAULT TREE ANALYSIS ON PERSONAL COMPUTERS

S. Contini, A. Poucet
Commission of the European Communities,   J.R.C. Ispra Establish.,
21020 Ispra (VA), Italy.

ABSTRACT

The paper presents the main characteristics of the SALP-PC
computer code for fault tree analysis. The program has been
developed in Fortran 77 on an Olivetti M24 personal computer (IBM
compatible) in order to reach a high degree of portability. It is
composed of six processors implementing the different phases of
the analysis procedure. This particular structure presents some
advantages like, for instance, the restart facility and the
possibility to develop an event tree analysis code.
The set of allowed logical operators, i.e. AND, OR, NOT, K/N,
XOR, INH, toghether with the possibility to define boundary
conditions, make the SALP-PC code a powerful tool for risk assessment.

1. INTRODUCTION

The fault tree technique is a very important tool in systems
reliability analysis. In the past a lot of computer codes for
logical and probabilistic analysis of fault trees have been
developed on main frame computers. In the last few years the
increasing performances of personal computers enabled the development of independent work stations for risk assessment, dealing
not only with analysis but also with model synthesis and mani-
pulation. On this line J.R.C. has started a project aiming at
producing an integrated software for fault tree - event tree
synthesis and analysis /1/. The SALP-PC, which represents one of
the analysis modules, is based on a new approach designed to
fullfil some important requirements and to overcome some draw-
backs present in other codes of the SALP series.

2. MAIN CHARACTERISTICS OF SALP-PC

The problem of developing efficient procedures for determining
the minimal cut sets (MCSs) of a large fault tree is rather
complex, since the running time has always to be kept within
reasonable limits; this problem becomes even more complex when
the memory working space is a limited resource too.   In order to
face with these problems the following solution has been adopted
in SALP-PC:
- use of cut-off criteria for determining only a subset of the
  MCSs;
- logical analysis of the tree at different levels of detail;
- use of efficient algoritms for cut set minimization;
- use of garbage collection procedures to reduce the probability

that the program may abort due to insufficient working space;
- pruning of the tree before determining the MCSs when NOT
operators or boundary conditions are present.
Each of these methodological aspects are briefly presented;the
main features of the code are summarised in Table I.

2.1 Use of cut-off criteria

Theoretically, all MCSs should be identified, as each of them
could produce the system failure. However, in practical cases,
the identification of all MCSs can be not only very expensive
because of the high running time, but also useless. Therefore,
only significant MCSs may be determined. The significance can be
defined either on a structural basis (order of a MCS) or on a
probabilistic basis (mission time unavailability). If the aim of
the analysis is to obtain the most important MCSs, a measure of
the approximation introduced (truncation error, Pe) must necessarily be determined, without actually finding all the MCSs. With
the use of the probabilistic criterion (a MCS is considered to be
relevant if its mission time unavailability is not less than a
pre-established threshold value Plim) this measure represents an
estimate of the comulative unavailability at the mission time of
not relevant MCSs. If such a measure is not determined the
probabilistic cut-off is of little value. The knowledge of Pe is
fundamental to judge whether or not the chosen cut-off value
Plim can be considered as appropriate; consequently, to be really
useful, the estimate of Pe must be as close as possible to the
exact value, but without requiring to determine actually the
disregarded MCS's.
A method for solving this problem was already been implemented in
the SALP-MP computer code /2 /, but the degree of conservatism of
Pe was too high with complex trees containing events or subtrees
replicated many times. In order to determine a good estimate of
Pe, independently from the typology of primary events, a new
method of analysis has been developed, based upon the concept of
pseudo-module. The application of such method also allows a
significant reduction of computer time compared with other available methods.

2.2 Logical analysis methodology

In order to reduce the computer time needed to determine the
significant MCSs it is of paramount importance to perform the
modularization phase, whose aim is to transform the input tree
into a forest of independent simpler subtrees; generally, the
more the number of subtrees, the less computer time is needed.
This is why efforts have been spent in the past to set up ways of
modularizing, a given tree, as much as possible.
In most part of computer codes the modularization is performed by
determining the so called simple modules, i.e subtrees containing
only unreplicated primary events. Some codes determine also complex modules i.e. containing all occurrences of one or more
replicated primary events.
The aim of reducing the computer time and of determining a good
estimate of the truncation error lead us to defined a new analy-

584

sis method based on the concept of pseudo-module. A pseudo-module
is defined as a complex module in which the occurrences of replicated primary events not necessarily must all be contained in
the module definition itself.

Fig. 1 shows a fault tree already modularized with independent
modules. The pseudo-modules are shown by dotted lines, i.e.
G4, G10, G12, G11 and G3. Gate G10 is the root of a repeated
subtree and G11 contains two occurrences of the primary event D;
other replicated primary events are contained in the description
of G3, G4 and G12.
When pseudo-modules are substituted in the main tree with single
variables the "macro fault tree (MFT)" is produced, as shown in
fig. 1 by heavy lines. By following this approach the fault tree,
modularised with independent modules, is therefore transformed
into an MFT and a forest of simpler and Dependent Subtrees (DS).
It can easily be realised that this approach always leads to a
strong reduction of the fault tree complexity, while this cannot
be garanteed by other methods.
The presence of DSs necessarily requires the definition of a two
stage analysis procedure.

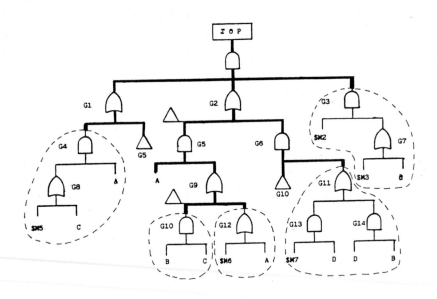

$Mx :   simple module
-----   Pseudo module
━━━━   Macro Fault Tree

Fig. 1 Example of pseudo modules and macro fault tree generation

In the first stage the MFT and all DSs are analyzed, according to the bottom-up approach, without making use of any cut-off technique; the set of minimal failure combinations of the MFT are here referred to as " Macro cut sets ". A macro cut is nothing but the conjunction of replicated primary events, simple modules and DSs. In the second stage dependencies among the elements of macro cut sets are solved. It is at this time that the cut-off technique is applied for retaining only the significant MCSs and estimating the truncation error value.(According to the results obtained the user may decide either to proceed or to restart with different threshold values without repeating the previous steps). A similar algorithm is applied during the simple module expansion for determining the significant MCSs of the input tree.

2.3 Cut set minimization procedure

The minimization procedure plays an important role in fault tree analysis: most of the computer time is spent to minimize cut sets. In order to reduce the computer time it is necessary, apart from using a powerful minimization procedure, to minimize only potentially non minimal cus when this is stricly necessary. In SALP-PC an efficient algorithm is applied at each gate level to determine whether its descendants are dependent or not; in case of dependency the set of combinations is partitioned and only those containing locally repeated events are minimized.

2.4 Garbage collection procedure

A problem that arises when the number of MCSs is too large to be dealt with is that of insufficient working memory space. In this case it is useful to apply a garbage collection algoritm to arrange data in some way so as to prevent the program from aborting.
During the analysis of the MFT the MCSs of repeated subtrees are maintained to be used when needed. In case of unavailability of working memory space the garbage collection procedure visits the part of the tree still to be analysed, identifies the references to repeated subtrees and deletes the MCSs of those subtrees no more necessary.
During the analysis of the macro cut sets the probabilistic threshold value is automatically increased each time the memory space is saturated. Therefore the new not significant MCSs can be deleted and their probability added to the truncation error value

2.5 Fault tree pruning procedures

The SALP-PC program allows the user to analyse fault trees containing the NOT operator. Compared with AND-OR trees, the analysis of an AND-OR-NOT fault tree poses many additional problems and hence the algorithms for determining the minimal form of prime implicants are time consuming. On the other hand a fault tree contains many variables, and negated events are defined to describe the "good" state of primary events, whose probability is generally either 1 or very close to 1. Examples of such applications are found in event sequence analysis and in the description of mutually exclusive events. In SALP-PC simplified methods, applicable when these conditions are satisfied, have been implemented giving, as a final result, the disjunction of minimal cut sets, on which the quantitative analysis can be applied /3/. Briefly, the algorithm is based on the a priori elimination of all unreplicated negated events before the modularization phase is applied. The remaining negated events are considered until they are no more needed to delete logically impossible combinations.

A similar pruning procedure is also applied, before the modularization, when a boundary condition is defined.

3.CONCLUSIONS

The modular structure of the SALP-PC code has proved to be extremely interesting. It allows to easily implement the program on various types of computers (from personal to mainframe). Moreover, it offers the possibility for applying the various processors for solving other problems, thus making it easy to develop a code for e.g. event tree analysis or analysis of marked trees (as in CCF analysis). The SALP-PC code is fast in comparison with other fault tree analysis codes (such as SALP-MP). Future developments include the application in event tree analysis and CCF analysis.

4. REFERENCES

/1/ A. Poucet, S. Contini, K.E. Petersen, N.K. Vestergaard
An Expert System Approach to System Safety and Reliability
Analysis. 2nd Workshop on Fault Diagnostic, Reliability and
Related Knowledge-based Approaches. Manchester, 1987

/2/ M. Astolfi, S. Contini, C.A. Clarotti, F. Picchia
"SALP-MP, a Computer Code for Fault Tree Analysis and Repairable Phased Missions". Eurocopi rep. n. 12, 1980

/3/ A. Amendola, S. Contini, C.A. Clarotti, F. Spizzichino
Analysis of Complete Logical Structures in System Reliability
Assessment. EUR 6888 en, 1980

Input	Fault tree and primary events data interactively entered (complete free format). 8 characters max for events description. Gates may have up to 6 descendants
Type of gates	AND, OR, NOT, XOR, K/N, INH (Inhibit)
Limit on number of gates or events	Depending on the available memory. For personal computers with 192Kb RAM: - n. of gates + n. of primary events: 300
Checking of input errors	Yes, on line; a check on existing loops is also performed
Methods of generating cut sets	Bottom-up according to different levels of fault tree definition Logical cut-off and /or probabilistic cut off with/without the estimate of the truncation error
Limit on number or size of cut sets	Depending on the available memory. For personal computers with 192 Kb RAM: 3000 of order 10 max
Quantitative analisis and importance anaysis	Unavailability, Expected number of failures for each MCS and for the top-event. Primary events criticality. Unrepairable, repairable and inspected components are allowed (sequential testing only)
Other features	- Boundary conditions - Restart facility at each step of the analysis procedure - Five different MCS's printing options - The INH gates may have dependent subtrees as descendants - High portability
Computer, operating system Programming language	OLIVETTI M24 and all IBM compatible. MS-DOS MICROSOFT FORTAN-77.

Tab. I Main features of the SALP-PC package.

CAFTA: A FAULT TREE ANALYSIS TOOL DESIGNED FOR PSA

James M. Koren [Scientific Applications International Corporation, Los Altos, California, USA]

John Gaertner [Electric Power Research Institute, Palo Alto, California, USA]

Abstract

The CAFTA workstation to streamline many of the PSA analysis steps and provide the utility with a maintainable PSA model. It supports a PSA methodology commonly in use today, which includes the use of modularized fault trees, linking and evaluation of accident sequence level models, and recovery, uncertainty, and importance analyses on the resulting cut sets. In today's environment, utilities are requiring PSA models to be functional well after the initial study is completed. This requires that the models be in a maintainable form. CAFTA can be used to support not only the initial PSA process, but also the utilities' continuing use of the models for decision-making.

Introduction

One of the outcomes of the OCONEE PSA (Ref. 1) was the realization that the process of building and quantifying the fault tree modules was much more resource intensive than needed. The system analysts spent a significant portion of their time building and modifying their models; those responsible for the component reliability data had to ensure all model data files were updated as new probabilities become available and there was a need for several technicians dedicated to the evaluation of the models.

In response to this need, EPRI assembled a contractor team of experienced PSA analysts as well as software engineers to specify the structure of a microcomputer work station that would eliminate many of the fault tree analysis problems. CAFTA (Ref. 2) was developed from this specification. CAFTA contains modules for editing and checking the fault trees, for managing the basic event data, for solving and quantifying the models, and for editing and sorting the resulting cut sets.

In addition to supporting fault tree analysis in general, CAFTA also proposes a specified methodological approach to the PSA. It supports fault tree modularization, a structural reliability data base management, and detailed cut set analysis. These features are each described below, along with a brief discussion of how, together with the other CAFTA features, a PSA model can be maintained.

CAFTA Overview

The CAFTA work station contains four major processors: fault tree editor, reliability data base, cut set editor and fault tree evaluation processor. Within these processors are utilities for uploading and downloading data, formatting models for evaluation by mainframe computer programs, report generation and interfacing between the processors.

The most central of all these processors is the reliability data base. It can receive input from both the fault tree and the cut set editor as well as the user, and provides failure probabilities for the evaluation processor and fault tree model formatting utility. This data base contains the reliability data as well as information about how and where the data came from. The <u>fault tree editor</u>, which is used to build and maintain the fault tree models, provides basic events to the reliability data base. Once the model is built and reliability data extracted from data base, CAFTA's <u>fault tree evaluation processor</u> can be used to obtain the cut sets. These resulting cut sets can be loaded into the <u>cut set editor</u> for review by the analyst. A functional block diagram of the CAFTA workstation is shown in Figure 1. The arrows show the direction of the data flow among the different processors.

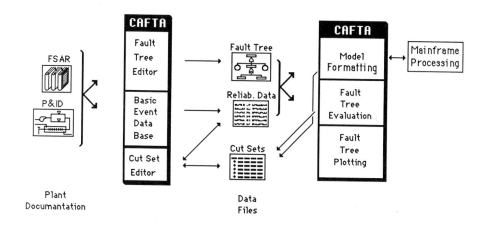

Figure 1 Functional Block Design of CAFTA

Fault Tree Modularization

In the past, PSAs of nuclear power plants were based on fault tree system models that contained thousands of gates and components. An example is the Oconee PRA (Ref. 2). These fault tree models contained various levels of detail down to the component level, and their solution was expensive and time-consuming. In some cases they were impossible to solve without modification by the analysts. This problem stems from the number and organization of the gate structure of the fault tree rather than the number of basic events in the fault tree. The Oconee PRA recognized this problem,and initial steps were taken in the study to improve model efficiency. One recent study had the same number of basic events as reference 1 (a similar plant), with approximately one-fourth the number of gates. This resulted in a model that could be requantified in less than 1 day with about 20 minutes of computer time, as contrasted with an estimated 2 weeks and many hours of computer time under the old system. The results obtained from both studies were directly comparable.

The major difference between the two studies was the extensive use of supercomponents The fault tree logic was constructed so that the basic events appearing in the system fault trees are organized in such a manner that they can be grouped and treated as a supercomponent during the quantification process. This process, called functional modularization, provides a great reduction to the level of fault tree complexity, as reflected in the number of gates in a fault tree. The supercomponents are defined by the analyst as part of the fault tree development process, and generally reflect a set of equipment that acts independently to perform a certain function, such as the components in a train of a specific system. Dependencies such as power, control or environment, are modeled specifically in the fault tree outside of the domain of the supercomponent.

A number of computer programs and procedures (Ref. 3 and 4) have been developed to automate the modularization process. However, automated approaches cannot apply all the available techniques and will manipulate the tree in such a manner that the supercomponents created will not make physical sense to an analyst. Therefore, a great deal of interpretation of the results is needed in which the analyst will have to expand each supercomponent as each cut set is reviewed.

CAFTA supports two approaches to the modularization process where the analyst identified the supercomponents. It also supports the automated approach where a computer program identifies the supercomponent through the interface it provides to the mainframe evaluation programs. However, the manual approaches are considered superior.

CAFTA supports the structuring of fault three models by the analyst such that functional independent sub-trees are created. These sub-trees are then evaluated separately from the main model and their cut sets stored. The sub-trees top gate can then be added to the basic event database and flagged as a "developed event". When the main model is then evaluated, all gates identified as developed events can be replaced and their supporting logic deleted. When this model is evaluated, the cut sets will contain developed event that represent clearly defined functions. CAFTA provides the utility needed to identify, evaluate, and replace gates with developed events.

This approach is not always needed, however, especially for simple independent sub-trees. Often it is easier for the analyst to simply input the independent sub-tree cut sets using CAFTA's cut set editor and then include only the top event name in the fault tree model. This approach, also supported by CAFTA, results in a smaller fault tree which is more readily understood by those not performing the analysis.

Cut Set Management

System level fault tree models produce at least hundreds of cut sets, and linked system or accident sequence models routinely yield many thousands of cut sets. Invariably these cut sets must be reviewed for accuracy and for physical insights about the systems that are modeled. Nearly always, cut sets must be modified or deleted because of model simplifications or incompleteness. Frequently, modeling errors, unavailability data changes, and design changes can be accommodated by editing the cut set list rather than changing the fault tree models themselves. The CAFTA Cut Set Editor has features to assist with each of the above needs.

The most important of these cut set editor features are:

- Provide documentation of the cut set result.

- Determine basic event importance measures.

- Provide for the removal of cut sets or addition of nonmodeled events including recoveries.

- Determine accurate top event failure probability.

- Update reliability database with developed events.

- Streamline the review of new cut set results after reevaluation of model.

- Prepare input for cut set analysis programs.

The different importance measures for the basic events are the means the analyst has to identify weaknesses in the system being modeled. The cut set editor calculates and displays the following importance measures for each basic event: Fussell-Vesely, Criticality, Birnbaum, Improvability, and Degradability.

The review of the cut set results often requires the selective removal of specific types of cut sets. There are several reasons for the removal of cut sets occur when many different initiating events are explicitly modeled, resulting in cut sets containing mutually exclusive initiating events. Another example would be a cut set that contained combinations of maintenance events that violated technical specification or system management policy. The identification and removal of these types of cut sets is often easier than the explicit modeling of the dependencies.

The process of reviewing the cut sets and making changes can be time consuming, especially with large numbers of cut sets. This work may have to be repeated if an error is found in the model and reevaluation is required. The cut set editor has a special "reload" command which attempts to retain as much of the old work as possible when new cut set results must be used. The editor attempts to match the original cut sets obtained during an earlier evaluation to the newer cut sets being loaded. If a match is found, any changes to the cut set are made and the cut set is flagged. The user must then remove the flag before the changes become permanent.

In addition, recovery events are most effectively applied to cut sets rather than included in the fault tree models themselves. This is true because the probability recovery usually depends on the specific combination of failures and on the time available, both of which are cut set specific. CAFTA enables the user to append a recovery event to a cut set, place its value in the database, reevaluate the cut set probability, and recalculate the top event probability with ease.

In total, the above features save calendar time and personnel hours in the cut set review task, the recovery analysis, and in any subsequent model updates.

Model Maintainability

Model maintenance is a necessity for large reliability modeling projects and PSAs. Models are continually modified during the project and are updated periodically after the initial project is complete.

Model maintainability requires keeping the fault tree models current and documented, keeping the database up-to-date and consistent with the fault tree models, and keeping the cut set files consistent with the fault tree models, and keeping the cut set files consistent with the fault trees and the data. The following three features of CAFTA are particularly suited for effective modeling maintenance.

- The database editor maintains failure information in two databases. The first database contains the basic events representing failure of components or human errors in the system models. The second database contains the failure rates for the deficient failure modes for each type of component modeled.

- Changes of failure rates in the second database file are propagated to each basic event database file automatically. This saves time and assures consistency.

- The most current basic event files are automatically accessed by the fault tree editor and the cut set editor. Therefore, fault trees and cut set lists are always up-to-date and can be easily updated.

- The "reload" capability of the cut set editor which retains as much of the old work as possible when new cut set results are generated is a great time-saver and improves the chances that changes are made properly.

Reliability Data Management

As a result of the OCONEE PRA, several areas were identified where the ability to better manage the reliability data could improve traceability, maintainability and consistency. The most important was the use of one central database for all the data. This would insure that if an event appeared in more than one model, one change would update all models. CAFTA's centralized database insures that all fault tree models linked to that database would use the same values. In addition to propagating events probabilities to all models, there was also a need to propagate the failure rate to all events representing similar types of component and failure modes. CAFTA handles this through the use of two linked databases. The first contains the basic events representing failure of components of the system, or human errors. The second database contains the failure rates for the different failure modes for each type of component modeled. For example, even though there may be many actuators modeled in the fault trees, and therefore, many unique basic events in the basic event database, the failure rate database many contain as few as three or four entries for the actuators, each representing a specific failure mode.

The importance of these two separated databases can best be seen by looking at a form of the equation defining the probability of failure:

$$P(BE) = 1 - e^{-\lambda \tau}$$

where

$P(BE)$ = probability of failure for a basic event BE
 = failure rate per unit time
 = the time required for BE to be operational

Although the failure rate, λ, may be the same for basic events in many of the models, different failure probabilities will be used for models of different systems. This is because mission success for each system may require the system to be operational a different amount of time. In general, the basic event database contains the τ values and failure rate database contains the λ values.

Data is passed between the two data bases through the use of a naming convention which typically refers to specific character positions within the basis event name to indicate both the type of basic event and its failure mode. CAFTA uses this naming convention to find and extract the correct failure rate data for this second database.

ON THE USE OF INTEGRATED COMPUTER TOOLS FOR POST-PROCESSING OF PSA RESULTS

Marit Bengtz, Michael Knochenhauer, Anders Törn
(AB ASEA-ATOM, Västerås, Sweden)

Abstract

Post-processing of PSA results is very much a question of efficient data handling. Large amounts of information are reviewed, quantified, modified and re-quantified. This work may be part of the PSA itself, of the review process, or of some other safety-related analysis concerning the plant. In all of these cases both handling of the information and analysis are required. The use of an integrated program package, including programs for both analysis and information handling, and with smooth interfaces between the programs included, will make the post-processing easier to perform. It will speed the work up and reduce the amount of errors inevitably introduced into analyses requiring much manual input and data handling. Furthermore, certain types of analysis difficult to perform using a more traditional approach will be facilitated.

1 Post processing of PSA Results

The performance of a Probabilistic Safety Assessment has provided the operating utility with an excellent plant model with focus on safety and reliability. A central part of this model is the set of detailed system fault trees, which include relevant findings from various activities performed within the PSA, for example

o systems analysis
o human error analysis
o dependent failure analysis.

A very useful characteristic of the fault tree model is its flexibility. Handled by adequate computer tools, fault trees can easily be modified, updated, or adapted to new boundary conditions.

This flexibility of the system models makes the PSA extremely useful for various kinds of safety-related analyses, such as:

o evaluation of considered changes in system lay-out,
o spotting of weak links in plant safety,
o evaluation of technical specifications,
o modification of emergency and operating procedures.

Currently, several analyses of this kind are being performed in Sweden. A short description of one of them is included in this paper.

However, a PSA contains an enormous amount of very detailed information, which indicates that the performance of the above mentioned analyses is not a trivial task, neither from the information handling nor from the analysis point of view. Post-processing of this kind would therefore be greatly facilitated if an integrated program package could deal with both analysis and information handling in an efficient way. SUPER-NET has been developed by ASEA-ATOM to perform this task /1/.

2 SUPER-NET

SUPER-NET is an integrated program package for reliability and risk analysis developed by ASEA-ATOM.

SUPER-NET has three main functions:

1. It works as an input and handling system for the plant model.

2. It provides tools for evaluation of the model with respect to parameters of interest.

3. It offers a possibility to generate reports with such structure and quality that they can directly form part of the documentation of the analysis.

The key features of the SUPER-NET reliability and risk analysis network are summarised in figure 1. As seen from the figure, the network has two main tasks:

o   to provide tools for the various kinds of analyses to be performed in the processing and post-processing of PSA results,

o   to link the individual programs and provide an efficient handling of their inputs and outputs.

The backbone of the package is the fault tree handling program SUPER-TREE, which contains the plant model. SUPER-TREE is used for:

o   input

o   editing

o   modification

o   documentation

of the plant model. It also provides a starting point for continued analyses by creating evaluation files in suitable formats.

The system evaluation is made with the fault tree analysis program FTAP, which for a given tree structure generates the minimal cutsets (i.e. events or combinations of events that bring about a suitably defined plant unavailability or failure). Cutsets are presented and ordered by the size of the contribution they give to the system unavailability or failure probability. The total unavailability for the evaluated case is also given.

The results from this fault tree analysis are treated further by the program SENS, which was originally developed for performing sensitivity analyses on the results from complex fault tree evaluations, and to make IMPORTANCE rankings of components.

Using the cutset list as a basis for a certain evaluation case, SENS creates the unavailability function which forms one part of the input to the programs FRANTIC and SAMPLE. FRANTIC computes the time dependent unavailability of a system, whereas SAMPLE computes the confidence interval of the computed unavailability, based on statistical uncertainty measures given for components in the data base. SENS also creates the actual input files for these two programs; component specific data is obtained from the SUPER-TREE file.

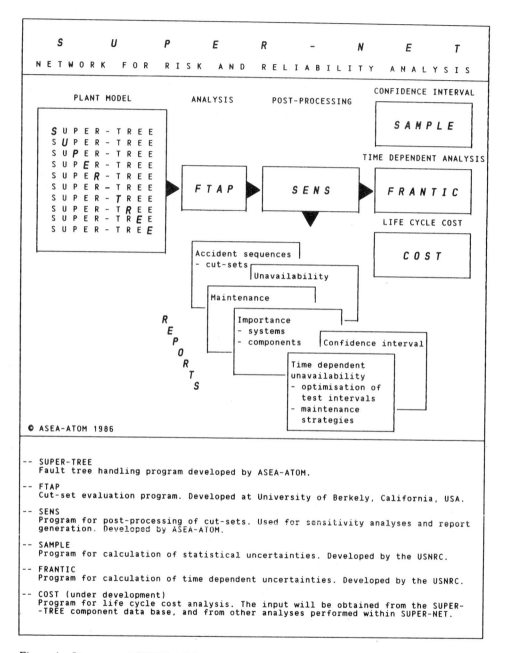

Figure 1: Structure of SUPER-NET

SENS has a further purpose: to generate reports. The program generates importance tables and documents the sensitivity analyses. In addition, it generates unavailability reports and maintenance reports for the sub-systems of a plant, based on detailed information supplied by the SUPER-TREE plant model.

Thus the main principles of SUPER-NET are:

o   to make use of SUPER-TREE as a data bank, containing all the specific information on individual components or basic events that is needed by the analysis programs of the network,

o   to provide smooth interfaces within the network, and

o   to provide built-in documentation of the analyses (fault tree plots, diagrams and reports)

3   Using SUPER NET for Post-processing

The application to be described deals with the introduction of preventive maintenance (PM) during power operation in stand-by safety systems in the Swedish Forsmark nuclear power plants. The work was performed within the joint Nordic research project NKA/RAS 450 (Optimisation of Technical Specifications by Use of Probabilistic Methods).

Using the SUPER-TREE plant model and the results from the Forsmark 3 PSA (performed in 1984/85), the effects of introducing PM were evaluated on system level and on plant level /2/. It was possible to make a complete re-quantification of the PSA within a couple of hours, including the adaptation of the input to the PM schemes considered. These re-evaluations were then followed up by extensive sensitivity analysis in order to assess the impact of e.g. common cause failure (CCF) parameter uncertainties on the outcome of the evaluations.

Some critical stand-by safety systems were analysed on system level. For these systems a crucial question was to what extent the results of the PM evaluations were affected by uncertainties associated with CCF parameters. The Multiple Greek Letter (MGL) method had been used to model CCF:s /3/. The results from a systematic sensitivity analysis performed with SENS, where CCF parameters were varied between two extremes, are shown in figure 2 below. The system analysed is the four-train containment cooling system with capacity 4 x 100% (4 x 50% in some cases).

Starting from the same PSA model, a number of different analyses have been performed within the same project. Thus, a detailed analysis of the impact of testing and preventive maintenance on the auxiliary feedwater system is under way. This analysis aims at giving a better over-all picture of the effects of testing and maintenance on system availability and reliability. For these kinds of analyses, the SUPER-TREE system model is used to produce the input to FRANTIC, which in turn is used to analyse the time-dependent unavailability of the system, concentrating on factors related to testing and maintenance.

The PM evaluations on plant level were concerned with the search for an optimal PM lay-out. Starting with the suggested PM scheme, re-quantifications of the Forsmark 3 PSA were made with boundary conditions given by the proposed scheme. Based on these initial quantifications, alternative schemes were suggested and evaluated resulting in the proposal of some important changes in the original PM lay-out.

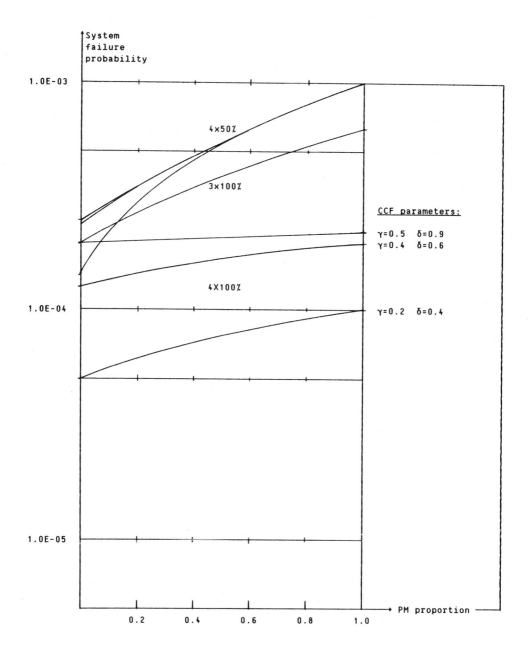

Figure 2: Influence of PM proportion and choice of CCF parameters on system unavailability

4   References

1. M. Knochenhauer, SUPER-NET - A Program Package for Reliability and Risk Analysis. SINTOM Seminar on Computer Programs for Reliability Analysis, Visby, Sweden, April 27-29, 1987.

2. M. Knochenhauer, The Forsmark 2 Preventive Maintenance Project. Probabilistic Calculations, ASEA-ATOM Report RPA 86-39.

3. K. N. Fleming, A. M. Kalinowski. An Extension of the Beta Factor Method to Systems with High Levels of Redundancy. PLG-0289, 1983.

Experience Using a PC-Based Workstation in a Level 1 PSS Effort

Y. D. Lukic
(NUS Corporation, San Diego, California 92127 U.S.A.)

Vincenzo Cavicchia
(ENEL-DCO Sede di Roma, Roma, Italia)

ABSTRACT

This paper describes various aspects of the experience gained in using a PC-based workstation in the performance of the Caorso NPP Level 1 PSS. It specifically addresses the experience with workstation functions designed to unburden the analyst from some fo the traditionally labor-intensive tasks within a PSS.

1   Introduction

The Probabilistic Safety Study of Caorso (Ref. 1) was initiated in August 1986 as a joint effort of ENEL and NUS Corporation. The primary motivation of the study was to provide a nuclear safety perspective of the plant from the probabilistic viewpoint in response to the public concerns arising from the Chernobyl accident. While accelerated by occurrence of this accident, the study also represents a continuation of the policy by ENEL and ENEA to subject all nuclear plants in Italy to a probabilistic scrutiny.

The top objective of the study was a thorough assessment of the severe core damage frequency associated with so-called internal events. An equally important objective was to provide a characterization of the dominant accident sequences that could leave the reactor core in a conditions considered vulnerable to severe core damage. Another objective was to obtain insights on contributors to public risk by grouping the dominant accident sequences with similar accident phenomenology, with respect to the magnitude of fission product source terms, and construct and quantify containment event trees that represent the containment response following an accident, for each of the groups.

The three month schedule for the Caorso PSS is, so far, perhaps one of the shortest schedules ever for the performance of a Level 1 PRA embodying a similar level of detail. Key to the success of such a complex task has been the NUSSAR (NUS Safety and Reliability) PC workstation software package (Ref. 2). The use of NUSSAR by project analysts was instrumental in simplifying and reducing the overall level of effort associated with:

(1) inputting system fault tree logic into the computer;

(2) performing human reliability analysis;

(3) verifying and correcting the fault tree logic;

(4) plotting the system fault trees;

(5) linking, i.e., merging, of front line system logic with support system logic;

(6) analysis of merged system fault trees to obtain system unavailability, cutsets, and basic event importance estimates; and,

(7) translating the fault tree logic and basic event data from its NUSSAR PC format into the mainframe computer SETS/SEP format, for the purpose of accident sequence quantification.

Each of these PC software-related tasks carried out within the Caorso project is described in Section 2.

2   Caorso PSS Experience with NUSSAR

2.1 Fault Tree Input

Detailed system fault trees were developed and quantified for the systems and operating modes listed in Table 1.

1.	Reactor Core Isolation Cooling	(RCIC)
2.	High Pressure Collant Injection	(HPCI)
3.	Manual and Automatic Depressurization System	(ADS)
4.	Low Pressure Core Spray	(LPCS)
5.	Residual Heat Removal	(RHR)
	1) Low Pressure Coolant Injection	(LPCI)
	2) Suppresion Pool Cooling	(SPC)
	3) Containment Spray Cooling	(CSC)
6.	Standby Liquid Control	(SLC)
7.	Electric Power (emergency and normal 6KV/380V AC, 120V AC instrument bus, 110V DC, 24V DC)	
8.	Reactor Building Ventilation and Cooling	
9.	Emergency Service Water	(ESW)
10.	Normal Service Water	(SW)
11.	RHR Service Water	(RHRSW)
12.	Reactor Building Closed Loop Cooling	(RBCCW)
13.	Alternate Rod Insertion	(ARI)
14.	Recirculation Pump Trip (end of cycle and ATWS RPT)	

Table 1. Detailed Fault Tree Models — Caorso PSA

These fault trees were input into the PC through NUSSAR's interactive, on-screen graphics. As each basic event was input on-screen, the reliability data and basic event description were automatically updated from data bases created for this project. Fault tree gate descriptions were input on-screen, as were the basic event and reliability data of basic events not defined within the data bases.

All front line systems and practically all support systems had expressed dependencies on other systems. These dependencies were handled within the fault tree logic through NUSSAR's "external transfer" definition which effectively set up the tree for the subsequent fault tree "merging" process.

Each system fault tree was generally saved in a separate file. However, at times it proved to be more effective to break up a system fault tree into separate logic entities, e.g., trains, when the logic of one entity was very similar to others. In this manner the fault tree logic was entered for only one entity whose file could subsequently be first cloned, then suitably modified in order to represent other similar logic entities.

In some cases, a different system fault tree had to be constructed for each initiating event and/or system mode of operation; this implied changes in fault tree logic, basic event data, or both of these. Here again the process of cloning the system fault tree file, and modifying it appropriately for the initiating event and mode of operation, proved to be a very effective technique.

A strong drive was made to modularize the Caorso project fault trees. This led in some cases to significant reductions in size and complexity of fault trees. In other fault trees the modularization proved not to be easy to implement because of various cross-tie piping connections and the overall difficulty in determining independent fault tree branches.

2.2 Human Reliability Analysis

The human reliability quantification methods used in the study are the human cognitive reliability (HCR) correlation developed by NUS for EPRI (Ref. 3), use of some of the tables from NUREG/CR-1278 (Ref. 4) and in some cases expert judgment.

The HCR correlation is of prime use in those situations in which time is a critical factor. The response of the crew is in part determined by their mental processing. The mental processing of the crew is a function of the amount of information that has to be processed, the complexity of the transient and the degree of difficulty for the crew to extract that information from the control board information (indicators, recorders and alarms). The ability of the crew to respond in time is a function of the stress induced in the crew by the accident and its perceived consequences.

In the Caorso PSS, the quantification of the non-response probability was accomplished by using the Human Reliability Analysis Module of NUSSAR. This module is an implementation of the HCR Correlation. All the data input is done on-screen and the analyst has to select the PSFs, the dominant cognitive behavior and the median response time together with the appropriate system time window.

2.3 Verifying and Correcting the Fault Tree Logic

After the fault tree logic was initially input into the computer, it was necessary to check that no errors were made in the input. Some errors/omissions, i.e., undeveloped gates, undefined internal and external transfers and basic events without data, were straightforward to detect thanks to the Fault Tree Status Report available to the analysts within NUSSAR. Other errors, e.g., OR gates erroneously input as AND gates (and vice versa), mistyped basic event names, etc., required different detection approaches.

One of the successful techniques was to develop a system cutset list which could be visually checked and compared, at least for the low order cutsets, against the analysts' expectations. Key to this approach was to "disconnect" the external transfers from a tree, thus reducing the complexity of the logic to verify. This technique was complemented by an extensive cross review of all fault trees by other analysts.

2.4 Fault Tree Plots

The review of fault trees by the Caorso project analysts was facilitated by the ability to create without additional effort both draft quality printer-plots and report quality Hewlett-Packard pen plots of the fault trees. NUSSAR's standardized graphic format feature also made it possible to quickly locate references to internal or external transfer gates within fault trees. This feature simplified the effort of fault tree peer review. An example of a fault tree page plot with NUSSAR is shown in Figure 1.

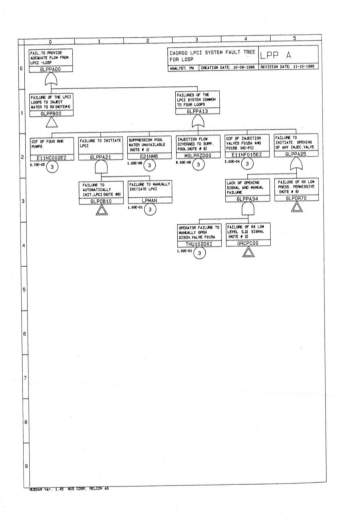

Figure 1: NUSSAR Fault Tree Page Plot

2.5 Merging Fault Trees

After the individual fault tree logic and data were found to be correct, each front line system was merged (e.g., external references from support systems were resolved) to obtain an expanded front line system fault tree. Each expanded fault tree, now containing all the front line and support system logic, was stored on a separate file, ready for system fault tree analysis.

2.6 System Fault Tree Analysis

Most of these expanded front line system fault trees could be quantified directly within NUSSAR, while a few others proved to be too comples to be effectively quantified within the workstation and instead were analyzed with the mainframe program SETS/SEP. Quantification of expanded fron line system fault trees was most successful where a high degree of modularization was achieved.

Analysis of front line systems provided the analysts with the estimates of system unavailability, probability-ranked cutset list and calculation of basic event importance using the Fuessell-Vesely algorithm.

2.7 Translation of NUSSAR Fault Tree Files into SETS/SEP Format

All front line and support system fault trees were translated into the SETS/SEP code format using the NUSSAR automated translation feature. Given the sheer number and complexity of the various fault trees, the automated, error free, translation feature proved to be a key element that allowed significant manpower savings.

2.8 Sequence Analysis

The sequence analysis was almost entirely performed within the mainframe computer using the SETS/SEP codes running on the CRAY-1-S2000 (CDC interface). SETS was used for generating the Boolean equations which were subsequently quantified with SEP.

3 Conclusions

The usefulness of NUSSAR as a tool in the performance of Level 1 PSS was established. Caorso PSS' ambitious schedule benefited from the application of this new, manpower-effective tool to unburden the analysts from the traditionally labor-intensive manual tasks associated with PSS performance.

The difficulties experienced in modularizing the system fault trees prevented the performance of accident sequence quantification within the PC. It is perceived that without effective fault tree modularization, the quantification of accident sequences remain mostly in the realm of mainframe computers.

User feedback during the Caorso PSS, and other projects where NUSSAR was used, have led to an expansion of present workstation capabilities which are embodied in NUSSAR-II. This expansion includes a fully integrated Monte-Carlo uncertainty analysis module, a cutset analysis module and an enhanced importance analysis module. In addition, the processing speed of the cutset analysis module was increased by 40%.

An additional software package developed by NUS is the NUPRA workstation whose objective is to automate the Probabilistic Risk Assessment (PRA), with ready application in the area of risk management.

4   References

1.   Caorso Nuclear Power Plant. Probabilistic Safety Study, Report No. ENEL DCO 401.VO40.VR.001, NUS-4954, November 1986.

2.   NUS Corporation and RELCON AB. NUSSAR, NUS Safety/Reliability Workstation, Version 1.45, 1985—1986.

3.   G. W. Hannaman, A. J. Spurgin and Y. D. Lukic. Human Cognitive Reliability Model for PRA Analysis, developed under EPRI contract, NUS-4531, December 1984.

4.   A. D. Swain and H. E. Guttmann. Handbook of Human Reliability Analysis with Emphasis on Nuclear Power Plant Applications, NUREG/CR-1278, USNRC, 1983.

REGULATORY USES OF PRA/PSA BY THE USNRC

Speis T.P., Office of Nuclear Regulatory Research
United States Nuclear Regulatory Commission, Washington, D.C. 20555

ABSTRACT

Probabilistic Risk Assessment is finding increasing acceptance by the U.S. Nuclear Regulatory Commission and is extensively applied in a number of safety assessments and regulatory activities. Specific issues highlighted and evaluated in this paper include safety issue prioritization and the issues of station blackout and containment leaktightness. PRA techniques and insights are also finding extensive usage in addressing the severe accident issue for nuclear power plants. Included in this are the development of methods and guidelines for individual plant examinations for severe accident vulnerabilities, the evaluation of the relative importance of containment failure modes from severe core melt accidents, and the development of mitigation strategies and fixes to enhance containment effectiveness against severe accidents.

1. INTRODUCTION AND OVERVIEW

Historically, regulatory decision making was based on information generated by the conventional "deterministic" approach. This approach is direct, simple to check, and is based on sound principles like defense-in-depth and the single-failure criterion, which strengthen inherent safety. However, this approach usually involves assumptions which are based on engineering judgement. These assumptions tend to introduce conservatism. Much of the conservatism arises from a caution generated by uncertainties associated with the current knowledge of phenomenology and of plant response to transients and accidents. The level of this conservatism in deterministic evaluations is very often hard to measure, thus depriving the decision-maker of a valuable piece of information. Moreover, deterministic evaluations are usually conducted on a case-by-case basis, and involve the evaluation against variously stated regulatory requirements separately for technical details of each of a number of sets of the plant's design and operational systems and safety functions (e.g., the reactor protection system, the decay heat removal function, the AC emergency power system, etc.). With the current available operating experience and accumulated insights about NPP safety, regulators increasingly regard plant safety as a combined function of plant design, construction, plant operations and operating-design interactions. Both the need and the possibility of a more coherent treatment of safety issues, with mechanisms based on probabilistic risk assessment (PRA), for enhancing consistency from issue to issue and from plant to plant are increasingly recognized.

As the methods of PRA and probabilistic safety assessment (PSA) approach maturity, regulators recognized its strength and potential. A major milestone in PRA utilization was the Reactor Safety Study [1] (RSS) which demonstrated that a Nuclear Power Plant (NPP) could be analyzed in an integrated and systematic way. The utilization of PRA was further stimulated by the accident at Three Mile Island (TMI). The TMI accident resulted in a realization that the potential for accidents other than design-basis accidents needed to be addressed more thoroughly in the U.S. regulatory process. PRA integrates into a uniform methodology the relevant information about plant design, operating

practices, operating history, hardware reliability, human reliability, the
physical progression of accidents, and potential environmental and health
effects in case of radioactive releases, in a systematic way. It uses both
logic models and physical models. The logic models define the combinations of
events (sequences) that could result in a core damage accident and are used to
determine the frequencies associated with each combination. The physical
models depict the progression of the resultant accident and the severity of
damage to the plant. For example, the combination of events that can lead to
a station blackout, and the probabilities that these combinations will occur,
are identified by a logic model, while, amongst others, the analysis of the
containment response to the accident is based on a physical model.

The results of the risk assessment are analyzed and interpreted to identify
the plant features and operational practices that are the most significant
contributors to the frequency of core melt, to vulnerability of the
containment, and to the frequency and amount of radioactive releases and to
risk. They can also be used to generate a variety of qualitative information
regarding the events and failures associated with various consequences. PRA
is subject to a number of known weaknesses and limitations. Maturity level,
weaknesses, and limitations in each segment of a full-scope PRA are discussed
in References [2] and [3]. Among these limitations are gaps and inadequacies
in the data base, modeling of core damage phenomenology, external events,
failure dependencies, human performance and equipment behavior under accident
conditions. Performance of realistic analyses is always one of the goals
claimed in PRA studies. However, when information is lacking or controversy
exists the analyst has no choice but to introduce conservatism, increase
uncertainties or exercise his judgement. The problems mentioned have as a
consequence that each risk analysis in the end provides an estimate of risk
and automatically involves subjectivity. Likewise the deterministic safety
evaluation cannot be performed without interjection of subjectivity. It is
less apparent in this case, however, than in the case of probabilistic methods.
In both cases, the engineering experience provides a substantial basis for
evaluation.

It is important to note that the recognition of negative aspects of the PRA,
contained in the preceding discussion does not mean that valuable insights
still cannot be derived from existing PRA results. Insights are based on
information extracted from the analysis of quantitative results including point
estimates, uncertainties, results of sensitivity evaluations, and possibly
results of importance analysis. The quality of derived insights reflects the
quality of this information base. An insight based on information that
exhibits reasonable uncertainties and sensitivities to modeling assumptions
should be given a heavier weight in decision making compared with other
insights lacking these qualities. Understanding all of the significant
strengths and limitations on the part of the decision maker will enable him to
make a more effective use of all available analysis including the information
obtained from deterministic and probabilistic evaluations. There are many
types of regulatory decisions, and the weight given to the quantitative PRA
results should vary depending on the degree of precision necessary and
attainable.

The USNRC has been making extensive use of probabilistic safety and risk
assessments [3] [4] in safety evaluations and in the regulation of nuclear
power plants. This paper discusses current applications in a number of areas
ranging from the regulatory analysis of safety issues to addressing the severe
accident issue for the existing NPPs.

2. REGULATORY APPLICATIONS

2.1 General Remarks

It is recognized that a PRA, due to its realistic integrated approach, presents the best available information concerning the specific ways in which critical safety functions at nuclear power plants can fail to be performed. This is valid in spite of PRAs known limitations and even though PRA models may be incomplete and evaluation uncertainties may be large. The wide spectrum of activities at NRC and the nuclear industry is utilizing the PSA/PRA information to guide and better focus these activities, as appropriate, in order to improve the safety performance of individual nuclear power plants. The use of PSA/PRA evaluations at NRC is marked by a steady increase and wider acceptability. The scope and level of technical detail in these evaluations is controlled by the objectives of the intended applications. Among these applications discussed in this section of the paper are the setting of regulatory priorities, and the regulatory analysis and resolution of safety issues: Specific examples of the latter are the issues of station blackout and containment leaktightness which are discussed below.

2.2 Prioritization of Safety Issues

The USNRC tracks reactor safety issues to help assure appropriate action for their resolution. Since it is beyond agency resources to seek resolution of all issues simultaneously, the agency has instituted a prioritization program to assist in the timely and efficient allocation of resources to those safety issues that have a high potential for reducing risk and in decisions to remove from further consideration issues that have little safety significance and hold little promise of worthwhile safety enhancement. Issues of such gravity that consideration of immediate action is called for are not included in this prioritization program, because of the compressed time scale on which decisions for such issues must be made. (NUREG-0933, Reference [5]).

The method of assigning priority rank involves two primary elements: the estimated safety importance of the issue and the estimated cost of developing and implementing a resolution. Special considerations may influence the proper use of those estimates.

Abbreviated PRA techniques are used to develop a quantitative estimate of the safety importance of the issue, measured in terms of the risk (product of accident probabilities and radiological consequences) attributable to the issue and the decrease in that risk that may be attainable by resolving the issue.

A numerical value-impact score is calculated by dividing the estimated potential risk reduction by the estimated cost entailed. This score denotes a value-impact relation, i.e., an estimated ratio of safety-improvement value to cost impact.

A priority rank (HIGH, MEDIUM, LOW, or DROP) is obtained by application of criteria in which both the safety importance of the issue and the value-impact-based numerical score are taken into account. The score is not always directly applied to determine the priority rankings. In some cases the safety importance of the issue is so great that it demands a HIGH priority, or so minor that only a LOW priority (or decision to DROP) is warranted, irrespective of the value-impact assessment.

The priority ranking is reviewed and modified if appropriate in light of any special factors that might (a) bring into question the applicability of the necessarily simplified calculation technique, (b) call for special consideration of often large uncertainties in the quantitative estimates, or (c) should for some other reason influence the ranking.

In summary, while the method has a quantitative emphasis, the calculated numerical values are used as an aid to judgment and not as determinative of the ranking results. The nature of the specific issue, the quality of the data base, and the scope of the necessarily limited analysis determine in each case the dependability of the numerical indications as a judgment aid.

2.3 Regulatory Analysis of Safety Issues

Many of the generic safety issues under review or resolved by the staff have been analyzed with risk assessment techniques to determine the impact of their resolution on plants, e.g., "Station Blackout," which is discussed in some detail in Section 2.4.1. Risk perspectives were also employed in the regulatory analysis of "Anticipated Transients Without Scram," "Pressurized Thermal Shock," "Water Hammer," and "Containment Emergency Sump Performance," among others.

2.4 Resolution of Safety Issues

2.4.1. Station Blackout

The term "station blackout" refers to the complete loss of alternating current (ac) electric power to the essential and nonessential switchgear buses in a nuclear power plant. Station blackout involves the loss of offsite power concurrent with turbine trip and the unavailability of the onsite emergency ac power system. Because many safety systems required for reactor core decay heat removal and containment heat removal depend on ac power, the consequences of station blackout could be severe.

The issue of station blackout involves the likelihood and duration of the loss of offsite power, the redundancy and reliability of onsite emergency ac power systems, and the potential for severe accident sequences after a loss of all ac power. Experience has shown that in numerous instances emergency diesel generators have failed to start and run during tests conducted at operating plants. In addition, a number of operating plants have experienced a total loss of offsite electric power, and more such occurrences are expected. The average loss of offsite power in the U.S. has been about once in ten site-years. In almost every one of these loss-of-offsite-power events, the onsite emergency ac power supplies were available immediately to supply the power needed by vital safety equipment. However, in some instances, one of the redundant emergency power supplies has been unavailable. In a few cases, there has been a complete loss of ac power, but during these events, ac power was restored in a short time without any serious consequences.

NRC's evaluation to resolve this issue included deterministic and probabilistic analyses. Probabilistic analyses were used in three areas: (1) to identify dominant accident sequences, (2) to develop recommended durations that plants must be able to withstand a station blackout, and (3) to calculate the estimated benefits in terms of reduction in risk to support the NRC staff's value-impact (backfit) analysis.

Calculations to determine the timing and consequences of various accident sequences were performed, and the dominant factors affecting station blackout likelihood were identified. Using this information, simplified probabilistic accident sequence correlations were calculated to estimate the likelihood of core melt accidents resulting from station blackout for different plant design, operational, and location factors. These quantitative estimates were used to provide insights on the relative importance of various factors, and those insights, along with engineering judgment, were used to develop the resolution. The NRC staff found that long-term station blackout sequences (e.g., that could result in depletion of station batteries or the condensate storage tank) can be a dominant contributor to core damage frequency (CDF). The major factors that contribute to CDF from station blackout are the estimated frequency of loss of offsite power, the diesel generator configuration (i.e., number of diesel generators needed compared to number onsite), diesel generator reliability, and the ability to cope with a station blackout. This is shown conceptually in Figure 1.

Insights from PRA were used to develop recommended station blackout coping durations. An attempt was made to achieve approximately an even level of estimated CDF from station blackout events for all plants of about 10^{-5} per reactor-year. Figure 2 shows that, everything else being equal, a plant with one-out-of-three diesel generators that can cope with a station blackout for four hours would achieve this target. Likewise, a plant with two-out-of-three diesel generator configuration would need to cope with a blackout for eight hours to reach the same target.

The proposed NRC resolution of this issue includes a rule that requires all nuclear power plants to be able to cope with a station blackout for a specified duration and to have procedures to withstand and recover from such an event. An associated regulatory guide provides guidance on acceptable plant-specific coping durations to comply with the rule. The acceptable coping durations are based on plant design and site-related characteristics that affect the reliability of offsite and onsite emergency ac power systems. The NRC staff used PRA to estimate the level of risk from station blackout with or without the proposed rule. This analysis (Ref. NUREG-1109) was used to support the final resolution of the station blackout issue.

2.4.2 Containment Leaktightness

A. Background

The technical specifications for each U.S. nuclear power plant includes an allowable containment leakage rate based on a plant-specific design basis accident (e.g., a large LOCA plus the release of a large amount of radio-activity in the containment) and characteristics of the reactor/containment system, site specific demography and meteorology. Analyses are performed to show that the use of this allowable containment leak rate will not result in calculated radiation doses at the site boundary which exceed those specified in 10 CFR Part 100 under the postulated accident conditions.

The applicant must demonstrate that the actual leakage rate is less than the allowable leakage rate before approval is given to start plant operation. At specified intervals during the operational life of the plant, leak rate tests must be performed to demonstrate continuing compliance. Test performance criteria and frequency for these tests are specified in Appendix J to 10 CFR Part 50, which requires two types of tests: an integrated (Type A) containment leakage test and local leakage tests (Types B and C).

Type A tests are required approximately every 3 years and involve pressurizing the entire containment and measuring leakage rate. Types B and C tests are required every 12 to 18 months (i.e., at refueling outages) and usually consist of pressurizing penetrations and the spaces between isolation valves.

B. Technical Findings

The resolution of the containment leaktightness generic issue is based in part on reviewing leakage testing carried out between 1965 to 1983, in accordance with Appendix J testing and reporting requirements. Leakages in excess of Tech Spec limits are reportable events. Figure 3 illustrates the total events reported, the distribution by reactor type and estimated levels of leakage. Of the 3447 reported Tech Spec violations, only approximately 16% were located in direct air pathways. A still smaller amount of these potential leakers were estimated to fall in the 10 to 100 La range. La is the allowable leakage and exceeding 0.6 La requires reporting. The chronological frequency of occurrence of these reportable events for valves and penetrations located in direct air pathways is shown in Figures 4 and 5 for BWRs and PWRs respectively.

The conclusions reached based on reviewing the 1965 and 1985 data are:

1. Type B and C tests are very effective, 99% of the reported events were detected by these test methods.

2. Procedural effects were a minor contributor to the reported events. Therefore, little would be gained by expending resources to revise administrative and procedural aspects.

3. Alternate leakage monitoring concepts were reviewed and the conclusion was reached that significant developmental costs would be required to bring them to a useable level. Current Type A instrumentation (i.e., RTDs and dew cells) could be used in a continuous monitoring capacity but would require additional recording equipment.

4. Prior assessments (NUREG/CR-4220) loss of containment isolation based on exceeding Tech Spec leakage limits significantly over estimated the safety significance of this safety issue.

This issue was also evaluated for risks associated with increased leakage levels and the results are reported in NUREG/CR-4330. These findings are shown in Figure 6 and show that leakages could be increased beyond 10 La without a significant increase to risk. Thus, based on those insights this issue has been judged to be of low safety significance and backfit actions cannot be supported.

While diffusive losses of a pressurized containment atmosphere during a postulated accident is of low risk significance, containment integrity is of paramount importance in limiting dose consequences. The NRC is therefore studying means of replacing the present emphasis on integrated leak rate with greater assurance against failure of containment isolation. Possible changes include a slight relaxation of the allowable leak rate, coupled with a more restrictive policy aimed at assuming that inadvertent breaches of containment integrity do not occur. For further improvements to containment performance against severe core melt accidents see Section 3 of this paper.

2.5 Safety Goals

In August 1986 the U.S. Nuclear Regulatory Commission issued a policy statement promulgating safety goals for the operation of nuclear power plants. (Federal Register, Vol. 51, pp. 28044 to 28049; August 4, 1986.) The safety goals include qualitative goals and quantitative objectives. Quantitative objectives are specified with respect to prompt mortality risk and delayed cancer mortality risk. The policy statement also includes a qualitative objective with respect to severe core damage prevention and a proposed quantitative guideline concerning large release frequency. The latter was proposed by the Commission for further staff examination. This additional objective and this proposed guideline may, in due course of further development of the policy's implementation, become associated with further quantitative objectives, in addition to the two mortality risk objectives mentioned. Also under development is quantitative guidance with respect to safety-cost trade-offs.

With the safety goals, PRA is used to develop risk estimates for use in comparisons of the effects of a potential regulatory action with the quantitative objectives. This PRA-aided safety-goal application is used in a process in which conventional approaches -- including conventional technical analysis and continued emphasis on defense in depth, siting, and performance of personnel -- retain their continuing value. The safety goals, including PRA-based comparisons with the quantitative objectives, are one factor among others in evaluation of potential changes in regulatory requirements. The quantitative objectives are a part of the evaluation standards applied in regulatory analyses of the need for a potential change in requirements and in selection from among available alternatives. The weight given to the comparison with the quantitative objectives is related to the degree of precision or uncertainty with which the quantitative risk evaluation can be made for the issue at hand.

No abrupt or radical change of the regulatory and licensing process is anticipated as the safety goals are introduced. The Commission's rules and staff standards remain the principal basis of licensing actions. However, the cohesion, predictability, and public understanding of further regulatory actions should be enhanced by appropriate application of the safety goals, implemented in a sound and consistent manner.

The following paragraphs summarize the provisions of the Safety Goal Policy Statement.

The qualitative safety goals are as follows:

"Individual members of the public should be provided a level of protection from the consequences of nuclear power plant operation such that individuals bear no significant additional risk to life and health."

"Societal risks to life and health from nuclear power plant operation should be comparable to or less than the risks of generating electricity by viable competing technologies and should not be a significant addition to other societal risks."

The following quantitative objectives are intended to be used in determining achievement of the qualitative goals:

"The risk to an average individual in the vicinity of a nuclear power plant of prompt fatalities that might result from reactor accidents should not exceed one-tenth of one percent (0.1 percent) of the sum of prompt fatality risks resulting from other accidents to which members of the U.S. population are generally exposed."

"The risk to the population in the area near a nuclear power plant of cancer fatalities that might result from nuclear power plant operation should not exceed one-tenth of one percent (0.1 percent) of the sum of cancer fatality risks resulting from all other causes."

In applying the objective for individual risk of prompt fatality, the Commission has defined the vicinity as the area within 1 mile of the nuclear power plant site boundary. If there are no individuals residing within a mile of the plant boundary, an individual should, for evaluation purposes, be assumed to reside 1 mile from the site boundary.

In applying the objective for cancer fatalities as a guideline for individuals in the area near the plant, the Commission has defined the population within 10 miles of the plant site as the appropriate basis of calculation. The distance for averaging the cancer fatality risk was taken as 50 miles in the 1983 proposed policy statement. The change to 10 miles could be viewed to provide additional protection to individuals in the vicinity of the plant, although analyses indicate that this objective for cancer fatality will still not be the controlling one. That is, if the quantitative objective for prompt fatality risk is met for individuals in the immediate vicinity of the plant, the estimated risk of delayed cancer fatality to persons within 10 miles of the plant and beyond would generally be much lower than the quantitative objective for cancer fatality. Thus, compliance with the prompt fatality objective applied to individuals close to the plant would generally mean that the aggregate estimated societal risk would be a number of times lower than it would be if compliance with just the objective for cancer risk were involved.

Along with the qualitative safety goals, the Safety Goal Policy Statement includes the declaration that "the Commission intends to continue a regulatory program that has as its objective providing reasonable assurance, while giving appropriate consideration to the uncertainties involved, that a severe core damage accident will not occur at a U.S. nuclear power plant." Efforts to give this objective quantitative expression are underway within the NRC.

The Commission, in its Policy Statement, has directed the NRC staff to conduct additional studies intended to result in recommendations to the Commission of an implementation approach, including specific guidance for determining whether regulatory actions are consistent with the safety goals. As a potential important part of this guidance, the Commission has proposed the following general performance guideline for further staff examination:

"Consistent with the traditional defense-in-depth approach and the accident mitigation philosophy requiring reliable performance of containment systems, the overall mean frequency of a large release of radioactive materials to the environment from a reactor accident should be less than 1 in 1,000,000 per year of reactor operation."

The specifics of an approach to implementing the safety goals in the regulatory process are currently under development within the NRC. Several significant elements of the implementation approach are not yet clear and are receiving at this time the active consideration of the Commission, its Advisory Committee on Reactor Safeguards, and the NRC staff.

3. THE SEVERE ACCIDENT ISSUE

3.1 General Remarks

Core damage and core-melt accidents are expected to pose the greatest potential risk to public health and safety. Studies such as "The Reactor Safety Study" WASH-1400 [1] as well as many PRAs performed both in the U.S. and elsewhere in the world have concluded that core melt accidents represent the major contribution to risk from commercial nuclear power plants. A number of these studies have also identified areas in both the design and operation of a nuclear power plant where appropriate hardware additions or modifications, often coupled with procedural improvements, could help reduce these risks and often in a cost-effective way.

The NRC began to give attention to severe accidents even before the accident at Three Mile Island (TMI) and has increased its emphasis in this area since that accident. Severe accident evaluations and research had progressed to the point that the USNRC issued a Severe Accident Policy Statement in August 1985 (50 FR 32138) that concluded that existing plants posed no undue risk to the public. However, the Commission pointed out that at each plant there will be systems, components, or procedures that are the most significant contributors to risk. Utilities should identify these contributions and develop appropriate courses of action, if and as needed to ensure acceptable margins of safety. Furthermore, the Commission stated that such examinations "will include specific attention to containment performance in striking a balance between accident prevention and consequence mitigation." In this section of the paper we will describe how this Commission policy is being implemented and how PRA techniques and insights - aided by phenomenological evaluations and engineering judgements are being extensively utilized to aid in the identification and prioritization of the important technical issues, and in arriving at conclusions on the approaches to be taken and the solutions to be implemented.

3.2 Individual Plant Examinations

The Commission's policy statement on severe accidents calls for the formulation of an integrated, systematic approach for the examination of each power plant now operating or under construction for possible significant risk contributions that might be plant specific and might be missed in the absence of a systematic search. Plant-specific analyses by NRC and the nuclear industry with PRAs, have in the past identified vulnerabilities to severe accidents that have typically been unique. Generally, it has been possible to reduce the un- desirable relatively high risk from these plant-specific unique features (design and/or operational) to an acceptable level by low-cost changes of procedures or minor design modifications [6], [7].

Through an initiative by the Industry Degraded Core Rulemaking Group (IDCOR), two separate methodologies have been developed for the examination process: one for BWRs and one for PWRs. These methodologies are structured to evaluate the plant's design and operation and will focus both on severe accident prevention and on mitigation (i.e., improvements to containment performance given a severe accident). Since the IDCOR Individual Plant Examination Methodology (IPEM) makes direct use of past PRA experiences, it requires a small fraction of the resources required to perform a full-scope PRA*. Further, it represents an effective tool for PRA technology transfer, especially for those utilities with very limited or no PRA experience. The IDCOR IPEM involves all of the basic elements of a level-1 PRA, i.e., plant familiarization, accident sequence definition, data assessment and parameter estimation, accident sequence quantification and interpretation of the results.

Among the efficiencies in the IDCOR IPEM are the building upon past PRAs in the same class of plants (learning-curve efficiencies), developing analyses mainly in areas that past PRAs have shown to be important, use of support states to reduce the number of event tree analyses (the PWR method also uses damage states) and it curtails the level of detail by use of conservative unavaila- bilities when the precision of system unavailabilities developed in detail is not required. Some of the limitations in the IDCOR IPEM are: its investigation of those features identified as outliers in previous PRA studies, i.e., the IPEM guidance on depth of analyses may not be sufficient to identify all outlier features unique to the NPP and some risk management decisions may require adding details to the models. Our review of the IPEM indicates that the potential for extension (front end to a level-1 PRA) exists. There is need for heavy reliance on judgement (choice of templates, adjustment factor/nodal questions). There is a need to have available a high level of PRA expertise. The IDCOR guidance provides for only limited verification of the IPEM independ- ent of existing PRA studies; also no uncertainty analysis is included (limited sensitivity analysis is used as an alternative). On balance the NRC staff has found the IDCOR IPEM, together with recommendations for enhancements to the methodology using insights provided by NRC sponsored studies [8], acceptable for utilization for individual plant examinations. In addition the NRC staff is specifying, in the generic letter to the utilities setting forth the examination, that a full-scope PRA or some other systematic method could be acceptable. The present schedule calls for full effort to be initiated in the latter part of this year.

---

* This might not be as true now as when the development of the methodology was initiated. More recent advances in the technology of computer-aided fault-tree generation have led to substantial cost reductions in the level of effort needed to perform a complete PRA.

While recognizing uncertainties in a number of phenomenologies, notably in areas which affect containment performance, the NRC staff is recommending that the IPEM should nevertheless proceed and be utilized to provide the basis for the utility's (i) appreciation of severe accident behavior, (ii) recognition of the role of mitigation systems and (iii) the development of a severe accident management program. For example where the uncertainties in phenomena lead to difficulties in reaching firm conclusions about the most probable outcome, a range of outcomes should be examined and evaluations should be performed of the strategies to manage and/or mitigate the consequences of those potential scenarios, e.g., in the case of high-pressure scenarios which have been postulated to lead to early failure of some classes of containments, pending a more complete understanding of the issue, strategies should be examined which could lead to primary system depressurization prior to the molten corium blowing directly into the containment, overpressurizing it to failure. Other "generic" phenomenological issues which have been identified from NRC's extensive research and evaluation programs, and which require additional work before a more complete understanding is at hand, include the issue of steam generator tube failures and hydrogen burning/detonations. These issues together with the direct heating of the containment are mainly the consequences of high-pressure scenarios. Issues associated with low-pressure scenarios include the crusting vs. quenching of deep corium melts covered with water and hydrogen stratification in the presence of condensation. Again the aim of the IPEM will be to develop event trees that cover the range of uncertainty and develop the appropriate prevention/mitigation strategies to account for these uncertainties. In Section 3.3.B we provide a summary of the relative probability of occurrence of the failure mode for each containment type utilized in the United States as a result of the phenomena and processes that have been found to be important. Among these are some of the phemomena discussed in this section.

3.3 Containment Improvements

A.   The Issue and Current Practices

The role of the containment as a vital barrier to the release of fission products to the environment has been recognized for some time. The public safety record of the U.S. nuclear power plants has been fostered by applying the "defense-in-depth" principle, which relies on a set of independent barriers to fission product release. The containment and its supporting systems are one of these barriers. Included among the latter are fission product cleanup systems such as containment sprays and filters.

Containment design criteria are based on a set of deterministically derived challenges. Pressure and temperature challenges are based on the so-called design basis loss-of-coolant accident. Radiation considerations are based on a postulated substantial core-melt accident. Also, criteria based on external events such as earthquakes, floods, and tornados are considered.

The Chernobyl accident has focused attention on whether containments for U.S. light-water reactors that were built using criteria based on design-basis accidents have adequate margins available to prevent the release of large quantities of fission products during severe accidents.

The margins in safety provided through U.S. practice have been the subject of considerable research and evaluation, and these studies have indicated the ability of containment systems to survive pressure challenges of 2.5 to 3 times design levels [9]. Because of these margins, the various containment types presently utilized in U.S. nuclear power plants have the capability to cope, to varying degrees, with many of the challenges presented by severe accidents. For each type of containment, however, there remain failure mechanisms which

could lead to containment failure, often to early failures with concomitant
releases of large quantities of radioactivity. Therefore the key question is
the capability of containments to prevent the release of large quantities of
fission products, whether the existing available margins are adequate or
whether additional improvements should be pursued to further enhance their
performance during severe accidents. A related question is the proper balance
between accident mitigation and accident prevention, i.e., whether it is more
cost-effective from a risk-reduction perspective to undertake additional
improvements which are directed towards reducing the probability of a severe
accident from happening or toward improving the containment performance given a
severe accident. Many times this is a difficult question to address, but as
was discussed in Section 3.2 the detailed plant specific examination will
provide input in addressing this question by identifying the important
sequences and their contribution to core melt and also challenge to its
containment and then be able to arrive at a more balanced view and perspective
of the relative effectiveness of the two approaches (i.e., prevention or
mitigation). In any event the NRC staff is proceeding to implement the
Commission's policy of defense-in-depth by undertaking evaluations and research
to examine and better understand the principal failure mechanisms for each
containment type and identifying the features which could be utilized to
mitigate such failure mechanisms. These efforts are closely coupled to the
PRA-aided Individual Plant Examinations and the results from both activities
will be utilized in reaching final decisions on the extent and the types of
improvements in containment system performance.

B. Containment Failure Modes and Mitigation Features

Although reactor containment buildings were designed to withstand the loads
generated in design basis accidents, subsequent analysis has shown that the
various containment designs can cope, to varying degrees, with many of the
challenges presented by core melt accidents. However, for each type of
containment, there remain failure mechanisms which could lead to early failure
and associated releases. In some designs these failure mechanisms are well
understood while in others, the failure modes are not very well understood, and
their likelihood is viewed as being high or low by various experts. In this
section, we present the principal failure modes for each containment type and
identify the design features which when implemented could mitigate such failure
modes. We have separated out those potential improvements for the mitigation
of station blackout sequences. Extended station blackout is currently believed
to be a leading contributor to core melt for all reactor types, and on a
relative basis will remain an important contributor despite the expected
reduction in core melt frequency due to the resolution of the station blackout
issue discussed in Section 2.4.1. Station blackout presents a more severe
challenge to containment than other sequences because of the inoperability of
active ESFs (e.g., containment cooling). The "station blackout specific"
improvements will provide an added measure of protection for a wide variety of
other accident sequences.

Tables 1 to 4 summarize our conclusions [8] [10] regarding potential containment
failure modes from severe core-melt accidents for the five types of containment
examined.

Table 5 contains a number of features which when implemented could mitigate
some of the more probable failure modes summarized in Tables 1 to 4. These
features alone and in appropriate combinations are presently being further
evaluated before we can judge their acceptability. Additional evaluations are
also underway to better understand the specific failure modes; these
evaluations include not only calculations/sensitivity studies, but research in
well focused areas for more information on the relevant physical processes and
phenomenology. The present schedule calls for these studies to be completed
by early 1988 and recommendations to be made to the Commission by mid-1988.
The containment improvements program is closely coordinated with the
individual plant examination activities discussed earlier.

3.4 Severe Accident Program

Insights obtained from previous PRAs involve not only technical matters but also lessons learned in both the management and performance of the tasks. An important aspect of severe accident prevention and mitigation is human involvement. Early recognition of abnormal occurrences, availability of procedures specifying corrections, and well trained operators and emergency teams can have a major influence on the cause of events in case of a severe accident.

As part of the IPE, dominant severe accident sequences will be analyzed and evaluated for potential intervention. Steps that could prevent core damage will be identified. All reasonable means will be provided to successfully execute these steps. This includes (1) appropriate diagnostic instrumentation, procedures, and alarms to recognize the approaching danger; (2) operator training and procedures to know what remedial actions are available; and (3) procedures, operator training, and reliable equipment to accomplish the necessary functions.

Similarly, when a sequence progresses beyond core melt, potential mitigative features will be evaluated. In this phase of the accident mitigation, containment integrity (i.e., avoiding early catastrophic failure) is likely to be the main goal. Heat removal from the containment, control of the containment pressure rise, and retention of fission products are the most important functions. Potential human interventions needed to accomplish these functions will be investigated.

An accident management strategy that has the capability to accomplish these functions for each of the dominant accident sequences despite the degraded state of the plant will be developed. The strategy will be checked against the existing organizational structure, responsibilities will be clearly defined, and changes made if needed. For example, one school of thought advocates limiting the responsibilities and training of the operating crew to design basis events and the very early stages of severe accidents. This way, the operators could concentrate on events that they are expected to face. Their training would not be overcomplicated with very unlikely events. Should an event progress into the core damage stage, a specially trained emergency team would take over. Obviously, these decisions must be made before emergency procedures and training programs can be finalized.

Good documentation of the accident management strategy is essential. Practically every aspect of plant operation is involved in accident management. Coordination and communication among the various organizational units is important. As an example, consider venting the containment. It should be clear (1) who has the authority to decide that containment venting is needed and should commence, (2) what information is needed to make this decision, (3) who is responsible for furnishing the information, (4) what instruments can plant personnel rely on to obtain the information, and (5) what steps must be taken and what equipment needs to function to initiate venting. Once venting has been initiated, a similar set of questions arises concerning the termination of venting.

Each organizational unit involved in the process must know its part and should be trained in order to be prepared in case of a severe accident. Managers and instructors should review the training programs of the operating crews and emergency teams and should supplement them as necessary. Committees responsible for developing the plant's emergency procedures and special procedures for emergency teams should take into account the evaluation of the dominant accident sequences and make appropriate changes. Plant maintenance personnel should be aware of the special demand placed on these instruments and equipment. It is expected that, in addition to regular equipment provided within the plant, emergency procedures will take advantage of special equipment, if needed, to prevent as well as mitigate severe accidents. Responsibility to take such action should be assigned, and the individuals responsible should know where to turn to get the needed equipment.

In summary, an important result of the IPE is the identification of preventive and corrective actions plant personnel can and should take in case of severe accidents. The documentation submitted to NRC will include this information together with the steps the licensee has taken to ensure that personnel are properly trained, procedures are in place, and instruments and equipment will be available and will function when needed.

4.   SUMMARY AND CONCLUSIONS

As the methods of probabilistic risk assessment approach maturity, regulators increasingly recognize its strengths and potentials. Among the strong points of PRA are its integrated and systematic approach to NPP safety, its consideration of failure dependencies, interaction among systems and their support systems, its consideration of the human element, and its ability to make an explicit statement about the magnitude of uncertainties associated with evaluation results. PRA insights and methods are finding increasing acceptability among regulators. This development is clear from the PRA applications, a number of which were highlighted in this paper. These applications include allocation of resources, setting of regulatory priorities, resolving safety issues, identifying plant-unique vulnerabilities, and better understanding of the nature of severe accidents and their consequences. The programs involving safety goal evaluations and severe accident policy implementation foreshadow the potential for an even greater use of PRA, its models and its insights within the broad field of decision making concerning nuclear safety.

However, the history of PRA is marked by cautious acceptance. Regulators are aware of PRA limitations: the continuing need for hard data, mature methods, verified models, and a better handle on uncertainties. At the same time, regulators are also aware of the strengths and weaknesses of the conventional deterministic approach to regulation.

However, PRA is making an explicit statement about uncertainties (which in some areas may be large) and how important these uncertainties are in terms of the ultimate effects on the public health and safety. The current practice at NRC is to use both types of evaluations and operating experience as an input to decision making.

ACKNOWLEDGEMENT

I wish to express my thanks to F. Eltawila, A. Rubin, A. Serkiz and G. Sege of the USNRC for their efforts and support in preparing this paper.

REFERENCES

1. USNRC, "Reactor Safety Study, For Assessment of Accident Risk in U.S. Commercial Nuclear Power Plants," WASH-1400, October 1975.

2. "Probabilistic Risk Assessment: Status Report and Guidelines," NUREG-1050, February 1985.

3. T. P. Speis and A. Jahns, "Risk Assessments for Nuclear Safety." Proceedings of Nuclear Energy Agency, OECD, an Interface Questions in Nuclear Health and Safety, held in Paris 16-18 April 1985.

4. "Applications of Probabilistic Techniques at NRC," A. Thadani, F. Rowsome, and T. Speis. Fifth International Meeting on Thermal Nuclear Reactor Safety, Karlsruhe, September 1984.

5. NUREG-0933, "A Prioritization of Generic Safety Issues," U.S. Nuclear Regulatory Commission, (1983 and periodic updating supplements).

6. "Review and Evaluation of the Indian Point Probabilistic Safety Study," NUREG/CR-2934 (SAND 82-2929), December 1982.

7. "Safety Evaluation Report of the GESSAR II (BWR/6 Nuclear Island Design)," NUREG-0979, Suppl. No. 4.

8. "Reactor Risk Reference Document," NUREG-1150, draft dated February 1987.

9. "Containment Performance Working Group Report," NUREG-1037, draft dated May 1985.

10. "Estimates of Early Containment Loads from Core Melt Accidents," NUREG-1079, draft dated December 1985.

TABLE 1

Failure Modes in Large Dry and Subatmospheric Containments

Failure Mode	Relative Probability of Occurrence
α Steam explosion: missile	Very low
β Failure to isolate *	Variable
χ Hydrogen burn/detonation	Low
δ_1 Overpressurization: early (due to steam spike)	Low
δ_1' Overpressurization: early (direct heating)	Variable**
δ_2 Overpressurization: late (over 8 hrs.)	High
ϵ Basemat melt-through	Medium
ν Interfacing LOCA: (Containment bypass)*	Variable

* Mitigation features are ineffective against these failures. Their probability can be reduced by procedural/design changes.

** Geometry dependent; also wide range of views on phenomena and consequences.

TABLE 2

Failure Modes in Mark I and II Containments

Failure Mode		Relative Probability of Occurrence
α	Steam explosion: missile	Very low
β	Failure to isolate*	Variable
γ	Hydrogen burn/detonation	Very low (inerted containment)
δ_L^ϵ	Overpressurization: early (due to steam spike)	Low
δ_L^ϵ	Overpressurization: early (corium/concrete interaction plus steam)	High
δ_T^ϵ	Overtemperature: early (corium/concrete interaction)	High
	Steel containment melt-through	Variable** (applies to Mark-I only)
$\vee$	Interfacing LOCA: (Containment bypass)*	Variable

*   Mitigation features are ineffective against these failures. Their
     probability can be reduced by procedural/design changes.
**   Depends on corium's ability to flow to and melt-through the liner.

TABLE 3

Failure Modes in a Mark-III Containment

Failure Mode		Relative Probability of Occurrence
α	Steam explosion: missile	Very low
β	Failure to isolate*	Variable
γ	Hydrogen burn/detonation	High (standing flames; from station blackout sequences)
δ_1^ϵ	Overpressurization: early (corium/concrete interaction)	Medium
$\vee$	Interfacing LOCA: (Containment bypass)*	Variable

*   Mitigation features are ineffective against these failures. Their
     probability can be reduced by procedural/design changes.

TABLE 4

Failure Modes in an Ice Condenser Containment

Failure Modes		Relative Probability of Occurrence
α	Steam explosion: missile	Very low
β	Failure to isolate*	Variable
γ	Hydrogen burn/detonation: early	High (For black-out sequences where power to igniters and air return fans is lost)
δ_1	Overpressurization: early (due to steam spike)	Low
δ_1'	Overpressurization: early (direct heating)	Variable**
δ_2	Overpressurization: late (over 8 hrs.)	High
ϵ	Basemat melt-through	Medium
γ	Interfacing LOCA: (Containment bypass)*	Variable

*   Mitigation features are ineffective against these failures. Their probability can be reduced by procedural/design changes.
** Geometry dependent; also wide range of views on phenomena and consequences.

Table 5

Potential Improvements For Mitigation of Severe Accidents

Containment Type	Mitigation Feature	Proposed Improvements	
		General Purpose Improvements	Station-Blackout Specific
Mark I and II	Drywell Sprays	-connect spray header to a diverse pump and water source.	-connect spray header to a diverse pump, water source and dedicated power supply
	Wetwell Venting	-Conduct a systematic evaluation of existing wetwell venting system: Verify valve capacity and operability; verify remote actuation from the control room; verify procedures, training and other human reliability factors; verify the adequacy of the vent path and verify effect of venting on EQ of essential equipment in the secondary containment.	-verify (or add) actuation capability in the absence station emergency power
	Core Debris Chanelling (Mark I only)	-Add a concrete curb to confine core debris on the drywell floor to prevent core debris from coming in contact with containment	
Mark III	Wetwell Igniters		-assure that igniters are powered from dedicated power supply*
Ice Condenser	Hydrogen Igniters		-assure that igniters are powered from dedicated power supply*
	Containment Sprays	- add diverse pump and water source	-add diverse pump and water source, and dedicated power supply*
	Air Return Fans	Extend availability in severe accident environment	Dedicated power supply*
	Core Debris Chanelling	-Concrete wall at the exit of the reactor cavity	
Large Dry and Sub-atmospheric	Containment sprays		Add diverse pump and water source, independent of station emergency power*
Steel Containment Melt-through	- Core Debris Retention		- Containment Sprays

* Independent of onsite power, offsite power and emergency power

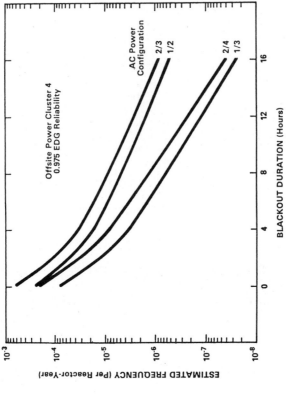

Figure 2, Blackout Frequency versus Duration
for Different EDG Configurations

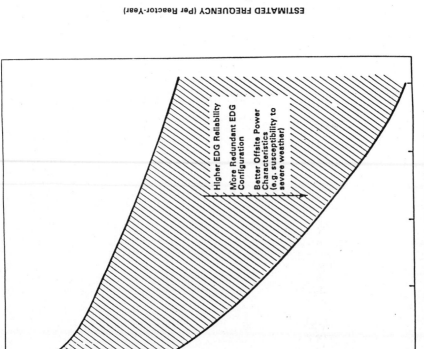

Plant's Ability to Cope with Station Blackout (hours)

Figure 1 Estimated Core Damage Frequency from Station Blackout Events

APPENDIX J REPORTABLE EVENTS
DIRECT AIR PATHS – BWRs

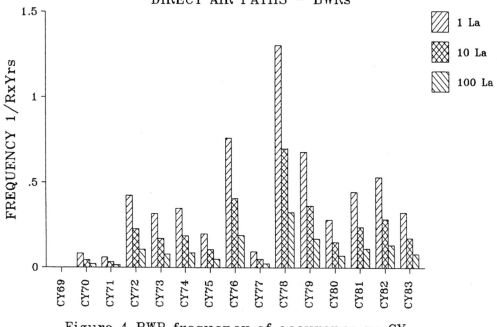

Figure 4 BWR frequency of occurence vs CY

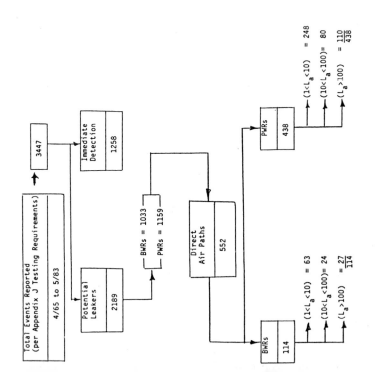

Figure 3 Overview of Containment Isolation History

APPENDIX J REPORTABLE EVENTS
DIRECT AIR PATHS – PWRs

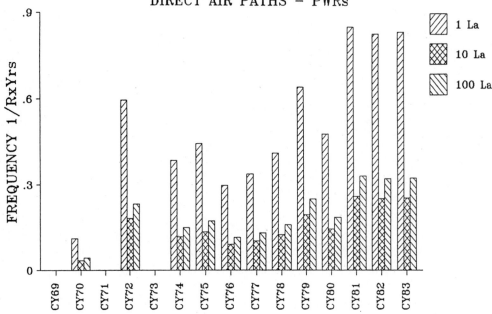

Figure 5 PWR frequency of occurence vs CY

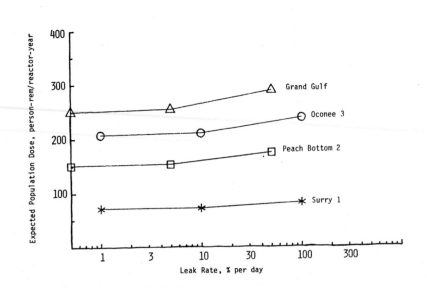

Figure 6 Sensitivity of Risk to Containment Leakage
(Ref. NUREG/CR-4330)

PROBABILISTIC STUDIES FOR THE SAFETY ASSESSMENT OF THE ITALIAN NPPs

A. Valeri and C. Zaffiro

(ENEA/DISP Rome, Italy)

ABSTRACT

This paper discusses the foundamental steps of the Italian approach to nuclear safety in which a wide use is made of probabilistic techniques with the application of probabilistic targets for the occurrence of core melt accidents and large releases.

The first step concerns the development of a level 1 PSS and includes consideration of specific analysis for identifying possible in-plant safety improvements. In turn the second step is devoted to the containment analysis for assessing the probabilities of the external releases. It also includes the studies to be performed for identifying the feasible provisions in the frame of the actual containment capability to cope with the severe accidents. The paper concludes with a few considerations on the uncertainties of the analyses and the effective safety level which can be assured through this approach.

1. THE ITALIAN APPROACH TO NUCLEAR SAFETY

The current approach to nuclear safety for the Italian NPPs includes the application of a Probabilistic Safety Study (PSS) with the use of probabilistic targets as far as the global probability of core melt accidents is concerned.

Generally the targets are set in the range from 10^{-6} to 10^{-5} per reactor year, and should be met through the adoption of feasible design improvements without altering the general consolidated characteristics of the plant. In addition the approach also includes an assessment of the actual capability of the containment to withstand the consequences of degraded core accidents.

The aim is the evaluation of additional in plant safety provisions which could be adopted for reducing and minimizing the public risk but without bringing drastic modifications in the containment design. The assessment is mainly based on the improved knowledge and understanding of severe accident phenomena due to the outcomes of the recent studies and research programmes. It doesn't exclude, however, that a probabilistic analysis of the containment behaviour during severe accidents is performed for the study of accident sequences beyond core melt and for the assessment of the corresponding external radiological releases. Results of this probabilistic analysis are used for verifying compliance with additional probabilistic targets related to the containment performance and thus to the acceptable external releases. The targets require that, if a core melt accident occurs, the external releases of the most volatile fission products (noble gases excluded) should exceed the 0.1% of the core inventory with a conditional probability less than 5%.

The Italian Regulatory Body for Nuclear Safety and Radiation Protection believes that an approach which includes probabilistic evaluations with the use of reference targets for making decisions, enhances the plant defense in depth and the protection of both the public health and the environment.

The approach should also provide guide for the consideration of external emergency preparedness which could be developed and decided on the basis of a probabilistic pattern of the source terms.

2. DEVELOPMENT AND USE OF PSSs

To verify compliance with the plant probabilistic targets, a Probabilistic Safety Study is normally carried-out for the Italian plants.

At present two levels of PSS are required. The first one (level 1 PSS) determines the overall probability of core melt accidents. The second one (level 2 PSS) determines the probability distribution of the release categories for specific core melt accident conditions.

The execution of the level 1 PSS is considered to be interactive with the design development and should provide support for any important design choice. In addition it should allow to assess balance of the plant defenses among different groups of sequences leading to core degradation. Finally it should allow identification of possible areas where it is appropriate or necessary to introduce design safety improvements or modifications. It is common opinion that the results of probabilistic studies strongly depend on the method of approach. For these reasons a few guidelines are used in the frame of the best available methodologies. Specific attention is given to the contribution of common mode failures to systems unavailaility which should not be less than 10^{-5}. This limit is applied to each individual not diversified system which performs a single safety function during the accident sequences.

The execution of the level 2 PSS requires that core melt accidents sequences are grouped in different classes that predict similar post-accident containment scenarios. Containment event trees are developed for each class. Nodal questions are considered for specific post-accident low probability phenomena, pre-existing leakage and human intervention which may cause or prevent different containment failure modes. As far as the various phenomenological events are concerned, the probabilities are usually assigned on a subjective way. Pre-existing leakages and operator actions are probabilistically treated according to the operating experience. External releases are calculated and binned in different source terms categories. The results of the analyses are usually presented under the form of probabilities associated to the various release categories.

3. APPLICATIONS TO ITALIAN PLANTS

3.1 Results of level 1 PSS.

So far, the application of probabilistic techniques has found a wide use in the safety assessment of the Italian NPPs. It provided support to the licensing decisions for the new projects, Alto Lazio BWR Mark III plant and the Italian PWR Standard Projects PUN, and for the old Latina Gas Graphite plant.

After the Chernobyl accident, the increased need of more plant safety for protecting the public health led the Italian Regulatory Body to extend the application also to other existing plants in order to assess their actual safety levels and to identify, if necessary, possible backfitting actions. The new applications regarded the Caorso BWR-Mark II plant and the old Trino Vercellese PWR plant.

The effectiveness of the plant modifications was assessed with reference to the probabilities of core melt accidents estimated by the level 1 PSS. Sensitivity studies and importance analyses on the first PUN-PSS results suggested a set of design modifications which provided a sensible reduction (about a factor 5) of the core melt probability. The PSS for Caorso provided results which confirmed possibility to decrease the core melt probability through the adoption of suitable safety related provisions including both in plant modifications and emergency procedures. Fig. 1 indicates the effect of new provisions on the PSS results. Fig. 1 also reports the core melt probabilities for two cases related to the ALTO LAZIO NPP. The two cases made use of licensing and realistic criteria respectively when assessing the system availability to provide the requested safety functions. They were performed under two specific steps of the licensing process. The first one was aimed at assessing the generic balance of the plant protective funtions, as requested by the technical specification attached to the issued Construction Permit. The second step was requested for judging the plant safety level on the basis of more realistic level 1 PSS results.

At last, fig. 1 indicates the estimated core melt probability value for Latina NPP which is higher than the others. It should be here pointed out that the Latina plant is different from the other LWR plants and thus the related plant safety levels cannot be directly compared through the assessed core melt probabilities.

3.2 Probabilistic assessment of the containment performance

A preliminary probabilistic assessment of the containment performance has been performed in Italy for PUN and Caorso Mark II BWR plant. The purpose was to provide support to some licensing decisions in the field of severe accidents taking also into account the probabilistic targets to be met for the external releases.

The first step of this analysis was the use of the information contained in level 1 PSS to identify the group of sequences which characterize the classes of accidents in the containment. Table 1 indicates the classes for PUN together with the corresponding probabilities, the main core melt events and the status of the Containment Safety Systems. It provides the basis for assessing the availability of the plant safety functions which are needed for mitigating and controlling the post-fusion conditions in the containment.

For the construction of the containment event tree and for the quantification of both the source terms and probabilities, the main containment events were hypothesized on the basis of the existing knowledge on the severe accidents phenomena, but serious containment failures were made very unlikely. Some prudential probabilistic relationships were made available for the pre-existing openings and the recovery actions. A broad range of accident consequences was investigated for PUN which implied a large number of containment sequences to be investigated for quantifying the source terms. This approach produced probabilistic distribution curves for each classes of accidents. Table 2 reports the external releases calculated at 5% conditional probability.

Table 3 indicates the classes of accidents for Caorso, and the corresponding core melt probabilities which were derived from the Level 1 PSS. In the preliminary study, probabilities were assigned to low, medium and high fission products releases in which: low is less than 0.1% I-Cs, medium is greater than 0.1% I-Cs but less than 10%, high is greater than 10% I-Cs. Table 3 also indicates both absolute and conditional probabilities for I-Cs releases greater than 0.1%.

If the 0.1% I-Cs is taken as the reference value at 5% conditional probability to be exceeded, the results of the probabilistic studies are useful for identifying some weak points of the containment system which could be improved through the adoption of additional mitigating provisions. For istance the PUN containment analysis confirmed the need of mitigating the consequences of the V sequence (interfacing LOCA) and/or decreasing its contribution to the global core melt probability.

In table 3 the Caorso classes of accidents in which the probabilistic targets are not met, have been underlined. The results of the analysis show that, although serious consequences of these accident classes are already expected to occur at very low probability values, there still exists the possibility to further reduce the probability of large releases through the adoption of additional in plant provisions which could include both some minor plant modifications and emergency procedures.

4. CONCLUSIONS

The following conclusive considerations are here made to clarify the validity of the applications described in this report in the light of the uncertainties which exist in the probabilistic analysis, expecially in the field of severe accidents.
It is generally recognized that, at present, the probabilistic techniques are rather well consolidated when used for estimating the probability of core melt accidents. Therefore it is reasonable to think this value represents a good estimate of the overall safety level of the concerned plant.
On the other hand, the analysis of the containment performance for estimating the probabilities of the external releases implies several issues related to the occurrence of poorly understood phenomena. Therefore the analyses need subjective judgements very often and may result more or less complicated, depending on the number of assumptions. NUREG 1150 report has well focused the range of variability of both the estimated probabilities and source terms. Therefore the PSS results should be used with great care for practical safety decisions.
To prevent confusion in the decision making process, the Italian applications of the probabilistic techniques in the field of severe accidents, excluded from the analysis all the events which are potentially capable to cause early or intermediate catastrophic containment failures, since these events are believed to be very unlikely. This approach addressed the analyses only on the areas of concern for the still credible phenomena and provided better confidence in the analyses results.

REFERENCES

1. R. Tononi, A. Valeri, C. Zaffiro "Regulatory Requirements and Implications of Probabilistic Safety Studies for the Italian NPPs". Proceedings of the International ANS/ENS Topical Meeting on Probabilistic Safety Methods and Applications. S. Francisco, California, 24-28 February 1985.
2. G. Petrangeli and C. Zaffiro, ENEA/DISP, Italy "Regulatory Implications of Source Terms Studies" IAEA Proceedings of an Internationl Symposium on Source Terms Evaluation for Accident Conditions. Columbus, Ohio, 20 October - 1 November, 1985.
3. ENEA/DISP "Report of the ENEA/DISP Task Force on a Possible Reassessment of Source Terms for Regulatory Purposes in the Light of Indications given by Recent Studies and Research Programs" DISP/SER/SIC(85).

4. A. Valeri and C.Zaffiro "The Use of PSA for Safety Decisions in the Italian PWR Standard Project" Procedings of the CSNI Workshop on Probabilistic Safety Assessment as an Aid to Nuclear Power Plant Management. Brighton, U.K., May 1986.
5. C. Zaffiro "Probabilistic Assessment of the Containment Performance during Severe Accidents in PWRs" CEC Seminar on Studies of Severe Accidents in LWRs. Bruxelles, 10-12 November 1986.

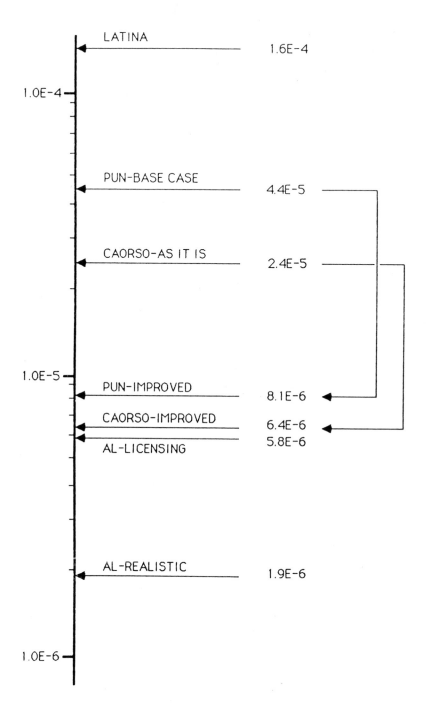

FIG. 1 - CORE MELT PROBABILITIES FOR ITALIAN NPPs

Table 1 – Containment Accident Classes for PUN

Classes	Dominant Core Melt Sequences (*)	Probability (E-6)	Main Core Melt Events	Containment Safety System Status
TE-D	TMLB'	0.08	Transient – Early Core Melt	All failed
TE-C	TMLB	0.98	Transient – Early Core Melt	All failed except one fan cooler
SE-D	S2B	0.71	Small Loca – Early Core Melt	All failed
AE-A	AD	1.70	Large Loca – Early Core Melt	All work properly
V	V	0.12	Containment Bypass	————

(*) According to the WASH 1400 terminology.

Table 2 – External releases for PUN calculated at 5% probability

Reference scenarios	Releases at 24 hr (%)				Noble gases (%)					Reference sequences	
	C_sI-C_sOH	Te-Sb	Ru-Rh	La-AcT	24hr	48hr	72hr	96hr	10gg	N.	Main events
TE – D (TMLB')	1.23 E-2	1.10E-2	2.7 E-3	3.94 E-5	23	40	53	63	100	914	P.O = 8cm^2 Sprays at 3,5 hr
TE – C (TMLB)	2.27 E-2	1.09E-2	3.45 E-2	5.14 E-4	25	41	53	63	100	817	P.O. = 16cm^2 Sprays at 8 hr
SE – D (S2B)	6.83 E-2	1.25E-1	3.86 E-2	5.4 E-4	25	41	53	63	100	936	P.O. = 16cm^2 Sprays at 10 hr
AE – A (AD)	1.1 E-3	3.8E-4	5.3 E-5	5.25 E-7	23	40	53	63	100	213	P.O. = 16cm^2 Sprays in operation!
V	2.73 E-1	9.58E-2	1.36E-2	1.36E-4	NC	--	--	--	--	--	Containment by-pass

Table 3 – Core Melt and External Releases Probabilities for Caorso NPP

ACCIDENT CLASSES	REFERENCE CORE MELT SEQUENCES	CORE MELT PROBABILITIES (E-6)	CONDITIONAL PROBABILITIES FOR I-Cs RELEASES GREATER THAN 0.1%
I-A	TQUX	1.35	0.2
I-B	TE	1.24	12.7
I-C	TC1 UX	0.03	0.2
I-D	TQUV	1.40	3.5
II	TW	0.08	48.7
III-A	R	0.27	0.22
III-B	SQUX	0.08	0.21
III-C	AV	0.31	3.6
III-D	AD	0.12	20
IV-A	TC1 C2	0.45	32
IV-B	TC1 W	0.02	45
V	V	0.01	70

DESCRIPTION OF THE INTEGRATED PROGRAM ON REALIZATION AND UTILIZATION OF PSA IN SPAIN.

José I. Calvo.
(Consejo de Seguridad Nuclear, Madrid, Spain).

ABSTRACT

An Integrated Program on PSA realization and use in Spain was issued by the Nuclear Safety Regulatory Agency, CSN. According to this Program, a specific PSA shall be done for each nuclear power plant in Spain. To facilitate the use of national resources and the development and assimilation of methodologies, analyses will be done in a phased fashion, with utilities wide participation. The CSN hopes that this Program will mean a major review of the safety of the plants and that the models developed for each plant can be the bases for future applications in many areas of NPP performance.

INTRODUCTION

The Spanish Nuclear Safety Regulatory Agency, Consejo de Seguridad Nuclear (Nuclear Safety Council, CSN), decided in 1983 to require that the utility operating the Santa María de Garoña nuclear power plant perform a specific Probabilistic Safety Analysis of the plant, for analyzing the overall safety and helping to decide about engineering modifications to be implemented at that plant, then with thirteen years of operating experience.

After this requirement, the CSN, in its second semiannual report to the Spanish Parliament of that year, included the intention on extending this type of safety analysis to the rest of Spanish NPPs. To go along this intended line, the CSN requested its technical staff to prepare a proposal on the needs, benefits and possibilities of doing these analyses to every nuclear plant in Spain.

The proposal, ellaborated as a program, was prepared and presented to the CSN after the preliminar results of the pioneer study in Garoña were obtained. The general improvement of the plant safety got from the analysis, the increasing utilization of probabilistic techniques for safety analysis all over the world and the future applications foreseen for the probabilistic modeling of each plant, were the bases for the proposing to implement and Integrated Program to carry out specific PSAs of each Spanish NPP.

The Proposed Integrated Program, due to its broad scope, was sent for comments to all the organizations in Spain with interest in the nuclear industry field. After the comments were received and analyzed, it appeared a fairly general support of the Integrated Program, with the only consideration of small differences on the way to implement it. The comments accepted were incorporated into the final proposal and the Integrated Program approved by the CSN in June 1986.

DESCRIPTION OF THE PROGRAM

The final "Integrated Program on Realization and Utilization of Probabilistic Safety Analysis in Spain" report is divided into two parts. The first part is an analysis of the needs, benefits and possibilities of such a program, as it was requested by the CSN. The second part is the Program itself, that is described in the following.

The Integrated Program consists of seven points, outlined to make a real integration of the activities needed to be able to arrive at the main goal and to satisfy the initial motivation of the Program, that is, to analyze in depth the safety of the Spanish NPPs and to have a logic-probabilistic model of each plant, to be used in future applications.

A brief description of the seven points is as follows:

- Probabilistic Safety Analysis Requirements. The general characteristics the requirements will have are defined, indicating their progressive scope and that there will be a time interval between the specific requirements to each plant. A schedule is included, as an initial work objective.

- Data Bank Development. The necessity of a data bank, where information about operational events and malfunctions of systems and components can be accumulated, is identified, to require that the Spanish utilities prepare a proposal for developing a computerized bank of this type.

- Rulemaking and Guidance. The convenience of including these requirements into a more general regulation frame is discussed. The need for issuing specific guides, regarding some aspects of the studies or some future applications, is also foreseen.

- Research Plans. There are need for research in several areas. A coordinated effort among concerned organizations is to be achieved.

- International Relations. Due to the continuous development of methodologies and applications, an adequate level of communication with international organizations and other nations has to be maintained for information exchange and integration into international work lines.

- Promotion of Technological Progress. From an Integrated Program of this kind and the nature of the probabilistic and reliability techniques, they can be deduced the benefits on the nuclear industry technological level in general and the possibility of extending the use of these techniques to other industrial areas in Spain.

- Recruiting and Training of Personnel. Increased human resources and training of personnel will be needed, at the CSN and the industry in general, to carry out all the activities of the Program.

Summarizing, the main features of the Program are as follows:

- The specific requirements to each NPP will be done in a time-phased fashion, to optimize the use of national resources.

- The initial level of the PSAs will be 1, as defined in NUREG/CR-2300, but a progressively increasing scope, within level 1, between requirements is visualized, to include more aspects. If a methodology for other levels is validated and a decision taken in that sense, it may be possible to start with higher levels from some of the requirements.

- Each PSA will be revised periodically and the revision made at the same scope of the latest PSA requirement.

- Personnel from the utilities staff shall take part of the teams performing the studies and personnel from the CSN technical staff or contractors will be assigned in parallel to the project, to make a continuous and interactive evaluation and get a final study review almost at the same time the study is presented to the CSN.

- The other points of the Program are aimed at providing the integration character and describing the supporting activities of such a Program. These activities are considered equally necessary and important to obtaine the benefitial results searched by the initial CSN concern. Maybe one of the most significant is the development of a data bank at plant specific and national levels, to accumulate information on operational events and system and component malfunctions, to be used for the reliability data base construction in PSA studies. This bank will have to be connected to an international bank to have more statistical significance since the beginning. It is also considered very significant the research on potential applications of the PSA models to improvements in several areas of the licensing, management and other aspects of NPP performance, for instance, to improvements in the so-called technical specifications.

PRESENT SITUATION

One year after the Program's approval by the CSN, activities have been done regarding all the points of the Integrated Program. According to these seven points, the activities achieved so far and results can be described as in the following:

- Probabilistic Safety Analysis Requirements.

The final report for the first version of the Garoña PSA is being issued after some improvements in several areas of the study have been made. The analysis was done following the IREP Procedures Guide methodology and has been the source of many design and procedures small changes for reducing in a considerable amount the core melt frequency. This pioneer study and its satisfying results was a major reason for the Integrated Program implementation.

The second PSA was required to the Almaraz NPP, a plant with two PWR units. A very general procedures guide, that of NUREG/CR-2815, Revision 1, was chosen, as a minimum, for the utility being free to decide about basic methodology to be used. The scope was enlarged to include fire risk and containment systems reliability analysis. The study is presently ongoing and is being realized by two Spanish engineering firms, with an U.S. company as consultant, and directed and managed directly by utility personnel. People from the utility Operations organization was again included in the team by CSN requirement. CSN staff is performing an interactive and continuous evaluation of the project, as was mentioned at the Program main features description.

The third PSA has also been required. The plant selected was Asco, another two-PWR plant. The requirement has been issued to the utility following the Program general lines, already described, and using also the NUREG/CR-2815, Revision 1, as the basic and minimum guide. The scope has again been enlarged according to the Program general philosophy. Another external event, internal floods this time, was chosen to be added to the scope required to the Almaraz PSA. The utility is preparing a proposal on the project organization and technical basic options of this study. After this proposal is approved by the CSN, the study itself will start. This process is the same for all the requirements.

Hence, they are in the completion stage or ongoing the first PSA version of five out of the eight units presently in operation.

- Data Bank Development.

The CSN required all the utilities to prepare a proposal on the development of a computerized data bank. This proposal was prepared by the joint Spanish utilities organization, UNESA, and evaluated and finally approved by the CSN. According to this project, two data banks, on operational events and on systems and components malfunctions, will be developed and implemented at each Spanish NPP and coordinated at national level, to be operative in 1989. The CSN will be evaluating this development proyect during these two years and will have access to the bank as an user. It is hoped that data from this bank can be used in the future revisions of the PSAs.

- Rulemaking and Guidance.

The regulatory framework is presently the individual requirements being done by the CSN to each utility. The need for a more general frame can be established in the future according to the experience being gained. Specific guides may be most likely issued for concrete applications of the models, for documentation or for project proposal presentations.

- Research Plans.

The CSN has initiated, in collaboration with a University, a research project on the use of PSA models for improvement of technical specifications. It is the intention of this project the ending on a training course about the techniques developed or assimilated during the project, for promoting the use of those techniques as a real application of PSAs. This work might also lead to the issue of a guide for potential users.

At international level, the reliability and risk analysis area has been included into a more general agreement between the CSN and the U.S. NRC on nuclear safety research. This agreement may give mutual benefits in the next future and help to the assimilation of methodologies in several areas.

Also at national level, the CSN has been consulted, by several Spanish organizations, about the definition and implementation of an overall national research program on risk analysis and on concrete research activities and focusing.

- International Relations.

CSN personnel is participating in working groups on risk and reliability that have been created in international organizations, like the IAEA and the CSNI. Relations are maintained also with other nations similar organizations for information exchange.

The CEC activities in nuclear safety have also been joined by the CSN, and Spanish organizations in general, during the last two years.

- Promotion of Technological Progress.

Other groups and organizations working in this type of analysis have been invited by the CSN to participate in workshops, meetings, surveys and other activities of the internatinal working groups where the CSN is the Spanish representative. Information about this work is normally distributed to concerned organizations.

CSN personnel have participated and advised on the arrangement of PSA training courses in Spain, in particular those prepared, by the Spanish research center CIEMAT, in collaboration with the U.S. DOE and the IAEA.

Participation has also been done in national-level meetings on the use and application of PSAs and related areas.

- Recruiting and Training of Personnel.

As can be obvious, the approval and implementation of this Integrated Program has created a great demand on PSA-trained personnel in Spain. This has obliged to elaborate training plans for future personnel. The CSN has followed this line and given several schollarships for training of personnel, either by means of courses, or by participation in specific development projects or tasks. This new personnel has to be needed in the next future to collaborate to the effort that the Integrated Program implementation is to cause.

ACKNOWLEDGMENTS

This paper has been commented with José I. Villadóniga. The latter, Rosa Morales and the author of this paper were the writers of the original Integrated Program proposal and the final and CSN-approved version.

It has also to be mentioned here the encouragement from the CSN Commissioner Eduardo González during the preparation and implementation of the Program.

REFERENCE

Programa Integrado de Realización y Utilización de los Análisis Probabilistas de Seguridad en España. Consejo de Seguridad Nuclear. Agosto, 1986.

APPLICATION OF PRA TO THE SAFETY SYSTEM DESIGN GUIDELINES OF STANDARD NUCLEAR
POWER PLANT IN KOREA

Koo-Woun Park, Sun-Koo Kang, Jae-In Shin, Sc.D.
Korea Power Engineering Company

Abstract

Korea has been developing a master program for the design of standard Nuclear Power
Plants (NPP) which will be a basic model for future Korea nuclear units. One of
the important programs is to establish Safety System Design Guidelines (SSDG), including major design considerations for the plant safety systems. The PRA technique
was applied as a way to the development of SSDGs.
An analytical methodology was developed to evaluate and select optimized design
alternatives resulting from the improvement on design vulnerability. Computer-aided,
Value Impact Analysis (VIA) was conducted for Decision-Analysis.
In this paper, procedures for developing SSDGs with the PRA technique were explained
step by step and some examples were also introduced.

1. Introduction

A set of Safety System Design Guideline (SSDG), providing a spectrum of basic deisgn
concepts of the plant safety systems, is one of the basic documents required for
designing a nuclear power plant.
Standard system configuration, design criteria, system interactions, evaluation
methods of design adequacy, and various design considerations are also included in
SSDGs to be utilized in design/engineering activities and decision making processes.
For preparation of SSDGs, experiences in construction, operation and maintenance
of NPPs, basic design concepts developed by utility and/or A/E companies, and
governing lincensing regulations, should be taken into consideration. A reference
plant has been selected and analyzed with the PRA technique to establish plant PRA
model followed by importance analysis for design adequacy evaluation. For inadequate
designs, several design alternatives were recommended based on the past experiences
to improved design vulnerabilities. A optimum design recommendation was then determined by the Value Impact Analysis (VIA). Results from these analyses were summarz-
ed as a part of SSDGs to help design engineers. In this paper, application methodology of the PRA technique, leading to the development of SSDGs, is described in
detail (Figure 1). Each procedure with its result is explained using examples.

2. Application

Development of Plant Analysis Model

NUREG/CR-2300, PRA Procedure Guide, was a basic reference for the development of
plant analysis model. To carry out Importance/Sensitivity Analysis with ease, the
SET/LET (Small Event Tree/Large Fault Tree) method was utilized. KNU 7&8, were
selected as a reference plant. PRA of the reference plant was performed with
generic data, giving rise to a plant analysis model. It turned out that loss of
off-site power (LOP) gives the highest contribution to the core melt frequencies.

Evaluation of Reference Design

Adequacy

Risk Reduction Worth (RRW) and Fussel-Vesely Improtance (F-V) were used to determine design adequecy of the reference plant. A computer program, WFIN code, was developed and linked to the plant analysis model. Adequate design features were selected as a part of SSDGs, while inadequate features categorized into design improvement items for the next step. Importance Analysis has shown that operator action is the most critical one, especially with respect to the off-site power recovery, followed by operations of Emergency Electric Power System (EEPS), Residual Heat Removal System (RHRS), Auxiliary Feed Water System (AFWS), and so on (Table 1). It is seen that design improvement is necessary for the Loss of Off-site Power.

Design merits of the reference plant are also identified as follows :

o Residual heat removal capability through the secondary system ;
   - Startup feedwater pump in addition to AFWS
   - Two PORVs per main steam line

o High reliability of NSCWS and CCWS
   - 2 x 100% pumps per train

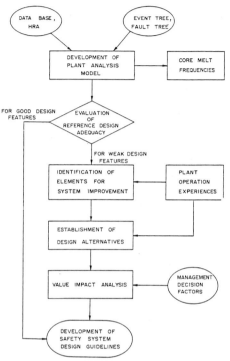

FIG. I   PRA APPLICATION FOR SSDG DEVELOPMENT

Table 1. Major results of plant importance analysis

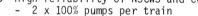

Item	RRW	F.V	remarks
o Operator error	3.125	0.64	
- Recovery from LOP	2.000	0.46	LOP related.
- Others	1.140	0.20	
o EEPS	2.000	0.46	LOP related.
o RHRS	1.282	0.22	
o AFWS	1.136	0.12	

Identification of Design Improvement Items/Design Alternatives

To investigate further on items requiring design improvement, operating and design
improvement experiences in the existing NPPs were examined. Plant Importance
Analysis revealed off-site power recovery and EEPS were two leading contributors
to the plant safety. EEPS, one of the two major contributors, was chosen as an
example to develop design alternatives. Two alternatives, additional D/G (100%
capacity) installation (to existing tow-100% capacity) and DC battery capacity
increase (withstanding 2.2 hr to 8.0 hr), were selected. System analysis and plant
analysis based on the plant analysis model with each design alternative were repeated. The resultant core melt frequency change is shown in Table 2. Core melt
frequency ratio for major Initiating Event (I.E) to the total core melt frequency
is depicted in Figure 2.

Table 2. CM frequency reduction for each Alternatives.

		Total CM	LOP	SBO	OTHER I.E
CASE I	BASE (Existing Design)	5.6E-5	4.5E-6	2.1E-5	3.1E-5
CASE II	Battery Capacity Increase	4.3E-5	4.5E-6	7.6E-6	3.1E-5
CASE III	D/G Addition	3.5E-5	1.4E-6	2.3E-6	3.1E-5

LOP : Loss of Off Site Power

SBO : Station Black Out

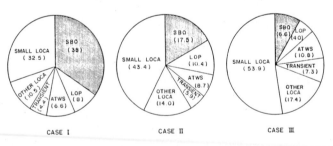

CASE I　　　　　CASE II　　　　　CASE III

FIG.2   CM CONTRIBUTION FOR EACH CASE

Value Impact Analysis

VIA was adopted for determination of optimum design alternatives. First, a computer
code, VIADUCT, was developed to incorporate construction and operation costs,
public risks, utility financial risk, discount and escalation rates, etc. with the

analysis. The analysis method and the computer code developed can be utilized as
an important decision making tool when designing a NPP. The VIA resulted in the
preference of battery capacity increase over additional D/G installation as shown
in Table 3.

Table 3. Results of Value-Impact Analysis

Alternative	Value/Impact Ratio		Improvement Probability	
	Mean	Variance	Source	Normal
Case II vs. Case I	8.20	24.7	98 %	99.4 %
Case III vs. Case I	0.553	0.107	9 %	8.5 %
Case III vs. Case II	0.214	0.020	—	—

* Improvement Probability of A vs. B ; probability that A is better than B.

   Source; Improvement probability from data generated by Monte Carlo Method

   Normal; Improvement probability from assumption that the PDF is a normal
                distribution function

Safety System Design Guideline

Examples of contents of SSDGs based on the above analysis are summarized as follows;

o Enhancement measures of off-site power reliability

o Enhancement measures of EEPS
   - DC battery capacity increase

o Improvement measures for residual heat removal capability
   - Utilization of a startup feedwater pump
   - Installation of 2 PORVs per main steam line

o System design improvement measures for operator error reduction
   - Automatic operation for long-term core cooling
   - Man-machine interface

o Operability/Maintainability Enhancement measure
   - Design simplification
   - Operation/Maintenance procedure standardization

o Optimum-design evaluation method
   - Application of computer-aided VIA methodology

3. Conclusions

The PRA/VIA methodology as a tool for the development of detailed procedures leading to establishing of the SSDGs for the plant safety improvement was explained.
In addition to the SSDG development, studies on determining system target unavailability, target core melt frequency, upper limit distribution for each I.E., etc.
with the PRA/VIA technique are also in progress.

To ensure higher confidence in the results from above explained methodology, uncertainty involved in the current PRA/VIA should be minimized. In KOPEC, further studies on how to reduce these uncertainties will be conducted in the near future.

References

1. Korea Power Engineering Company, 1985. Design Studies on the Standardization of Nuclear Power Plants, KOPEC/RR-02/85, Ministry of Science and Technology, Seoul, Korea.

2. Andrew, W.S., et al. 1983. Guidelines for Nuclear Power Plant Safety Issue Prioritization Information Development, NUREG/CR-2800, Pacific Northwest Laboratory, Richland, Washington.

3. McCormic, N. 1981. Reliability and Risk Analysis, Methods and Nuclear Power Applications, Academic Press, New York.

4. Science Application Inc. 1980, Value-Impact Analysis, EPRI-NP-1237, Electric Power Research Institute, Palo Alto, California.

5. U.S. NRC. 1983. PRA Procedures Guide : A Guide to the Performance of Probabilistic Risk Assessment for Nuclear Power Plants, NUREG/CR-2300, Washington, D.C.

6. Nuclear Safety Analysis Center, 1984, A Probabilistic Risk Assessment of Oconee Unit 3, NSAC/60, Palo Alto, California.

INVESTIGATION OF CURRENT AND FUTURE APPLICATION OF PROBABILISTIC METHODS FOR
THE SAFETY ASSESSMENT OF NUCLEAR POWER PLANTS*

Dr. M. Herttrich, G. Breiling
(BMU, Bonn, - BBR, Mannheim, Federal Republic of Germany)

Abstract

An investigation conducted by the Federal Ministery of Interior (FRG) addressed the current and future role of determinitic principles and probabilistic
methodes for the safety evaluation of nuclear power plants. The results of
this study are presented and further expplained by use of examples. Conclusions regarding future application of probabilistic safety analysis methods
are drawn and discussed in light of growing international experiences.

Introduction

The atomic law of 1959 /1/ states that a licence to construct and operate a
nuclear power plant in the Federal Republic of Germany may be granted only if,
among other prerequisits, the necessary precautions against injuries and damage are taken according the state of science and technology. The respective
safety requirements for design and licensing of NPPs have been codified in
mandatory safety criteria, ordinances, regulatory guides and guidelines. When
practical experience with design, lincensing, construction and operation of
NPPs has led to a common opinion of all parties involved, nuclear codes and
standards have been laid down, describing technical solutions and procedures
that represent an accepted standard. So the safety assessment of a NPP follows
a mainly deterministic approach. Safety decision making during design and licensing is essentially reduced to a verification of compliance with the pre-
scribed technical requirements.

Obviously, with this approach, the process of evaluating the necessary amount
of protection and the decision about technical requirements takes place inside
the rulemaking committees. Results of probabilistic safety analyses (PSA) of
nuclear power plants influence on the one hand the process of developing the
deterministic rules. On the other hand, the application of these methods in
the licensing process is considered as information supplementory to the
deterministic safety evaluation.

Objective of the present investigation was:

-    to describe and evaluate the role currently played by PSA within the
     mainly deterministic safety practices

---

*   Results of an investigation of the Federal Ministry of Interior (FRG)
     under contract SR 347, 1985:
     Untersuchung zur Anwendung probabilistischer Methoden für die
     Sicherheitsbeurteilung von Kernkraftwerken

–   to elaborate and demonstrate, how PSA – applications exceeding current
    practices can be used as an investigative tool for further technical
    improvements of NPP–safety

–   to assess, if a more explicite use of PSA as a communicative tool can
    help to improve discussions and decision making on actual safety issues
    between the different parties involved.

Methods of Safety Assessment

The deterministic approach as developed in the Federal Republic of Germany is
the base of a high safety standard that has gained world wide acknowledgement.
The rules and guidelines that define this standard address very basic design
requirements and specify a large variety of criteria to be met and procedural
guidelines to be followed (Table 1). These rules have e.g. led to a PWR design
that is known by the abreviation GPWR, a pressurized water reactor of German
standards, see Fig. 1 as a reference for system design.

Protection against external events requires outer containment

Systems under primary pressure must be contained in a
pressure containment

The pressure containment must be designed for large break
LOCA conditions

Meet requirements for emergency cooling under the assumption of
  1. Possible accident impact (like feeding the break etc.)
  2. One component out for repair
  3. One component fails on demand
  4. One reactor protection signal systematically failed

Design redundant subsystems non intermeshed, spatially separated
of each other, protect against flooding etc.

No credit shall be taken of operator actions during the first 30 min.
after initiation of an accident

Table 1: Examples for deterministic rules and guidelines

One example, typical of this German standard is the use of HP–injection pumps
with a shut off head below the primary system safety valve setpoint. The
underlying deterministically ruled principle is not to increase primary pressure above nominal values by means of safety injection, in a situation in
which the loss of coolant signal has been actuated. Another example is the
requirement to terminate steam production inside the reactor vessel during
emergency cooling after LB-LOCA situations. Both these deterministic requirements define in many aspects design specifics of PWR safety systems. They
exclude reliance on a containment cooling system as the heat sink for long
term emergency core cooling.

In consequence, GPWRs are not equipped with containment coolers as those found
in US-PWRs. This in turn puts more weight upon the emergency functions of the
steam generator. This example shows how single principles adopted to justify

specific deterministic design rules influence the safety design as a whole. The interest in a holistic concept of safety evaluation is therefore quite obvious. The justification of the overall safety system concept cannot be established by means of statistics of real accidents, so a different analytical approach - the PSA-approach - has been developed. Since the issue of the American Reactor Safety Study in 1975 PSA methods have considerable matured and are more and more used to provide an overall safety evaluation. The German Risk study phase A was published in 1980 , phase B is in progress.

As far as licensing decisions in the FRG are concerned, current regulations require probabilistic analyses to supplement the deterministic safety evaluation /2/. Beside the more general requirement of a "sufficiantly reliable" design /2,3/, probabilistic methods are basically considered as a means to assure a "balanced safety design" or to avoid a dominating influence of certain subsystems (power supplies, C & I) versus the unavailability of complete safety functions. As such, probabilistic methods are mainly used to demonstrate adequate reliability of safety functions and to identify weak points. In a more general sense the requirement of a balanced safety design will also assure that even for very different frequencies of initiating events a comparable

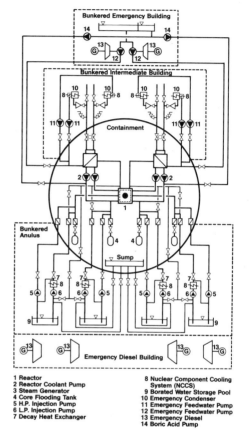

1 Reactor
2 Reactor Coolant Pump
3 Steam Generator
4 Core Flooding Tank
5 H.P. Injection Pump
6 L.P. Injection Pump
7 Decay Heat Exchanger

8 Nuclear Component Cooling System (NCCS)
9 Borated Water Storage Pool
10 Emergency Condenser
11 Emergency Feedwater Pump
12 Emergency Feedwater Pump
13 Emergency Diesel
14 Boric Acid Pump

GPWR Emergency System Design
(NPP Mülheim-Kärlich)

level of control and mitigation is achieved. This for instance has led to an emer- gency feedwater design appropriate for the more frequent loss of station power event as compared to the less frequent loss of coolant accident.

In compliance with these requirements, an applicant for a construction license in the FRG submits quite extensive reliability analyses to the licensing authority as part of the system documentation. These analyses address various accident initiators and quantitatively show the probability of failure for the required safety functions and other probabilistic measures. In general one can say that for the actual licensing procedures PSA-information of level 1 /4/ is available although a risk analysis is not required. For probabilistic measures of safety in general, no absolut quantitative requirement has been established although some have evolved out of actual practice.

The experience gained world wide with the application of probabilistic methods justifies an intensification of the role of probabilistic methods in the decision making process. Deterministic rules and guidelines define the applicable characteristics of system design and thereby induce a concept, whereas probabilistic methods constitute an investigation and evaluation tool. The effectiveness of these methods is e.g. illustrated by the insight gained with respect to the severity of the small break loss of coolant accidents when the US reactor safety study was published in 1975 or by safety improvements undertaken as a consequence of the German risk study /5,6/. These insights have - of course - influenced the updating of technical codes and standards. An overview about the positive experience gained with probabilistic analyses may be found in the many papers presented to the ANS/ENS Inernational Topical Meeting in San Frncisco /7/, which contains also a review of practices within OECD member states /8/. Among the many obvious advantages of such methods, the most important to be mentioned are

- methodical principles of the PSA-approach aim for complete covering of all possible events that can challenge the safety of the plant

- introduction of a quantitative measure of safety into the process of safety design and evaluation

- applicability to different types of nuclear plants or different design alternatives, including prototype plants as well as conventional

- allows to select optimal technical solutions by using the safer of competitive alternatives

Conclusion and Perspective

The conclusion to be drawn is summarized in table 2. While the suggestions given in item 2 and 4 address the more formal aspects of the use of probabilistic methods for the evaluation of plant safety, item 1 and 3 need some additional comments.

1. Define targets for the frequency of safety related events and conditional probabilities for control and mitigation of these events on the plant level and/or integral safety functions

2. Revise regulatory requirements to reflect probabilistic safety targets and applicable probabilistic methods, allow modification of deterministic requirements to optimize safety

3. Apply probabilistic methods to determine the reliability of safety functions of operating plants

4. Establish standards for applicable methods

Table 2: Major conclusions

Probabilistic safety analyses for operating or for new plants have been made a requirement in many countries. The modifications that evolved out of such practices underline the importance of such methods as a means to opmimise the already high safety standard of deterministically designed plants. Due to uncertainties of quantitative PSA-results, the application of safety goals has been a subject of great dispute in the past. Nevertheless, from the individual risk point of view, today's NPP ca be considered as acceptably safe. However without a quantification of safety by probabilistic methods the remaining uncertainty in the process of deterministic rulemaking is not smaller as can be seen by comparison of the different safety standards that are in use in different countries. While the deterministic approach as practiced in the Federal Republik of Germany assures an acceptable fundamental safety level, PSA can be used for verification and optimization beyond this level. PSA-application is a tool to verfy that the intented safety level is achieved and maintained during the whole plant life. Furthermore they can be used to elucidate the continual efforts of all parties involved to improve the safety performance even beyond acceptable limits.

From a nuclear industry point of view the target for a quantitative safety standard should be sufficiently high, that among the nuclear power plants operating world wide no severe core degradation accident should be expected for the rest of their designed life span with a sufficiantly high level of confidence. The possible impact of such accidents across whole continents has been demonstrated in the course of the Tschernobyl accident. With about 400 plants operating todate and an estimated remaining life span of, for example, 25 years a target for the core melt frequency of less than $5 \cdot 10^{-6}/a$ per plant should be aimed for in order to reduce the probability for not meeting the above stated goal below 5 %. This number is not easily achieved for currently operating plants. The average for 5 US plants is about 10 times larger /9/, what reduces the level of confidence in the above calculation to a 50/50 chance. This result quite obviously shows the need for further efforts to improve nuclear safety on an international scale.

References

/1/ Atomgesetz (FAG), Bundesanzeiger, 23.12.1959

/2/ Sicherheitskriterien für Kernkraftwerke, BMI, 21.10.1977

/3/ RSK-Leitlinien für Druckwasserreaktoren, GRS/RSK, 14.10.1981

/4/ PRA-Procedures Guide, NUREG/CR-2300

/5/ Heuser, Kraut:
     "Anwendung probabilistischer Methoden im atomrechtlichen
     Genehmigungsverfahren", GRS, 1985

/6/ Vetterkind, Schütte:
     "Design Optimization Case Study PWR Biblis",
     IAEA-Seminar, Oldbury UK, 13.9.1985

/7/ EPRI-NP-3912-SR, Februar 1985

/8/ Herttrich, Köberlein, Schwager, Andrews:
     "Applying the Results of Probabilistic Safety Analyses of Nuclear Power
     Plants: A Survey of Experience", see /7/ for reference

/9/ Nuc. Engineering Int., April 1987

THE USES OF PROBABILISTIC SAFETY ANALYSES IN THE LICENSING AND REGU-
LATION OF FINNISH NUCLEAR POWER PLANTS

Reino Virolainen
(Finnish Centre for Radiation and Nuclear Safety (STUK), P.O. Box
268, Kalevankatu 44, 00101 Helsinki, Finland)

Keywords   Deterministic criteria, Reliability analysis, PSA,
                      Probabilistic Safety Criteria (PSC), Safety func-
                      tions, Licensing of NPPs

1   Introduction

The formal licensing process of Finnish nuclear power plants has
been based on deterministic rules and criteria, such as specific
accidents, single failure criterion, diversity and redundancy. However, the probabilistic safety assessment has played a supporting
role in the licensing. The reliability analyses at the system
level has provided an independent review of the nuclear power plant
systems. Besides the system reliability analyses, a so-called
mini-PRA up to level 2 dealing with large break LOCA was performed
for Loviisa 1 unit in 1973-1975. At the end of 1984, the Finnish
licensing authority required the utilities to perform PSA studies
up to level 2 for the operating plants. The level 1 parts of the
studies are expected to be ready by the end of 1987.

With respect to possible new Finnish nuclear power plants, the PSA
approach will play, along with the deterministic criteria, an essential part in the licensing process. However, the PSA does not replace
the so-called deterministic safety analyses but both methods are
used side by side so that they complement each other.

The PSA is to be used in dealing with low-probability events, involving an unacceptable performance of safety systems or containment. Accordingly, the PSA is closely connected with the design,
construction and operating phases of NPPs.

To ensure sufficient safety of new plants, the numerical safety standards have been included in the regulatory guide. However, no fixed
acceptance standard is set forth in terms of the public risk or the
probability of a core damage. Instead, the licensing authority sets
forth numerical reliability objectives for the most important safety
functions, the unreliabilities of which shall remain below the set
limits.

2   PSA applications in the licensing of the operating plants

A considerable number of reliability analyses, over 20 altogether,
was performed during the construction phases of the Loviisa nuclear
power plant units from 1972 to 1980.

The failure rates used in the analyses of the Loviisa units during the construction phase were rather on the conservative side in comparison with the data used for WASH-1400.

Assembling of plant-specific data for the Loviisa units was organized after starting the commercial operation, and some of the most important systems have been re-analyzed as soon as the assembling of the plant-specific data was accomplished.

		Generic data	Plant specific data
Emergency make-up system	Injection phase	4×10^{-5}	2×10^{-4}
Emergency feed water system given loss of off-site power	Start	2×10^{-4}	2×10^{-3}

In addition to the reliability analyses at the system level, a probabilistic safety assessment called "mini-PRA" was performed for Loviisa 1 in 1973-1975. Only one initiating event, the large-break LOCA, was analyzed. The accident sequences leading to the damage of the reactor core were resolved utilizing the results of the system reliability analyses. The behaviour of the containment and the amount of radionuclide releases into the environment was assessed and categorized with the techniques used in WASH-1400.

The study showed that the accident sequence including the failure of the nuclear intermediate cooling system and the over-pressurization of the containment are the greatest contributing factors of the risk.

The reliability data used for the analyses of the Olkiluoto BWR plant are substantially similar to those used in the analyses of the Loviisa plant.

The results of these studies are presented below:

System	Unreliability
Safety/relief valve system	2×10^{-4}
Normal shut-down cooling system	3×10^{-3}
Auxiliary feed water system	3×10^{-4}
Core spray system	1.5×10^{-4}
Hydraulic scram system	10^{-7}

3 Analyses used in the licensing and regulation of new nuclear power plants

A Guide on the use of PSA in the licensing and regulation of NPPs has been prepared by the Finnish licensing authority, and it is intended to be used in connection with new plants.

The guide /1/ shows how probabilistic safety analyses are used in the regulation of the design, construction and operation of light water reactor plants in order to ensure that the safety functions of the plant are carried out reliably enough.

The probabilistic analyses do not replace the so-called deterministic safety analyses but both methods are used side by side to complement each other in the assessment of the plant safety. The deterministic analyses are used to demonstrate that the systems and components fulfil the design objectives set for them. The assumptions of the analyses on the loading of components, operating parameteres of systems, and faults impairing the performance of systems are determined in the design requirements. Because the deterministic analyses lack a quantitative assessment of the risks, they give only limited information on the total risk of the plant or the balance of the plant design. The deterministic analyses are dealt with in a different Guide YVL.

3.1 Mini-PSA

A prerequisite set by the authorities for the issuance of the construction permit is that a so-called mini-PSA has been completed.

It comprises the analyses relating to PSA Level 1. The Mini-PSA is based on the design concept from the preliminary design phase of the power plant and only on the most important initiating events.

The purpose of the mini-PSA is to give an idea of and reveal the interconnections and interactions between various systems and supporting systems, as well as the reasons for common failures and weak points at the function, system and redundancy levels. In achieving this purpose, the qualitative PSA methods play an essential role.

The calculations made in connection with the mini-PSA are not intended for showing that the probabilistic objectives of safety functions, set forth in the guide, are met. Above all, the purpose is to find out, which safety-related factors affect the crucial accident sequences and safety functions and, by means of a good design, to ensure that the probability of failure of the most important safety functions will even during operation remain below the objectives.

3.2 PSA

After the contruction permit has been granted, a PSA study of level 1 is commenced, including the by-pass chains of the containment. The safety analysis must be supplemented with a study of level 2 before the operating license can be issued.

Only the events that are initiated by internal faults of the plant are regarded as initiating events, with the exception of the loss of off-site power. Fires and floods inside the plant are also taken into account. Table 1 gives an outline of the timing of the PSA during the design, construction and commissioning of a NPP.

3.3 Updating PSA

The licensing authority (STUK) requires the power company to update the PSA during the design and construction phases always if the design concept is changed. In addition, it is required that the operators of the plant continuously supplement, follow, analyse and maintain the data base on operating experience and safety-related systems, and update the PSA to correspond with the operating experience, as far as substantial deviations from the earlier data base are detected during operation.

The purpose of the PSA presented in the Guide is not only to be a disposable analysis tied to the design and construction phases, but it is also meant to provide a tool for controlling and regulating the safety of a nuclear power plant all through its service life. It is a tool for both the plant management and the regulatory authority, and it helps the decision-makers to approach safety problems in an objective way.

Table 1 Timing of the PSA at the design, construction and commissioning phases

Decision in principle on the construction of a nuclear power plant

     Mini-PSA started

Application for a construction permit

     Mini-PSA completed and submitted to STUK for review

Construction permit

     PSA Level 1 and concise Level 2 started
     Review of PSA Level 1 and concise Level 2 started in STUK

     Supplementation of PSA Level 2 started

Application for an operating license

     Review of PSA Level 1 and concise Level 2 finished in STUK
     The power company provides STUK with the supplemented PSA
     Level 2
     Review of PSA Level 2 finished in STUK
     Conclusions

Operating license (inspections before the loading permit)

Commercial operation

     Assessment of an operating plant.

4 Safety analyses in the licensing and regulatory use

STUK uses the PSA in licensing for identifying the risks relating to the structural features, operation and maintenance and administration of the plant.

Before granting an operating license, STUK prepares a safety assessment, which includes at least the following reviews in regard to PSA:

-        Objectives, assumptions, methods

- Grouping of initiating events and an estimate of their
  frequency
- Reliability analyses at safety function level
- Accident sequences and their treatment
- Treatment of dependences, common-cause faults, human actions
- Treatment and utilization of the data base
- Uncertainty analyses
- Results and their interpretation
- Comparison with other PSA's
- Deficiencies in safety and their significance and prioritiz-
  ation, as well as their comparison with the results of
  deterministic analyses.

No fixed acceptance standard is set forth for the probability of a
core damage associated with the accident sequences. The estimated
probability is compared with the known probabilities of a core damage
at other nuclear power plants, and the probabilites associated with
the various accident sequences are compared with each other. These
comparisons give some insights into considerations whether there
is a need to take any measures to diminish the probability of a
core damage or the probability of releases into the environment.

One prerequisite for an operating license is that the unreliability
of the most important safety functions is below the numerical design
objectives set forth by STUK (section 4.1 below).

STUK also controls that the power company maintains an acceptable
standard of safety during operation. When necessary, the power
company must be able to demonstrate this by means of PSA methods.

4.1   Numerical design objectives for the reliability of safety
functions

To ensure the high reliability of the most important safety functions, STUK requires that their unreliability be below the following
design objectives, at least with a confidence of 90 %

Safety function	Probability of failure/requirement
Making the reactor subcritical	10^{-5}
Isolation of the containment (includes pipelines that are part of the reactor coolant system or directly connected to the open space inside the containment and penetrate the containment)	10^{-3}
Supply of feed water when the off-site power is lost or the main feed water system has failed (all loops)	10^{-4}
Operation of emergency core	

cooling, including long-term
recirculation, in the case of
a small reactor coolant leak 10^{-4}

Rapid reactor pressure reduction
and long-term cooling of the
condensation pool inside the
containment (BWR) 10^{-4}

The probability of failure for these safety functions is calculated
using a data base, which contains analyzed data on the operating
experiences from similar plants. If such data base is not available,
a generic data base is utilized. To determine the confidence limits
for the reliability data one can either use the Bayesian method or
classical methods.

Any dependencies between systems and components affecting reliability
are included in the analysis.

4.2   Utilization of the results of PSA

To avoid severe reactor accidents and to mitigate their consequences,
the results of PSA shall be utilized in the following matters relating to the training of the operating personnel and to the operation
of the plant.

-        The operating personnel shall familiarize themselves with
         severe accidents by means of the scenarios found and de-
         scribed by PSA.

-        The licensee must prepare instructions for preventing
         severe reactor accidents and for mitigating their conse-
         quences. If there exist some alternative actions, these
         shall also be included.

-        Simulator models must be developed and applied to those
         accident sequences that are important due to their probabil-
         ities and releases into the environment.

Bibliography

1.   Guide YVL 2.8, Probabilistic Safety Analysis in the Licen-
         sing and Regulation of Nuclear Power Plants. Finnish Centre
         for Radiation and Nuclear Safety, 1987

2.   Guide YVL 2.7 Failure criteria for the design of a light-
         water reactor. Finnish Centre for Radiation and Nuclear
         Safety, 1973

SAFETY PHILOSOPHY AND THE ROLE OF PRA IN LICENSING NPPs

Shinaishin M.A., and Hammad F.H.
(Atomic Energy Authority, NRSC, Cairo, Egypt)

Abstract

An incentive to this work is to find a guidance in decision making on whether - and what - to consider as Probabilistic Risk Assessment (PRA) criteria in establishing our safety philosophy for NPPs. The objective is, thus, two folds. First to investigate proposed scope and extent of implementation of probabilistic safety criteria and applications in licensing NPPs in various countries allover the world; and Second to propose, in view of these investigations, reference guidelines for admissible risk, and frequencies of plant conditions.

1. Introduction

The aim of this work is to form a consensus of the prevailing probabilistic safety principles used in licensing Nuclear Power Plants (NPPs) allover the world; and to come up with a proposal for the guidelines to be applied in Egypt.

2. Evolvement of PRA in Licensing NPPs

In this section we investigate the scope of practice, as well as the probabilistic safety criteria and principles in use or in prospect, in the safety assessment of NPPs in various countries of the world [1-18]. However, due to space limitations presentation shall be consize, and emphasis shall be put on the final findings of - and on cross comparisons made in - that investigation.

In this respect, it was found that actual application of PRAs of varying scope extends from specific safety system reliability analysis as in France and in Spain, to complete PSA as in Sweden and Italy, and to full-scope (Level-3) PRAs in USA and the FRG, in addition to Sizewell PRA in UK.

In most countries PRA criteria have not replaced but supplement
existing deterministic criteria; however, in a country such as
UK probabilistic criteria complement (not supplement) deterministic engineering principles which have been established as a
result of experience; and in a country like Canada probabilistic
criteria are a head of the deterministic.

Reliability analysis of safety systems have already become part
of the nuclear licensing process. They include system design
comparisons and optimization; as well as establishment of testing and maintenance strategies including identification of
admissible duration of downtimes, as in France, FRG, and UK.

Safety systems unavailability target lies in the range $10^{-4}-10^{-3}$
per demand, as in the FRG, Canada, and UK, complemented by a
common cause failure target which should be in the range $10^{-5}-10^{-3}$,
as in UK. In a country like France reliability targets aims,
also, at the fulfillment of specific safety functions and emergency procedures.

The majority of countries, e.g. USA, France, FRG, Canada, UK,
Italy, Japan, and Switzerland, have established plant conditions'
classification scheme tied to event frequency ranges and off-site
max. limits, or reference guidelines, for individual whole body
(or thyroid) doses. In addition, a country like Canada has specified max. population (integrated) dose limits. Also, in countries such as Canada and UK a complementary criteria for accident
conditions is to keep the release of radioactivity from accidents
which might occur within the life time of a NPP well below those
levels of release which would be acceptable for the plant normal
operation. An overview of such schemes shows, however, that
there are differences in classification frequency ranges and dose
limits.

Although differ in values (and implications) core melt frequency,
acceptable release frequency, or core coolability targets have,
also, been established in most of the countries; USA 10^{-4},
France $\leq 10^{-6}$, Canada $< 10^{-5}$, UK 10^{-6}, Japan $< 10^{-6}$, Italy
$10^{-6}-10^{-5}$. A subsidiary criterion to this is that the frequency
of occurrence of any one sequence of events leading to core melt,
unacceptable release, or to exceeding core coolability target
should be $\leq 10^{-6}$ per year in USA, $10^{-7}-10^{-6}$ in Italy, and $< 10^{-7}$
in the others. In addition some countries, e.g. Italy and France,
have the view that a conditional containment performance target
should also be established, this target is $10^{-2}-10^{-1}$ in Italy.

As regards quantitative risk targets, a prelevant opinion shared
by countries such as France, Japan, Finland, and Switzerland

holds that at present it may not be desirable to develop such
safety goals. In other countries emphasis is put on limitation
of individual risk, e.g. USA, UK, FRG, and Argentine. An Individual Risk target of 10^{-6} fatality per year per person in USA and
the FRG, and of $\sim 10^{-7}$ fatality per sequence per year in UK and
Argentine is seeked. This target corresponds to 0.1% of the
total risk from other sources in USA, and to 1% of the total risk
in the FRG.

Societal risk targets for the public in the vicinity of a NPP has
not yet been established except in : USA at less than 0.1% of the
total risk to the population, within 1 mile of the NPP site boundary for prompt fatality, and within 50 miles for cancer fatalities; in Sweden at 5 man-SV/year per 1000 MWe from installed nuclear power; and in Canada as indicated above.

Cost-benefit guidelines, on the other hand, are not established
any where except in USA, at 100 US dollars per MSV averted; but
it is not clear how could this be applied to early fatality risk.

Cumulative frequency - risk or - dose criteria curves are proposed in USA, FRG, Canada, UK, and in Netherland, with the purpose
of restricting the total risk, but are not enforced.

Finally, it is to be mentioned that, consideration is given to
Beyond Design Basis Accidents (BDBAs) in Environmental Impact
Statement as in USA, and Emergency Plans based on BDBAs have been
established as in USA and in the FRG (where leeward areas defined
by isodose lines are identified), and established to some extent
(considering the S3 source term) in France.

3. Probabilistic Principles in the Safety Philosophy of NPPs in
Egypt

In this section emphasis is put on suggested risk and other probabilistic criteria for prospective NPPs in Egypt within the framework of an overall safety philosophy which is based on deterministic as well as probabilistic principles.

In view of the findings of the previous section, risk criteria
are established in four areas as follows:

o Radiological societal risk to life and health from a NPP operation (normal operation and accidents) shall be As Low As Reasonably Achievable (ALARA) taking into account economical and social
factors. Acceptable criterion would be that NPPs' risk to the
public shall be comparable to or less than the risk of generating

electricity by viable competing technologies in the vendor country. (The reasoning behind such a criterion is to be guided by international limits in the nuclear industry.)

o Increase in Individual Risk from radiological exposure shall not exceed 0.1% of the fatality risk to which an average member of the public is exposed in his daily life. (The reasoning for setting the criterion to 0.1% and not to 1% as in the European countries is that we feel that the industrial risk in Egypt is an order of magnitude higher than in those countries.) International guidelines for average individual radiological fatality risk per reactor year are as follows : ICRP limit 10^{-5}, USA 2.5×10^{-6}, FRG 10^{-6}, UK 3×10^{-7}, Denmark 10^{-8}-10^{-7} fatality per year.

o Core Melt Frequency shall be kept as low as possible. Acceptable frequency target is 10^{-6} per reactor year from all sequences.

o Unavailability of a safety system shall be maintained at acceptable level consistent with the core melt frequency target. International guidelines are 10^{-4}-10^{-3}.

Criteria for acceptable frequency of occurrence per reactor year for the various categories of a nuclear power unit conditions and the accompaning acceptable individual whole body dose limits are shown in Table (1).

Table (1), Accident Categorization and Radiological Dose Limits 2,3-5,10,12

Plant Condition	Category	Reference Frequency of Occurrence per Reactor Year	Reference whole-Body Dose Limit	International Guide-lines for Acceptable Ref.Whole Body Dose Limits					
				USA	FRANCE	FRG	UK	JAPAN	SWITZER LAND
Normal Operation &	1		Less Than	$3/5 \times 10^{-5}$ gas-uous	site by site	Below 3×10^{4}		5×10^{5}	
Operational,Transients			Authorized Limit	and Liquid Effluent					
Abnormal Occurrences	II	10^{-1}- 10^{-2}	Authorized Limit		site by site	3×10^{-4}	$5/3 \times 10^{-3}$		2×10^{-4}
Improbable Accidents	III	10^{-2}- 10^{-4}	Below 5×10^{-3}		Below 5×10^{2}	Below 0.05	5×10^{-3}	Below 5×10	1×10^{2}
Design-Basis Accidents	IV	10^{-4} - 10^{-6}	Below 0.1	0.25	Below 0.15	0.05	0.1	Below 0.05	0.1
Beyond Design Basis Accident	V	Below 10^{-6}	Below 0.25		Above 0.15	Above 0.05	Above 0.1	Below 0.25	

* All Doses Except those for Category- I are in SV/event, Doses for Category-I are in SV/year.

In site selection those characteristics of the site that have bearing upon safety consideration shall be taken into account and weighed by their consequences including environmental impacts. The consequences of any single postulated event or a combination of random events having an estimated probability of occurrence less than 10^{-7} per reactor year need not be considered in the design.

The proposed philosophy to achieving safety of NPPs follows basically the consensus of placing most emphasis on accident prevention. However, if inspite of that an accident had occurred, means shall be readily available for : rapid and reliable shutdown of the reactor and for maintaining it in a safe shutdown for as long as it is necessary; for core cooling and residual heat removal to a reliable and effective ultimate heat sink; and for limiting the potential for the release of radioactive materials from the core, and from fuel storage and nuclear waste systems. If the gravity of the accident exceeds what has been designed for, an ultimate level of defence shall still be provided to cope with such accidents. At that level so-called ultimate procedures shall be available for the operator to manage the accident, and to control the release of radioactive materials into the environment to a level compatible with practically feasible off-site emergency plan, which further reduces the radiological risk to the public.

Issues of particular concern in Egypt which stem from being an importing country, and from our particular environment and national grid reliability should be identified.

Lessons learned from operational experience and in particular as a consequence of TMI-2 and Chernobyl-4 accidents should be fully comprehended and accounted for in plant design and operation.

Finally, it remains to point out that, although safety analysis shall basically follow a deterministic approach, probabilistic analysis shall be used as a support in providing a means for : determining the probability of occurrence of an accident or an event, and its consequencial risk, assisting in establishing the design bases for the plant, as well as for assessing comparative performance of safety systems on common bases, and for revealing possible weaknesses.

4. References

1. IAEA-TECDOC-308, "Survey of Probabilistic Methods in Safety and Risk Assessment for Nuclear Power Plant Licensing", a Technical Document Issued by the IAEA, Vienna, 1984.

2. Commission of the European Communities, "Status Report on Safety Goals/Objectives," Directorate General for Science, Research and Development Joint Research Centre, Brussels, May 1983.

3. W.F. Vink, "Quantitative Safety Objectives and Criteria, Liaison with Deterministic Safety Approaches," Commission of

661

the European Communities, Belgium, PRA-Training Course at ISPRA to NRSC Staff Members, Mar. 1986.

4. A. Birkhofer, H.R. Denton, K. Sate, and P.Y. Tanguy, "The Approaches to Reactor Safety and Their Rationale," SPERRFRIST bis 16, April 1985.

5. D.J. Higson, "Nuclear Reactor Safety Goals and Assessment Principles," Nucl. Safety, Vol. 26, No. 1, pp. 1-13, Jan-Feb. 1985.

6. L. Soffer, "Status Report-Role of PRA in Regulatory Policy in the U.S.," IAEA-ITC in PRA Methods in Safety Analysis for NPPs, ANL, USA, Oct. 1983.

7. W.E. Vesely, "Safety Goals," IAEA-ITC in PRA Methods in Safety Analysis for NPPs, ANL, USA, Oct. 1983.

8. USNRC, "Safety Goals for Nuclear Power Plants : A Discussion Paper," NUREG-0880, Feb. 1982.

9. A.L'Homme, and J. Pelce, "French Regulatory Requirements Concerning Severe Accidents in PWRs and Associated Research Programme," CEA/IPSN, B.P. No. 6-92260, Fontenay Aux Roses, France, Private Communications.

10. A. Kraut, "Applications of SRA and PRA in the FRG," IAEA-ITC in PRA Methods in Safety Analysis for NPPs, ANL, USA, Oct. 1983.

11. AECB-ACNS-4, "Recommended General Safety Requirements for Nuclear Power Plants," INFO-0116, June 1983.

12. R.D. Anthony, "Nuclear Safety Philosophy in the United Kingdom," Nucl. Safety, Vol. 27, No. 4, pp. 443-456, Oct.-Dec. 1986.

13. M.R. Hayns, "Application of SRA and PRA in the United Kingdom," IAEA-ITC in PRA Methods in Safety Analysis for NPPs, ANL, USA, Sept. 1983.

14. OECD-NEA, "The Use of PRA in the Italian Regulatory Process," Steering Committee for Nuclear Energy, Committee on the Safety of Nuclear Installations, Sub-Committee on Licensing, SIN DOC (83), Paris, June 1983.

15. G. Naschi, "Nuclear Safety in Italy," Italian Commission for Nuclear and Alternative Energy Sources, Private Communications.

16. B. Pershagen, and R. Nilson, "Nuclear Safety in Sweden, Policy and Practice," Nucl. Safety, Vol. 25, No. 1, pp. 1-18, Jan.-Feb. 1984.

17. A. Alonso, "The Application of SRA in Spain," IAEA-ITC in PRA Methods in Safety Analysis for NPPs, ANL, USA, Sept. 1983.

18. A.J. Gonzalez, "The Regulatory Use of Probabilistic Safety Analysis in Argentina," NUREG/CP-0027, 1983.

STATE OF THE ART OF PROBABILISTIC SAFETY ANALYSIS (PSA) IN THE FRG,

AND PRINCIPLES OF A PSA-GUIDELINE

Hans-Peter Balfanz
TÜV - Technischer Überwachungs-Verein Norddeutschland e.V.
Hamburg
Federal Republic of Germany

Contents:

Introduction

State of the art of PSA in the FRG:

During the past 15 years of licensing procedures for NPP the use of PSA for evaluating nuclear safety systems has steadily in-creased.
The extent and the depth of PSA appear from the spectrum and the types of analyses drawn up during licensing procedures.Also shown are examples on how to find representative accident sequences that will help reduce the extent of an analysis.

Motivation for a PSA-guideline:
The acceptability of using PSA for varifying the adequacy of nu-clear safety concept depends - apart from on adequate probability data - on a clear understanding of the methods used and their ad-vantages and limitations.

Because of our national approach towards a high standard of PSA - a striving pursued internationally as well - the creation of a PSA guideline for narrower analysis justification and its accept-ability appears adequate and recommendable.   It would, moreover, contribute to the use of uniform analyses as a working tool.

The principles of PSA methodology to be used as a guideline will be treated in this document;they are based on our own experience, which will be recorded here.

Due to the limitedness of this paper, not contained in same are the aspects of probability data and their uncertainties, the eval uations of analysis results (safety goals or relative judgement), nor reliability assurance at long term plant operation (used as a "living PSA"); the author's experience on these aspects appears under /1,2/.

1. State of the art of PSA for NPP in the FRG

1.1 Survey of PSA performed during NPP licensing procedures

Probability analyses of NPP safety systems have been used since more than 15 years now, mainly to support the evaluation of safety system designs for licensing procedure purposes of NPPs.

The first detailed fault tree analyses were set up for
- emergency core cooling systems
- reactor shut-down systems

and were mostly restricted to large LOCA. They were based on the safety design philosophy of a maximally considerable acci dent (MCA) (Table 1).

The location areas of the plants are shown in Fig.1.

Along parallel lines with the development of detailed safety analyses, PRA and plant experience grew the spectrum of PSA. The PSA established during licensing procedures for the modern German PWR at Brokdorf (KBR), Grohnde (KWG) and Philippsburg (KKP-2) are shown here as an example of the use of PSA in the FRG (Table 2).

As a result of the definitions made of different accidents, additional safety functions could be analysed and evaluated by the probability methods of:
- emergency core cooling, required through
  . large LOCA
  . medium LOCA
  . small LOCA

- decay heat removal systems of the secondary cooling loop, required through
  . small LOCA
  . emergency power case
  . external events
  . steam generator tube leaks

- containment isolation system, required through large LOCA

- primary circuits isolation system.

Also the functions of the cooling system for fuel element storage pools are analysed by consideration of relevant incidents and accidents (Table 3).

Based on PSA results, the surveillance test intervals of each analysed system and component function, important for limiting undetected unavailabilities of the systems and components were optimized and taken over to the plants' operation manuals (Table 4).

Similar PSA-extensions were made for BWR's.

Based on the experience with these PSA studies, the German manufacturer KWU developed a so called Reliability Handbook for the new PWR (Konvoi plants) GKN-2, KKE and KKI-2. It contains detailed analyses on safety systems in respect of
  - small LOCA
  - emergency power cases
These events are called "reference events" because of their
- relatively high frequency, and
- because these events require the largest number of safety
  system functions.

The analyses referred to above may be used in a more simplified way for assessing other system functions related with other events.

1.2 German nuclear standards' requirements on the reliability of safety systems

In several German Standards, reliability requirements of safety systems are mostly formulated by qualitative statements like - sufficiently reliable -.

The most important probabilistic requirement is contained in the NPP Safety Criteria of the Federal Ministry of the Interior /3/, here recorded in a shortened form:

1. Incidents shall be avoided with sufficient reliability and, in addition,

2. Safety features shall with sufficient reliability control incidents.

These two requirements have to be met so as to adequately balance the safety concept, and probabilistic methods shall as much as possible be used in accordance with the current state of the art.

In order to meet these requirements, the important safety functions of most PWR and BWR in the FRG are asessed as described in the above chapter.

2. PSA-guideline for NPP: Principles and suggestions

2.1 Motivation and tasks of PSA

Basically, there are two types of PSA application:
a) Probabilistic assessment of Plant Safety Systems (PSA)
b) Evaluation of mitigation measures beyond design accidents

a) Probabilstic assessment of Plant Safety Systems (PSA):

Presently, the safety concept of NPPs is based on the deterministic principles, such as:
- safety features to prevent or control incidents and accidents
- reactor containment as a passive barrier against radioactivity releases
- redundant and diverse safety systems for high system reliability.

These safety principles are steadily being improved and made precise by the increase of conventional safety analyses and systematic PSAs, supported by plant-operational experience. With the analytical tool of PSA, plant safety standards could be better balanced, thus preventing over- or underdesigning of safety features.

The merit of a plant-specific PSA exists in its offering a different analytical tool for evaluating a safety concept, based on deterministic principles.
Furthermore, PSA delivers explicit results on the actual safety standard of a plant.

Up to now, PSA is developed for evaluating all system safety functions in respect of the spectrum of possible incidents and accidents that result in sequences of a core melt accident. This level of analysis is called a level-1 analysis of PRA.

The broad application of level 1-PSA in national and international fields /4/ indeed justifies precision of the PSA-tool in a guideline.
Setting up such a guideline corresponds with German safety standards, considering the multiple statements on the highly reliable safety system being required.

For plants already in operation, such PSA guidelines would find application in
- reevaluating and optimizing surveillance test procedures and safety related operational procedures;
- evaluating desired plant and system modifications and for optimizing backfitting measures;
- evaluating actual operational experience, e.g. increase of component failure rates.
For this type of application, reliability analyses already available of safety systems can then be used for similar systems of other plants also. This has been practised already,

for example, for new PWRs in conjunction with the Reliability Handbook, as well as for the new reactor protection system
as mentioned in Section 1.2. The purpose of that application
is the one of standarizing safety standards of different
plants by this technique.

b) Evaluation of mitigation measures for beyond-design-accidents

Probabilistic methods can also be used for optimizing mitigation measures for beyond-design-accidents.
Dominant and representantive accident sequences can be selected on a basis of a level 1-analysis.Simple measures of accident mitigation can be found by a detailed event tree analy-
is, e.g. by indicating time intervals of core heat up and by
the possibility of activating additional system capacity.

2.2 Aspects of the methodology of safety analyses

Probabilistic analyses of safety-important systems are used
on very different system levels, ranging from an electronic
device up to hypothetic accidents.
The huge number of components and systems in an NPP makes a
complete analysing of all potential component failure combinations impossible.
The widely known deductive analytical method used in the
fault tree analysis brings a reduction of components to be
analysed. The main event undesired on the level 1-analysis is
a core melt accident. It is the task of the analysis to find
all causes (possible failure modes) which may lead to that
accident.
The logic structure of this event level is shown in a simplified drawing for the PWR (Fig.2), indicating both analytical
forms:
- deductive analysis (Fault Tree Analysis FTA)
- inductive analysis (Failure Mode & Effect Analysis FMEA and
  Event Tree Analysis ETA).

The American Procedure Guide /5/ uses the "Master Logic Diagram" (Fig.3) for discussing the spectrum to be analysed and
to help find and select the important accident sequences.

The graphic presentation of the logic of accident sequences
in Fig.2 also indicates the safety-importance of individual
components in connection with the sequences. For example, the
containment isolation valves (CIV 1,2) have safety functions
of different importance, one for LOCA and one for a core melt
accident .

The isolation valves (PIV 1,2) installed between the primary
system and the low pressure injection system (outside the containment) are marked as highly important because of the possibility of core melt and containment bypass accidents (Interfacing System LOCA).
Furthermore, Fig.2 shows that on failing to close the isola-
lation valve (PRIV) in the discharge line of pressure relieve
valve PRV, a small LOCA is imminent.

Experience with many PSA shows that the methodology of combining
- event tree analyses and
- fault tree analyses
is the best way to describe the spectrum of important accident sequences and, under these circumstances, the important
system safety functions of an NPP.

For the purpose of an adequate use of the PSA-methodology at
NPPs, the following section will deal with the principal aspects and the extent of analyses.

2.3 Structure of event tree and fault tree analyses

Finding all failure possibilities of a core melt accident
(Level 1-analysis) requires assessing a more or less complete
list of initiating events that may result in a core melt if no

safety system responds (Section 2.4 contains further data on this point).
The following initiating events are starting point examples in an Event Tree Analysis (ETA):
- loss of main heat sink
- emergency power case
- LOCA.
The initiating events are to be linked with the required system safety functions, and the logic of their failure combinations up to hazard events, such as core melt or overpressure of primary circuits, shall be drawn in the event tree diagram (Fig.4, Example of an ET of a BWR emergency power case).

Although the system safety function required can be derived from the initiating event, the structure and the sequence of system functions can be varied in respect of the extent of each system function defined and of the sequence of these functions in the event tree.

For the purpose of getting a more or less uniform ET and for an optimal use and interpretation of ETA, a number of important statements on ET and FT structuring are being listed below:

1. The system functions required for controlling a presumed initiating event are structured in ETs, according to the sequence of points of time at which the system functions are required.

2. For a good interpretation of ET and for reducing the number of FTs, even if these may get bigger, each system function should be defined in an ET as extensively as possible.

3. Similar system functions should be combined only if the failure effects of these functions in connection with the initiating event are also similar. For example, the system functions of an emergency core cooling (e.g. flooding the

reactor core and decay heat removal) should be kept apart, as the time durations of core overheating differ substantially. Similarly, development of the subsequent accident sequence of both also differs,due to release of radioactivity and its effect on the containment structure. Furthermore, different time scales of accident sequence give different possibilities for back-up measures by operational personnel mitigating the accident consequences.

4. The system functions' denominations should closely resemble the system's response to accident sequence.These system functions are called "front line systems", e.g. shut-down system (SDS), high and low pressure injection of emergency core cooling systems (HPIS/LPIS of ECC) (Fig.4).
Secondary systems like ancillary systems, e.g. power supply, control devices, reactor protection systems,component cooling systems, will be classified as "support systems" and are not shown in the ET.

5. Support systems shall also be taken up in fault trees of front line systems. It must be observed that support systems can be used for different types of front line systems (e.g.component cooling system).In this case the dependency of front line systems will have to be adequately modelled in FTA.

6. Because of a possible interdependency of different front line systems, e.g.system-specific dependency or common cause failures of similar components in different front line systems, the FT of each system function of a single ET accident sequence or of all ET sequences shall be combined in "Super Fault Trees" for assessment of these dependencies.
Just because of the dependencies, a simple multiplication of the failure probabilities of each system function's individual FT would deliver incorrect results.

7. Component failures of support systems can also cause initiating events (e.g. failure of an electric energy power bus). This dependency must also be taken in consideration.

2.4 Extent of safety analyses

Completeness of an analysis for assessing all failure possibilities of a core melt accident (level 1-analysis) is more complex to realize than assessing the failure modes of a system in a fault tree.

According to the methodology of event tree analysing, initiating events are compiled and based on theoretical analyses, engineering judgement (as a postulating component and structure failures), and on plant operation experience.

These events are compiled in e.g.

- the German "Störfall-Leitlinie für Kernkraftwerke mit DWR" (Guideline for incidents and accidents at NPP with PWR) /6/;
- the American "Procedure Guide" NUREG 2300 /5/.

The German guideline explains the list of events as follows: "The events are compiled on a basis of the actual experience with safety analyses and safety assessment during the licensing procedure and operational experience with PWR, and the events shall be considered in the NPP safety design against accidents."

The "Master Logic Diagram" (Fig.3) can be used for checking this list of events against the plant's safety fatures. In addition, the functions indicated in the diagram canbe used for events structuring.

Experience with PSA has taught that it is possible and even convenient to reduce the extent of analysis by grouping the events and to define a representative event of each group.

For a typical BWR, the large number of different types of transient events can be summarized in 6 groups:
1. Emergency power case
2. Failure of main feedwater system
3. Failure of main heat sink
4. Getting stuck open of a pressure relieve valve

5. Overflooding of a primary circuit
6. Power transient (this event must be elucidated by more detailed failure causes).

The first three events are of differing nature, due to their
frequencies of occurrence and because of the fact that in emergency power cases the decay heat removal system depends on
emergency power supply.
Most of the system safety functions that must necessarily respond to these three events are identical (Fig.4):
- shut-down
- automatic pressure limitation
- automatic pressure relieve in case of the high pressure injection system failing
- decay heat removal.

For this reason, the event trees of these three events are
very similar,permitting the use of most fault trees decribing
the functions. This also permits limiting the extent of analyses without causing any restriction to the overall result of
same.

The event of group item 5 (overflooding of a primary circuit)
is dependent on different safety systems, such as isolation
and shut-down of the main water feed or other high pressure
pumps. This type of accident sequence may also be relevant to
plant conditions other than that of full power operation.

The spectrum of LOCA inside the containment of a typical BWR
can be summarized in 3 groups:
- small LOCA in the primary circuit
- small LOCA at the bottom of the reactor vessel
- large LOCA in the primary circuit.

The distinction between small and large LOCA is constituted
by the necessity or not of automatic pressure relieve.

The type and combination of injection systems necessary for controling the three events are different but,again here, the decay heat removal systems are similar.

Apart from the events discussed for BWR, there are other events of importance for PWR:
- leakages and breaks in the secondary loops
- leakage of a steam generator tube.
In these cases, it is important to analyse additional safety functions such as failure detection and measuring of isolation leakage.

Further PWR and BWR accidents not included in the above ET are:
- leakages of external containment pipes connected to the primary circuit (steam and feedwater lines of BWR);
- interfacing system LOCA;
- leakage of pipes connected to the condensation water pool of a BWR;
- excessive flooding of reactor building or of other safety-relevant buildings, due to large pipe leakages of e.g. service water;
- overpressure protection system of the big vessels in the turbine hall, and main turbine overspeed protection system;
- cooling system of fuel elements storage pool.

Safety features covering other accident sequences such as external events, fire hazards, crashing down of heavy loads are usually assessed on deterministic principles.

3. Performance and limits of PSA, Conclusions.

Advantages:

- PSA is a powerful instrument for checking and improving NPP safety systems designed on deterministic principles.

- In principle, PSA provides the complete logics structure of the interfaces of safety system functions and accident sequences. This picture illustrates the importance and the interactions of system and components and can be used for a better understanding by the plant designer and plant engineers, of plant safety features.

- Using probability values and probability calculations on a system's reliability level, the importance of components and systems are quantified by numbers. A plant's safety design can thus be balanced on a basis of quantitative numbers.

- Quantitative evaluation of safety features is mostly used in a relative sense. Therefore, this evaluation is less sensitive to the uncertainties of the absolute numbers.

- The extent of analyses can be limited to safety-important systems and components by using deductive methods (Fault Tree Analysis), e.g. by defining undesired events and analysing the causes of such events only).

- PSA is used to optimize, in a quantitative way, operational safety procedures up to accident management procedures and surveillance test procedures.

- The actual plant operational experience of system and components can be checked on a basis of a plant-specific PSA study, called "Reliability Assurance" or "Living PSA".

- PSA provides explicit (quantitative) results of the actual safety standard of a plant design as well as of a plant in operation.

Limitations:

- PSA cannot be used to determine the impossibility of specific accidents.

- Its quantification of absolute plant risks suffers of:
  . uncertainties of numbers, e.g. rare events
  . quantification of human reliability and of measures un-
    planned
  . incompleteness of accident analyses (unknown events)
  . simplified models, e.g. of complex accident conditions,
    that cannot be simulated in practice.

- PSA being based on a completely correct system layout, design erors cannot be quantified.

An impressive number of examples verifies PSA as an analytical tool for assessing NPP safety features. Observing its limitations, PSA is a powerful instrument that cannot be substituted for any other instrument. For these reasons a PSA guide
line is to be considered highly recommendable.

References:

/1/ H.-P.Balfanz, G.Becker, Methods and Requirements for a Com-
     puter-aided Information System on Safety Parameters and
     PSA for Operational Safety Management, IAEA-Meeting, Vienna,
     March 16 - 20, 1987

/2/ H.-P.Balfanz,TÜV Hamburg, Reliability Assurance of Long Term
     Nuclear Power Plant Operation in the FRG, State of the Art,
     Requirements and Experience, PSA-Workshop, Brighton UK, May
     20 - 23, 1986, OECD Report Nr.125

/3/ Bekanntmachungen des Bundesministers des Innern, Sicherheits-
     kriterien für Kernkraftwerke vom 21.10.1977, Bundesanzeiger
     Nr. 206 of 03.11.1977

/4/ OECD/NEA, A Survey of the Applications Made of the Results
     of Probabilistic Safety Analyses of Nuclear Power Plants,
     CSNI, Report 124, Paris, October 1986

/5/ NUREG/CR-2300, PRA Procedure Guide, A Guide to the Performan-
     ce of Probabilistic Risk Assessment for Nuclear Power Plants
     Final Report, January 1984

/6/ Störfall-Leitlinien für Druckwasserreaktoren, Bundesanzeiger
     Nr. 245a, October 18, 1983.

Table 1 : RELIABILITY ANALYSES OF ECCS OF NPP

NPP	Accident	Systems analysed	Assumptions Test interv.	Unavailability (max. values)
GKN (PWR)	large LOCA	LPIS, ACCS heat remo- val system, electr.po- wer supply (EPS)	1 m for sys- tems, 1 a for checkval- ves at prima- ry circuit.	2.5×10^{-4}
Biblis A	- " -	- " -	- " - long term cooling 4000h	3.7×10^{-4} failure prob, 4×10^{-4}
Biblis B	- " -	- " - a)without EPS b)with EPS	6 weeks of systems	3.7×10^{-4} 5×10^{-4}
KKP-1 (BWR)	- " -	LPIS, heat removal system,EPS	similar to GKN	4.5×10^{-4}
KKB (BWR)	-"-	- " -	- " - heat removal sys- tem of cooling condensation sup- pression pool 2 w	5×10^{-4}

w = weekly
m = monthly
a = yearly

Table **2**: Results of PSA of Primary and Secondary Emergency
Heatremoval Systems of PWR

Event/ incident	Frequency 1/a	Unavailability of Safety System	Frequency of Sequence 1/a
large LOCA	$3 . 10^{-4}$		
heat removal syst.		$4,1 . 10^{-4}$	
containment isolat.		$1,3 . 10^{-4}$	$1,6 . 10^{-7}$
medium LOCA	$8 . 10^{-4}$	$5,4 . 10^{-4}$	$4,3 . 10^{-7}$
small LOCA	$3 . 10^{-3}$		
small leak to	$2 . 10^{-3}$		
pessurizer valve			
primary-side		$5,4 . 10^{-4}$	
secondary-side		$1 . 10^{-4}$	$3,1 . 10^{-6}$
emergency power case	$3 . 10^{-2}$	$5 . 10^{-5}$	$1,5 . 10^{-6}$
SG-tube leak	$1 . 10^{-2}$	*)	-
external events	*)		
heat removal syst.		$3 . 10^{-3}$	
Primary circ.isol.		$4,6 . 10^{-3}$	
Loss of main feed water	$4 . 10^{-1}$	$1 . 10^{-5}$	$4 . 10^{-6}$
Leak in second. circ.	$3 . 10^{-3}$	$1 . 10^{-3}$	$3 . 10^{-6}$
Total			$1,2 . 10^{-5}$

*) only qualitative assesment by comparing other events

Table 3: PSA OF FUEL ELEMENT STORAGE TANK COOLING SYSTEM

Initiating Event	Accident frequency 1/a	Unavailability	Probability of Event $T > 80°C$ *) 1/a
Failure during normal operation			3×10^{-7}
LOCA	3×10^{-3}	1×10^{-4}	3×10^{-7}
External event - earthquake - gas explos.) - plane crash)	$10^{-4} - 10^{-5}$ 1×10^{-6}	1×10^{-4} 1×10^{-2}	
Emergency power case - short term - long term revision phase	5×10^{-2} 1×10^{-3} 1×10^{-4}	1×10^{-5} 5×10^{-5}	
Pipe break of cooling system at plant operation revision phase	1×10^{-4} 1×10^{-5}	1×10^{-2}	1×10^{-7}

*) Failure criterium: increase of storage pool water temeperature $T > 80°C$

Table **4**: Surveilance Test Intervalls assessed by PSA

Emergency core cooling system	4 w
Nuclear component cooling system	4 w
Service cooling water system	4 w
Check valves to primary circuit	1 a
Pressurizer-blowdown isolation valve	8 w
-blowdown valve	1 a
Containment isolation valves	
Volume control system	1 a
ECCS	4 w
Nuclear ventilation system	4 w
Nuclear building drain system	4 w
Nuclear component cooling system	1 a/4 w
Fuel element storage pool cooling system	4 w
Emergency heat removal system second. side	4 w
Check valves to SG	1 a
Emergency power supply	4 w
Start-up and shut-down of cooling system	3 m
Volume controlsystem spray valve	4 w
Steam dump valves	1 a
Primary isolation valves	1 a

a = annually

m = monthly

w = weekly

atomwirtschaft, April 1987

Figure 1: NPPs of FRG

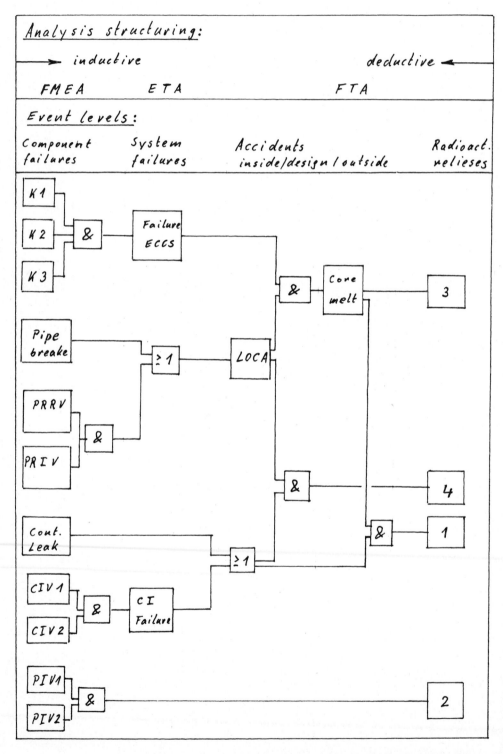

Figure 2 : Simplified logic-structure of hazard event levels of PWR

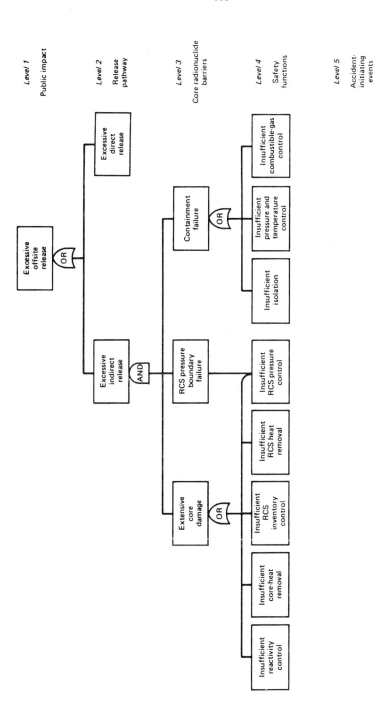

Level 1
Public impact

Level 2
Release pathway

Level 3
Core radionuclide barriers

Level 4
Safety functions

Level 5
Accident-initiating events

Figure 3-5. Master logic diagram. See Table 3-5 for a summary listing of the safety functions, initiating events, and system-response groupings derived from this master logic diagram.

Figure 3, taken from 151

686

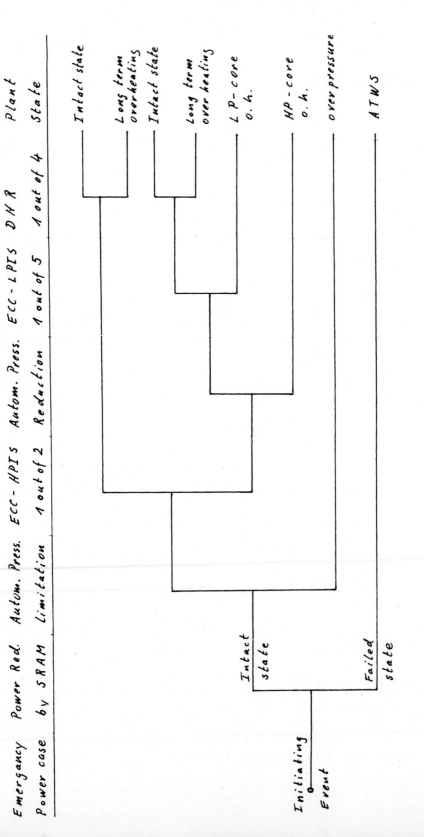

Figure 4: Event tree of emergency power case of a BWR

COMPARISON OF TWO PROBABILISTIC SAFETY STUDIES, ONE USING LICENSING CRITERIA AND THE OTHER USING REALISTIC CRITERIA

V. Cavicchia, G. Toccafondi
(ENEL - DCO Rome, Italy)

ABSTRACT

Two different probabilistic studies have been performed for the Alto Lazio nuclear plant.

The first analysis has been the evaluation of the frequency of occurencies exceeding the licensing acceptance limits using licensing models. This analysis is mainly used as basis for the Technical Specifications.

The second analysis has been the evaluation of the core damage frequency, using realistic criteria. This analysis is being used to perform a complete risk assessment analysis, including the consequences on the population, which will provide the basis to make decision on the plant modifications required to mitigate the severe accidents.

The paper presents the differences in the methodologies, in the thermal-hydraulic models and in the results.

1. INTRODUCTION

The Alto Lazio Nuclear Plant is a two BWR/6 units plant presently under construction in Italy, about 100 Kilometers northwest of Rome. The fuel loading is foreseen by 1990.

The Alto Lazio design presents a few improvements in comparison with the BWR6 Standard plant design. The major difference in the NSSS is the introduction of the Special Emergency Heat Removal (SEHR) system, which has the capability of automatically removing heat from the core and the containment for 10 hours without human intervention. The SEHR system has redundant active components and its own independent auxiliary systems, including two diesel generators. The SEHR system and its auxiliary systems are designed in class 1E as the other ECCS.

Two different probabilistic studies have been performed for Alto Lazio plant.

The first analysis, called Alto Lazio Station Reliability Analysis (ALSRA), has been completed in December 1984 with a total effort of about 250 man-months. The final goal of the ALSRA was the evaluation of the frequency of occurences exceeding the licensing acceptance limits using licensing models to find the minimum number of mitigating systems required.

For example the ALSRA thermal-hydraulic model for the core cooling function is the standard 10 CFR 50 Appendix K licensing LOCA model.

The second analysis, called Alto Lazio Station Probabilistic Safety Study (PSS/AL), has been completed in September 1986. The final goal of the PSS/AL is to evaluate the core damage frequency using realistic criteria, such as a best estimate model for the thermal-hydraulic analysis. The latter study is similar to the level 1 PRA normally performed in U.S. and in Europe. The PSS/AL study was performed modifying the reliability model of the ALSRA introducing the realistic criteria instead of the licensing ones. This study required a total effort of about 24 man-months (including the performance of the unique Alto Lazio best estimate thermal hydraulic analysis).

This paper presents the main methodological differences between the ALSRA and the PSS/AL, their different purposes and the difference of the results.

INITIATING EVENT	FSAR ANALYSIS	ALSRA (LICENSING) MINIMUM CONFIGURATION	PSS/AL (REALISTIC) MINIMUM CONFIGURAT.
LARGE LIQUID LOCA	HPCS + 2 LPCI + 7 SRV OR HPCS + LPCS + 1 LPCI + 7 SRV OR LPCS + 3 LPCI + 7 SRV	1 LPCI + LPCS OR SEHR + LPCS OR 1 LPCI + HPCS OR SEHR + HPCS	SHORT TERM HPCS OR LPCS OR LPCI OR SEHR LONG TERM HPCS OR LPCS OR 2 LPCI + SEHR OR 3 LPCI
SMALL LIQUID LOCA		HPCS OR LPCS + 4 SRV OR 1 LPCI + 5 SRV OR SEHR + 5 SRV OR 2 LPCI + 4 SRV OR SEHR + 1 LPCI + 4 SRV	1 FW OR RCIC OR HPCS OR LPCS + 3 SRV OR SEHR + 3 SRV OR LPCI + 3 SRV

TABLE 1: EMERGENCY CORE COOLING SYSTEM CONFIGURATIONS

2. METHODOLOGICAL DIFFERENCES BETWEEN ALSRA AND PSS/AL STUDIES

The main differences between ALSRA and PSS/AL are in:
a)   the limits of the safety functions (acceptance criteria);
b)   the model used to evaluate the minimum configurations for the mitigating systems (success criteria) and to evaluate the time available for operator recovery actions when automatic systems fail to operate;
c)   the credit taken for the non-safety grade systems.

2.1. DIFFERENCES IN THE ACCEPTANCE CRITERIA

For the acceptance criteria, the biggest difference between licensing and realistic bases is in the containment cooling function. In ALSRA the limit of the containment pressure is 15 psig (design limit) and the limit of the suppression pool temperature is 185° F.
In PSS/AL the containment pressure limit is the rupture pressure limit evaluated as 45 psig for Alto Lazio, by an analysis in the elastic field.
The use of a 45 psig limit gives a much longer time available for manual recovery from system failures before the limit is reached.

2.2. DIFFERENCES IN THE MODEL

The ALSRA and PSS/AL analyses use different models to evaluate the minimum configurations of the mitigating system required in response to the various scenarios.
For example the success criteria for the core cooling have been evaluated in ALSRA using the standard 10 CFR 50 Appendix K licensing models and in PSS/AL using the "best estimate" model, which is different mainly because it uses a decay heat rate about 20% less than that used in licensing and because it takes credit for the steam cooling when the core is uncovered.
The result is that in ALSRA a larger number of mitigating systems are generally needed and less time is available for the operator to perform recovery actions before the limits are exceeded.
Table 1 shows an example of the differences of the minimum mitigating systems which are needed in ALSRA analysis and PSS/AL study for the large liquid LOCA and for the small steam and liquid LOCA. In the Table 1 the configurations used in the FSAR analyses are also shown. These configurations are not the minimum ones, but they are established assuming only the single failure criterion and without considering the SEHR system.
As an example of the differences in the timing, in ALSRA the allowable time for the recovery of one ECCS in an isolation event with failure of the automatic logic is 15 minutes, for the high pressure systems, and 8 minutes for the low pressure systems. In the PSS/AL the recovery of one ECCS system within 25 minutes is successful. This difference in the timing leads in ALSRA to larger values of the probability of human error to manually start the ECCS, when the automatic initiation logic has failed.

2.3. DIFFERENCE IN CREDIT FOR NON-SAFETY SYSTEMS

In ALSRA the same assumptions made in the licensing process have been assumed; in particular the non-safety systems are never considered in the mitigation of an accident event. In PSS/AL analysis, credit for non-safety systems is taken, if they are available after the event.

3. DIFFERENT PURPOSES OF THE ALSRA AND OF THE PSS/AL STUDIES

Both ALSRA and PSS/AL studies are used during the design and licensing processes, but with different purposes.
In particular the ALSRA study provides:

a) a model to obtain more rational and unique Technical Specifications which are based on licensing criteria;
b) an indipendent design verification, providing an integrated plant view following the same bases used during the design;
c) a support for the resolution of licensing issues.
The PSS/AL study is used:
a) as a basis for the modifications of the emergency operating procedures;
b) as a plant model for a complete risk analysis, which studies probabilistically the consequences of an accident on the population, and which will be used to make decisions on the plant modifications required to mitigate the severe accidents;
c) to compare the Alto Lazio plant to other plants for which a risk assessment has been performed.
As said above, the ALSRA study, instead of the realistic PSS/AL study, is used as basis of the Alto Lazio Technical Specifications to define the Limiting Conditions for Operations, the maximum allowable repair time and the surveillance test interval. The reason of the use of a licensing basis probabilistic study is that the Technical Specifications are the restrictions on the plant operation deriving from the design such that the licensing limits are not exceeded, using the same hypotheses used in the licensing, except for the single failure criteria. Another reason is that ALSRA does not take credit for the non-safety mitigating systems during an accident and therefore the conclusions derived from this study are much more appropriate for the Technical Specifications application than those derived from the PSS/AL, since Technical Specifications are not imposed to non-safety systems.

4. RESULTS OF THE ALSRA AND PSS/AL STUDIES
Table 2 compares the results of the two studies in term of yearly frequency of exceeding the limits for the core cooling function for different initiating events. The absolute values decrease for all events when the realistic criteria are considered, but in different way.
The last column of table 2 provides the ratio between the ALSRA and the PSS/AL percentage contribution to the total frequency of exceeding core cooling limits, this value is a measure of the conservatism of the present design licensing criteria.
The highest values of this parameter were obtained for the large and intermediate LOCA due to the larger number of pumps required for these events in the licensing model, as shown in Table 1. That means that the present design criteria are much more conservative for the LOCA events than for accidents initiating from other events.
The core damage frequency due to loss of Control Building (CB) and Control Room (CR) ventilating systems during normal operation was left equal to that found in ALSRA; additional heat transfer analysis and additional realistic investigation on the survival of the electrical and logic components would reduce this value in the PSS/AL study.
The main reason for the low value expected for the frequency of core damage at the Alto Lazio plant is due to the presence of the SEHR system, which is completely independent of the ECCS systems.

EVENT	ALSRA		PSS/AL		ALSRA/PSS
	FREQUENCY PER YEAR	PERCENTAGE	FREQUENCY PER YEAR	PERCENTAGE	PERCENTAGE RATIO
LOSS OF OFF-SITE POWER	2.2×10^{-6}	36.9%	8.3×10^{-7}	43.7%	0.84
OTHER TRANSIENTS	1.8×10^{-6}	30.3%	3.1×10^{-7}	16.3%	1.86
LARGE LOCA-INSIDE DW	5.9×10^{-7}	10.1%	9.8×10^{-9}	0.5%	20.2
LOSS OF CONTROL BUILDING/CONTROL ROOM HVAC	5.9×10^{-7}	10.1%	5.9×10^{-7}	31.0%	0.32
INTERMEDIATE LOCA-INSIDE DW	4.6×10^{-7}	7.9%	1.1×10^{-8}	0.6%	13.2
ECCS LINE BREAK LOCA	2.5×10^{-7}	4.3%	1.5×10^{-7}	7.9%	0.54
SMALL LOCA AND OTHER LOCA'S	2.2×10^{-8}	0.4%	4.4×10^{-10}	0.02%	20
TOTAL	5.8×10^{-6}		1.9×10^{-6}		

TABLE 2 : FREQUENCY CORE DAMAGE FOR INITIATING EVENTS

GENERIC SAFETY INSIGHTS FOR INSPECTION OF BOILING WATER REACTORS

J. C. Higgins
(Brookhaven National Laboratory, Upton, New York, USA)
B. M. Hillman
(U.S. Nuclear Regulatory Commission, King of Prussia, PA, USA)

Abstract

Generic safety insights, to aid in the inspection of U.S. Boiling Water Reactors
(BWRs), are developed using existing BWR Probabilistic Risk Assessments (PRAs).
These generic insights can be used directly to inspect BWRs without PRAs or to
develop detailed plant specific inspection guides for those plants without PRAs.
Methodology as well as some examples of the generic insights are presented.

1. Introduction

As the number of operating nuclear power plants (NPP) increases, safety inspection
has increased in importance. The broad scope of the NPP inspection program, coupled with the technical complexities of a nuclear power plant, make the understanding of safety significance a difficult task. What is important, and what is not
important? What should one focus inspection efforts on? The inspector's engineering judgement alone cannot be trusted to accurately answer these questions. Such
judgement must be assisted by systematic evaluations of what is and what is not of
safety significance. Over the last two years Probabilistic Risk Assessment (PRA)
techniques have been developed to aid in the inspection process.

Brookhaven National Laboratory (BNL) has been involved in the development of these
PRA-Based inspection methods for the U.S. Nuclear Regulatory Commission, Region I.
A number of inspection methods have been developed and utilized including: inspection methods based on event trees and system fault trees, PRA-based system inspection plans, computer-based risk tools, common cause methods, human error methods,
and generic PRA methods. Broad interest in generic PRA-based methods has arisen in
the past year, since only about 25% of the U.S. nuclear power plants have completed
PRAs, and also, inspectors want PRA-based tools for these plants. This paper describes the NRC program to develop generic BWR PRA-based inspection insights or
inspection guidance designed to be applied to plants without PRAs.

2. Generic Insight Development

The first step in this generic applications process was to develop a document listing generic BWR PRA-based insights. BNL developed the procedure described below in
order to produce this document. The process consisted basically of a review and
analysis of all available BWR PRAs[2] individual PRA reviews, and the various already
completed PRA review and oversight documents. As an example, each BWR PRA was
reviewed to extract and list the dominant contributors to risk. Both core melt and
offsite consequences were used as risk measures. Then after the dominant risk contributors had been obtained for each plant, they were reviewed again to determine
which items appeared for a majority of the plants. Those items which appeared
repeatedly were considered to be generic. Already completed PRA review documents

(for example Reference 1) were then reviewed to gain additional insights and confirm those from the first task. Additionally, PRA-based insights in the two important areas of common cause failure and human error were incorporated into the generic insight document. These last three mentioned tasks served mainly to confirm the validity of the initial list developed from actual plant PRAs and did not add a significant number of additional items to the generic insight document. Upon completion of these various reviews, the BWR insight document (Reference 5) was consolidated.

After the generic insights list was completed, an analysis was performed to determine approximately what percentage of risk was covered by the items in the list. Each of the nine BWR PRAs used for the task was compared with the generic list. The percentage of risk at each plant addressed in the generic list was determined. An average was then taken across the nine plants. The results showed that approximately 70% of the risk-significant items at any plant are covered by the generic list. This, of course, varies somewhat from plant-to-plant, but over all it is a good estimate as to how much risk would be addressed by the generic list at any given BWR without a PRA. This is probably just about the best that could be achieved in such a generic list, as the remaining 30% of risk-significant items usually vary from plant-to-plant, and hence, are not generic. Also, one should realize that unique plants, such as Big Rock Point, differ significantly from the norm; hence, the generic list should be applied cautiously at such plants.

This generic PRA-Based BWR Insight document is now being used in two ways. First, it is being used directly by NRC personnel to aid in inspection of BWRs without PRAs. Secondly, it is being in the continuing work to develop plant specific PRA-based guidance for BWRs without PRAs. These two uses are discussed in more detail below.

3.   Summary of BWR Generic Insights

At the beginning of this project, it was not obvious how many significant generic insights would be obtained, since it is well known that many aspects of plant risk are plant unique due to the diversity of nuclear system designs. The results of the study, however, identified a significant number of items which were common dominant risk contributors at many BWRs. A sample listing of items from the BWR generic PRA-based insight document, along with related inspection areas, are presented in Table 1. In applying these items to a BWR without a PRA, one must realize that for the plant in question: (1) there may be dominant risk items not on the list, and (2) there may be items on the list which are not dominant for this plant. Nonetheless, based on comparisons between completed PRAs and the generic list, it is judged that about 75% of the dominant risk items at any given plant will be included. Since this will be used merely to supplement and focus other inspection techniques the lack of 100% completeness is not a major concern. The document provides an excellent means to focus limited resources into key risk significant areas and hence, contribute to overall nuclear safety.

TABLE 1 - SAMPLE BWR GENERIC INSIGHTS

The items listed in Column 1 are considered to be generic dominant contributors to risk. (Not all of those in the actual generic document are included here.) The areas listed in Column 2 are sample areas to be inspected to minimize the risk from the Column 1 items.

COLUMN 1	COLUMN 2
I. Initiators: 1. Loss of offsite power. 2. Major transients in the power conversion system.	I. Procedures for operation of switchyards, main steam and feedwater systems.
II. Sequences: 1. Station Blackout 2. ATWS 3. Transient, failure of PCS, loss of HPCI & RCIC, ADS failure. 4. Transient plus failure of long term RHR. 5. Interfacing systems LOCA (offsite risk)	II. Review of operator training & procedures for station blackout and ATWS.
III. Failure of Systems: AC/DC Power RPS Suppression Pool Service Water HPCI/RCIC ADS RHR Drywell Spray	III. Selection of surveillance tests, maintenance items, operating procedures to be reviewed. System walkdowns.
IV. Common Cause Items: 1. Diesel Generator Failure 2. DC System Failure 3. Service Water Failure 4. Common mode mechanical failure leading to ATWS 5. Fires in common areas such as cable rooms & equipment rooms	IV. Special reviews for commonalities in maintenance, calibrations, and support systems.

Table 1 (Cont'd)

COLUMN 1	COLUMN 2
V. Human Errors	V. Emergency procedures and operator training.
1. Failure to manually initiate ADS or SLC.	
2. Failure to recover offsite power (OSP).	
3. Failure to manually initiate SLC and defeat ADS on ATWS.	
4. Failure to vent wetwell before containment overpressurization.	
5. Miscalibration: RV level sensors, DW pressure, injection valve differential pressure for CS and LPCI.	
6. Recovery actions to address failures in dominant accident sequences.	
7. Failure to properly restore components after test and maintenance.	
VI. Component Level Items: HPCI - Turbine and Governor Failure SW - components in maintenance RHR - Injection valve permissive circuitry	VI. Equipment condition & maintenance training.
VII. Additional Important Insights: 1. Wetwell venting to prevent containment overpressurization. 2. Containment bypass sequences.	VII. Emergency procedures and training.

4. Uses for Inspection and Review Purposes

The BWR generic insights were developed primarily for NRC inspection purposes, but they could also be used for general insight by management and for various review purposes by either NRC or utility personnel. Some sample methods of use are described below. These would all take place at a BWR without a plant specific PRA.

1. Inspectors can familiarize themselves with the generic insights and be sensitized to what is generally important at BWRs according to PRA studies.

2. A special generic PRA-based review could be conducted at a BWR without a PRA to verify that appropriate steps had been taken to minimize the occurrence of the identified dominant failures.

3. During routine inspections performed by the NRC or QA personnel, the generic insights could be used to partially replace random selection for choosing areas, systems and components to review.

4. The dominant human errors could aid in the review of emergency procedures, operator training, and operator licensing.

5. Important component failures give guidance into areas to review during in-plant walk-throughs and in review of surveillance test results.

6. The important systems list can aid in inspection area selection and in review of maintenance backlogs.

5. Plant Specific Inspection Plans

As mentioned above, a second use for the generic insight document is in the development of plant specific PRA-Based Inspection Plans for BWRs without PRAs. These plans would be similar to PRA-Based Inspection Plans already developed for plants with PRAs. The PRA-Based Inspection Plans already developed for plants with PRAs consist of three main parts:

1. A prioritized systems list with systems placed into high, medium, and low importance groups based on importance measures.

2. Plant or systems level insights gleaned from the PRA event trees.

3. Dominant system failure modes at the component level obtained from system fault tree minimal cutsets along with supplemental information tables based on these failure modes.

In order to develop similar plans for plants without PRAs, the generic insights document is used, together with detailed system and component level failure mode tables, and plant specific information for the plant under study. A number of the detailed system and component level failure mode tables have been prepared. One is constructed for each BWR system. For example, the High Pressure Coolant Injection (or HPCI) table is constructed primarily from the dominant minimal cutsets of the HPCI system fault trees in the available BWR PRAs completed to date. This produces essentially a generic table of HPCI system dominant failure modes. When such tables are completed for each BWR system then a complete PRA-Based Inspection Plan can be developed for Plant A that does not have a PRA. These tables would be used along with the generic insights document discussed in paragraph 2, tempered with plant

specific design information for Plant A. When completed, the PRA-Based Inspection Plan will be used to aid inspectors in deciding which systems and
components in Plant A are more important or risk significant and hence, where
to focus their inspection efforts. Several U.S. plants with PRAs already have
such PRA-Based Inspection Plans developed and in use successfully. Those
plans developed using this generic process for plants without PRAs would be
used similarly.

6.   References

1.   NUREG 1050, Probabilistic Risk Assessment (PRA) Reference Document.

2.   Actual PRAs for the following nuclear power plants: Big Rock Point,
     Browns Ferry (IREP), Grand Gulf (RSSMAP), Limerick, Millstone-1 (IREP),
     Oyster Creek, Peach Bottom (NUREG-1150), Shoreham, and Susquehanna (IPE).

3.   "PRA Insights," BNL, R. Fitzpatrick, et al., NUREG/CR-4405, December
     1985.

4.   "Prevention and Mitigation of Severe Accidents in a BWR-4 With a Mark I
     Containment," BNL, T. Pratt, et al., Draft Report, April 1986.

5.   "Generic PRA-Based BWR Insights," BNL Technical Report A-3453-9-86, J.
     Higgins, 1986.

6.   "PRA Applications," BNL, J.C. Higgins, NUREG/CR-4372, January 1986.

7.   "Limerick Generating Station, PRA-Based System Inspection Plans," BNL,
     A. Fresco, et al., July 1986.

8.   "An Overview of Insights Gained and Lessons Learned from U.S. Plant
     Specific PRA Studies," NUS, Joksimovich, article in Nuclear Safety, March
     1986.

9.   "Loss of Safety System Function Events," NRC-AEOD, Trager, Case Study
     Report, December 1985.

10. "Insights Gained from PRAs, NRC-NRR, Sarah M. Davis, Report, September
     1984.

ORGANIZATION OF RISK ANALYSIS CODES FOR LIVING EVALUATIONS (ORACLE)[a]

Doyle L. Batt, Philip E. MacDonald, and Martin B. Sattison (Idaho National Engineering Laboratory, EG&G Idaho, Inc., Idaho Falls, ID, USA) and William E. Vesely (Science Applications International Corporation, Columbus, Ohio, USA)

1   Abstract

ORACLE (Organization of Risk Analysis Codes for Living Evaluations) is an integration concept for using risk-based information in United States Nuclear Regulatory Commission (USNRC) applications. Portions of ORACLE are being developed at the Idaho National Engineering Laboratory for the USNRC. The ORACLE concept consists of related databases, software, user interfaces, processes, and quality control checks allowing a wide variety of regulatory problems and activities to be addressed using current, updated PRA information. The ORACLE concept provides for smooth transitions between one code and the next without pre- or post-processing.

2   Introduction

A significant body of probabilistic risk assessment (PRA) information exists which provides an important resource that can be used by the Nuclear Regulatory Commission (NRC) in carrying out its responsibilities. However, no unified mechanism exists for using this resource in an effective, routine manner in NRC regulatory applications. This paper presents a concept to provide risk analyses results, models, and tools in a form that will aid plant inspections and audits, decisionmaking, and formulation of policy, as well as other regulatory applications. The concept consists of related databases, software, user interfaces, processes, and quality control checks allowing a wide variety of NRC regulatory problems and activities to be addressed using current, updated PRA information. Plants not having PRAs can also be evaluated using summarized models. The user interfaces are constructed so the NRC regulators do not need to know PRA techniques and nomenclatures to successfully use the available information.

The ORACLE concept is specifically designed to satisfy user-oriented objectives. The general objective of this effort is to develop risk-based approaches which can be used effectively in the NRC regulatory process. This objective can be broken into the following specific user-oriented objectives:

1.   Provide a system which allows risk monitoring of plants

2.   Provide a system which allows evaluations to be made of the risk impacts of design and operating changes

3.   Provide a system which allows evaluations to be made of the risk significance of regulatory issues

4.   Provide a system which assists NRC regulatory inspection and evaluation activities by identifying the risk important activities

---

a. Work supported by the United States Nuclear Regulatory Commission, Office of Nuclear Regulatory Research, under DOE Contract No. DE-AC07-76ID01570.

5. Provide a system which uses PRA technology to aid in managing accidents.

These objectives are briefly described below.

3 Description of ORACLE Objectives

3.1 Plant Risk Monitoring

Monitoring the risk and safety of plants is an important NRC objective. The ORACLE concept includes a system for risk monitoring which allows failures and incidents to be input in a routine manner and then processes the new information to give an updated risk level of the plant. The plant risk is thus monitored on an ongoing basis. The risk readings produced by the system can include the public health risk, core melt frequency, and system unavailabilities. The system will incorporate risk models of the plant to evaluate the risk implications of plant configurations and status, as well as events which occur. The system will also be designed to accommodate new analyses and approaches being developed within the NRC. Brookhaven National Laboratory is presently developing this system under a program titled, "Risk Based Indicators."

3.2 Risk Impacts of Design and Operating Changes

Evaluation of the risk implications of proposed design and operating changes is another important NRC function, encompassing backfitting and technical specification changes. The ORACLE concept includes a system for risk impact evaluations which allows simple user interactions to produce the risk impacts and net costs associated with proposed changes. The system will contain a library of updated plant models to show the individual plant effects and generic effects of the proposed changes. The system will also include summarized risk models for scoping evaluations and detailed models where further detailed analysis is desired. Emphasis will be placed on using existing PRAs when available. Summarized models will be used to evaluate potential changes at nuclear power plants not having full PRAs.

3.3 Risk Impacts of Regulatory Issues

Issues associated with plant regulation continually arise, and evaluation of the risk implications of these issues is another major NRC function. The Systems Analysis and Risk Assessment (SARA) System, designed for issue evaluations, allows the issue description to be input in a simple manner and then produces the risk implications on both a plant-specific and generic basis. Multiple issues can be prioritized based upon risk importance. Figure 1 shows graphically one type of information that this system can provide. Bounding analyses, as well as more detailed analyses, can be accommodated by the system. Sensitivity analyses are also simple to carry out using the SARA System.

3.4 Risk Importance Prioritization Regulatory Activities

NRC regulators carry out many daily routine activities which can be made more effective if the activities are prioritized according to risk importance. Tasks in inspection modules and technical-specification-associated reviews are examples of activities which can be assisted by risk importance information. The Plant Risk Information Status Management (PRISIM) System provides activity prioritization on specific activities and describes the risk importance actions in ways they can be acted upon. PRISIM is able to produce results usable in the field as well as in the NRC offices. Figure 2 shows a typical risk importance

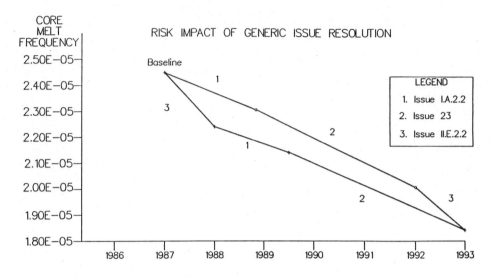

Figure 1: Core melt frequency vs assumed implementation schedule.

```
FRONT LINE SYSTEMS RANKED BY RISK REDUCTION IMPORTANCE
                                                    RISK REDUCTION
                   SYSTEM                             IMPORTANCE

    High Head Safety Injection System                   0.47

    Reactor Coolant System (Pressure Control)           0.43

    Auxiliary Feedwater System                          0.22

    Low Head Safety Injection System                    0.16

    Reactor Protection System                           0.02

    Chemical and Volume Control System                  0.01

    Component Cooling Water System                      0.01
    (RCP Thermal Barrier Cooling)

    Accumulator Safety Injection System                 0.01
```

Figure 2: Typical PRISIM risk information printout.

printout from PRISIM. This information can be used by the NRC resident inspector at a plant to determine risk-based inspection priorities. PRISIM also
produces risk importance guidance efficiently when timely action is required by
the NRC.

3.5 PRA Technology Use as Aid in Managing Accidents

When incidents and accidents occur, the NRC needs to identify effective strategies and evaluate the licensee's strategy for bringing the plant back to a

stable, safe condition. These effective strategies or success paths need to be identified quickly in certain cases to prevent further degradation of the plant situation. The effective success paths and strategies for mitigating an accident should be identified based on their likelihood of success and their use of available resources. The ORACLE concept provides the opportunity to develop an Accident Management System, presently being considered by the NRC.

4   Program Description

The process of collecting, analyzing, and updating PRA model input, and updating the PRA models is a means of providing current PRA results, in a useful form, to the various end-users of such information.

Figure 3 provides a functional overview of the ORACLE concept for integrating PRA-related research activities. The goal of this program is to aggregate a set of processes and computer codes capable of providing current PRA information to assist the NRC in meeting their objectives. Three basic products are being developed:

1.   Data gathering, evaluation, and storage activity for obtaining and retaining the various types of data needed for revising and updating PRA models and for use by end-users. This database would include plant PRA data, reliability data, plant design and operational data, and thermal-hydraulic and accident data. Additionally, results from PRA analyses would be stored for further analysis and reporting.

2.   PRA analysis program for creating, manipulating and updating the detailed PRA models for selected plants, based upon the revised data, and for downloading information and models to special purpose PRA-application codes. The PRA update process must ultimately be mechanized

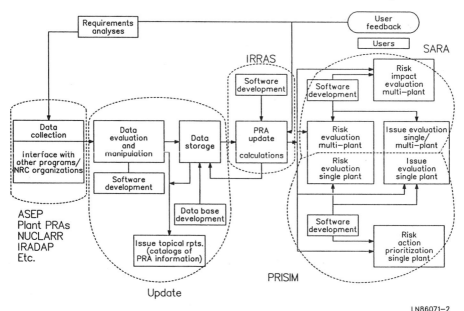

LN86071-2

Figure 3:   Relationship of existing programs to ORACLE.

to the maximum extent possible to bring to fruition current PRA-related results for use in the NRC regulatory process with minimum delay. The Integrated Reliability and Risk Analysis System (IRRAS) developed at the Idaho National Engineering Laboratory presently fulfills a major portion of this function.

3. Special-purpose PRA codes which serve as front-line tools in meeting end-user objectives for use of PRA in NRC applications. Companion papers on PRISIM and SARA/IRRAS present some of ORACLE's front-line tool capabilities.

The ultimate success of this program depends on a strong, clearly defined initial understanding of the relationship of existing programs to each other and a clear determination to integrate these programs. Figure 3 indicates the relationship of existing programs to this strategy for integration purposes. Definition of end-user needs and assessment of the applicability of PRA information must also be included as part of the development scope for the special-purpose codes.

The products presented above clearly indicate three user types:

1. Experienced PRA practitioners who produce and analyze PRA models/results using PRA analysis codes and the data gathered in the data program mentioned above.

2. Persons with some knowledge of PRA who are involved in analyzing safety issues/events but have no need for full scope PRA analyses.

3. Engineers with little or no PRA background who need PRA-related information or insights in performing their work.

5 Conclusions

The ORACLE concept includes: (1) a data collection/coordination effort to obtain, evaluate, and update PRA input data; (2) capabilities to store and access PRA models, results and data; and (3) software for manipulating and updating detailed PRA models and special-purpose codes designed to directly address the above-mentioned, user-oriented objectives. Databases and codes are structured to incorporate newly developed data and methods, as appropriate. The process of collecting, analyzing, and updating PRA model input, and updating the PRA models results in creating "living" PRAs which can be used to provide current PRA results, in a useful form, to the various end-users of such information. This ORACLE concept is being applied in all PRA programs at the Idaho National Engineering Laboratory. To date, the concept appears to be extremely viable.

NOTICE

APPLICATION OF PROBABILISTIC SAFETY ASSESSMENT (PSA) TECHNIQUES IN THE UNITED
STATES NUCLEAR REGULATORY COMMISSION (USNRC) INTEGRATED SAFETY ASSESSMENT PROGRAM
(ISAP)

Bahman Atefi, Daniel W. Gallagher, Phuoc T. Le, [SAIC, McLean, VA, USA]
Paul J. Amico, [ARTECH, Columbia, MD, USA]
Glenn B. Kelly, [USNRC, Washington, D.C., USA]

Abstract

This paper discusses the use of probabilistic techniques to complement the
deterministic analyses performed as part of the USNRC Integrated Safety Assessment
Program (ISAP). The results of a plant-specific PRA are used to form the basis of
probabilistic evaluations of safety-related ISAP topics. These topics include
issues identified in the Systematic Evaluation Program, pending licensing
requirements, and licensee initiated topics. A prioritization scheme has been
developed to rank the safety significance of each of the analyzed ISAP topics.
This ranking is used to facilitate the development of an integrated living
schedule that would allow the utlity to resolve the most safety significant issues
first and better allocate available resources.

Introduction

The Integrated Safety Assessment Program (ISAP) was developed by the United States
Nuclear Regulatory Commission (USNRC) to comprehensively examine the outstanding
regulatory requirements and safety-related issues pertinent to each nuclear power
plant. The primary objectives of this program are 1) to assess the importance of
each requirement or issue with respect to its impact on the risk associated with
the operation of the plant, 2) to prioritize the issues and 3) to develop an
appropriate schedule for implementing changes necessary to resolve these issues.
The ISAP pilot program was initiated in 1985 on the basis of voluntary
participation by licensees. The first plants that were volunteered by their
licensee to participate in the pilot program were Northeast Utilities' Millstone
Nuclear Power Station Unit 1 and Connecticut Yankee Atomic Power Company's Haddam
Neck Nuclear Power Plant.

The issues, or "ISAP topics," that are considered for each plant include:

1. Issues identified in Phase II of the Systematic Evaluation Program
    (SEP), pending licensing requirements including TMI Action Plan items
    for the particular facility, pending Unresolved and Generic Safety
    Issues, and licensee-initiated improvement projects.

2. Significant events that have occurred during the operation of the plant.

3. Dominant contributors to plant risk based on a plant-specific
    Probabilistic Safety Analysis (PSA).

ISAP Review Process

The procedure used for identification and resolution of all ISAP topics is as follows. An initial screening of the issues identified by the programs mentioned above is performed by the NRC to arrive at a set of ISAP topics that are appropriate for the plant under consideration. The licensee also identifies utility-initiated topics to be considered in the ISAP Process.

The licensee performs a complete plant-specific PSA and detailed deterministic evaluations of all the topics. For those topics suitable for analysis using PSA techniques, the licensee is requested to submit a probabilistic analysis for the topic using the models and results developed in the plant-specific PSA.

In addition to the PSA and deterministic evaluations, an operating experience evaluation is conducted which consists of an analysis of all data on forced shutdowns, power reductions, and reportable events for the plant under consideration. The objective of this review and analysis is to identify any events or trends that might point to an inherent weakness in the design or operation of the plant that may not be readily revealed in the PSA or the deterministic reviews. The operating experience analysis provides useful insights into the need for plant-specific performance data, as opposed to generic reliability values, and into significant accident precursors for the PSA. Moreover, the operating experience analysis provides an important perspective which should be used to temper judgments regarding the uncertainties in the conclusions drawn from both the PSA and the deterministic evaluations.

The NRC's analysis of the licensee's submittals consists of a detailed review of the plant-specific PSA and of each topic analyzed by the licensee using deterministic and/or probabilistic techniques. The review of the licensee's PSA is directed toward ensuring that the analysis methods and application correctly represent the risk profile of the plant. A unique aspect of the ISAP approach is the utilization of the PSA to develop new topics which would explicitly address plant-specific vulnerabilities in design, hardware, or procedures. As plant improvements are subsequently made and as operational events occur in the future, the PSA can be updated so that it becomes a "living" tool to evaluate safety issues and the need for additional plant improvements. This approach would enhance the return on the licensee's investment in the initial PSA.

The final set of topics that must be considered for each plant would consist of 1) the initial set of topics based on NRC-required programs discussed earlier, 2) utility-initiated topics that are important to safety, 3) any safety-related topics identified as a result of the review of the plant's operating history, and 4) areas of plant vulnerability due to design, hardware, or procedural problems identified by the plant-specific PSA.

Prioritization of the Topics

For all the topics analyzed (either probabilistic or deterministic), the licensee first ranks the importance of the resolution of each topic with respect to the plant operational risk. The licensee next identifies specific corrective actions which would resolve the topic and help determine the relative importance/ranking of the actions or issues involved.

For the ISAP topics analyzed using probabilistic techniques, several considerations must be kept in mind when choosing a method for ranking these topics. The first is that the method should be simple, straightforward, and should not require a substantial amount of effort. The variables used to rank each topic should be a good measure of the probability of occurrence of an accident and release of radioactive material outside the containment, i.e., a good measure of risk associated with the operation of the plant. Even though public health and safety are the primary objectives of the NRC regulations, the ranking method should indirectly address the substantial onsite and offsite financial costs associated with a major accident.

With all these factors in mind, a two-step ranking scheme considering change in core-melt frequency and total population exposure may be appropriate. The first step consists of evaluating the change in core-melt frequency as a result of resolving the topic. Change in core-melt frequency is proposed as the primary measure of importance of the issues for several reasons. First, it provides a direct measure of the importance of any proposed hardware or procedural change as implemented to resolve an issue. The only exception would be a change that affects containment or accident mitigation performance. Also, calculation of change in core-melt frequency is relatively straightforward and the level of confidence in the final numerical results is higher than in numerical results for risk measures that must include containment and consequence analyses.

Table 1 shows a ranking scheme based on change in core-melt frequency. As can be seen in this table, the numerical criteria used for ranking of the issues are fixed, and not based on a percentage of core-melt frequency for the plant under study. Thus, this method will not penalize plants with low core-melt frequency.

The cutoff change in core-melt frequency of $5x10^{-5}$ per year for ranking an issue high is based on consideration of the Commission's proposed safety goal core-melt frequency of 10^{-4} per year, and on our previous experience with the SEP Phase II which highlighted that issues resulting in changes in core-melt frequency of about $5x10^{-5}$ per year and higher are important contributors to the dominant core-melt sequences (1,2). The other cutoff points are one and two orders of magnitude lower than the high cutoff rate.

The second step in this ranking process is to estimate the total population exposure as a result of resolution of the issue. The purpose of this second step is to upgrade a ranking which is based solely on change in core-melt frequency to take into account low frequency events that could lead to large consequences. In addition, this second step allows ranking of those issues that only affect containment performance and would not be ranked in step 1 above. Table 2 shows a supplemental ranking scheme using change in total population exposure.

For example, based on the results of the Sandia Siting Study(3), the total population exposure as a result of an SST2 release is on the order of $2x10^{6}$ man-rem. The SST2 corresponds to accidents involving loss of core cooling with containment emergency safety functions available. For this type of release category the 5000 man-rem criteria approximately corresponds to the $5x10^{-5}$/year core-melt frequency which is the lower limit for a high ranking based on change in core-melt frequency. The total population exposure for an SST1 release is on the order of $2x10^{7}$ man-rem. The SST1 corresponds to the most severe radioactive release following a core-melt accident. It involves failure of core cooling and containment emergency safety functions with severe breach of containment. For this type of release category the 5000 man-rem criteria (a high ranking) corresponds to a $5x10^{-6}$/year core melt frequency, which is the lower limit for a medium ranking based on change in core-melt frequency.

Thus, for the case where the change in core-melt frequency is on the order of $5x10^{-6}$ and involves a severe containment failure and radioactive release, the issue would be ranked medium using the change in core-melt frequency criteria.

Change in Core-Melt Frequency as a Result of the Resolution of an Issue (per year)	Rank
$\Delta CM > 5 \times 10^{-5}$	High
$5 \times 10^{-6} < \Delta CM < 5 \times 10^{-5}$	Medium
$\Delta CM < 5 \times 10^{-6}$	Low

Table 1: Proposed Ranking Scheme Based on Change in Core-Melt Frequency

Change in Total Population Exposure as a Result of the Resolution of an Issue (man-rem)	Rank
$\Delta E > 5000$	High
$500 < \Delta E < 5000$	Medium
$\Delta E < 500$	Low

Table 2: Proposed Supplemental Ranking Scheme Based on Change in Total Population Exposure

But the total exposure criteria of Table 2 would upgrade this ranking to high, ensuring that low probability events with large consequences are ranked appropriately.

With respect to the implication of the various rankings shown in Tables 1 and 2, a high ranking for a topic is meant to imply that its resolution results in a high safety and/or economic benefit and should be implemented as soon as possible. A medium ranking for a topic implies that its resolution results in a desirable safety and/or economic benefit and should be implemented over a longer period of time. A low ranking for a topic implies that its resolution results in little or no safety and/or economic benefit and should be implemented last, if at all.

Also, it should be emphasized that for most plants a simple containment and consequence analysis using existing information and surrogate source terms would be sufficient for developing the total population exposures for this ranking scheme. Therefore, a large effort need not be expended to perform a sophisticated containment and consequence analysis.

For the deterministically-analyzed topics, engineering judgment is used for ranking the topic in the same categories of high, medium, or low. The type of considerations that are factored in ranking the deterministically-analyzed topics using engineering judgment include: safety and/or economic implications of resolution of the topic, existing generic or plant-specific regulatory requirements, estimated personnel exposure for implementation of the topic, and cost associated with resolution of the topic vs. the potential benefits.

Results

The NRC review of the Millstone Unit 1 ISAP topics is completed (4). For this plant, a total of 85 regulatory or safety-related topics were analyzed. Of the 85 topics, 21 topics (25%) were analyzed using probabilistic techniques. Of the 85 topics a small number of topics were completed (modifications implemented at the plant) while this study was in progress. Of the remaining topics that were analyzed using probabilistic techniques, approximately 18% were ranked as high importance to safety, 47% as medium importance to safety and 35% as low importance to safety. Among those topics analyzed using deterministic techniques, approximately 12% were ranked as high significance to safety, 40% as medium significance to safety and 46% as low significance to safety.

For the Haddam Neck Plant, the ISAP effort is near completion. For this plant a total of 82 topics were analyzed. Of these, 40 topics (49%) were analyzed using probabilistic techniques. The preliminary result shows that of those topics analyzed using probabilistic techniques, approximately 20% are ranked as high significance to safety, 20% are ranked as medium significance to safety and 60% are either resolved or ranked as low significance to safety (5).

Conclusions

The experience gained thus far in the ISAP pilot program indicates that the most valuable and unique features of this program are the comprehensive nature of the "topic" definition, the prioritization of issues using a uniform set of plant operational and risk-related measures, and the development of a comprehensive schedule for implementation of all plant improvements. This process promptly identifies the most safety-significant issues for a given plant and implements the necessary changes at the earliest possible time.

Preliminary results of the pilot program study show that when all the regulatory and safety-related topics for a plant are prioritized using a uniform ranking scheme, a significant number of the topics are ranked low. If this conclusion is valid for most plants, this process ensures that the limited utility resources are allocated in the most efficient manner for changes that have the most significant impact on the safety of the plant.

In addition, ISAP is an effective approach in which PSA techniques and plant-specific PSAs are being used extensively for regulatory purposes. In this regard, plant-specific PSA vulnerability analysis provides substantial benefits in reducing the plant operational risk. Experience gained from the Systematic Evaluation Program (SEP) and the ISAP pilot program indicates that PSA techniques in general and plant-specific PSAs in particular are extremely valuable tools for identifying and prioritizing safety-significant problems and resolving regulatory issues. These tools will continue to be important supplements to traditional deterministic analyses.

References

1. "Safety Goals for Nuclear Power Plant Operation", NUREG-0880, May 1983.

2. Systematic Evaluation Program: San Onofre Nuclear Generating Station, Unit 1, NUREG-0829, April 1985.

3. Strip, D.R., "Estimates of the Financial Consequences of Nuclear Power Reactor Accidents," NUREG/CR-2733, SAND82-110, September 1982.

4. Integrated Safety Assessment Program, Millstone Nuclear Power Station, Unit 1, NUREG-1184, April 1987.

5. Atefi, Bahman, et. al. "Review of Risk-Based Evaluation of Integrated Safety Assessment Program Issues for the Haddam Neck Plant", SAIC-87/3004, May 29, 1987.

APPLICATIONS OF PSA METHODOLOGY IN STANDARD DESIGN REVIEWS AND ROUTINE REGULATORY ACTIVITIES AT THE U.S. NUCLEAR REGULATORY COMMISSION

Mark P. Rubin and William B. Hardin
[U.S. Nuclear Regulatory Commission, Washington, D.C., USA]

Keywords

Probabilistic risk assessment, Probabilistic safety assessment, Regulatory decision making, U.S. Nuclear Regulatory Commission

Background

Probabilistic risk assessment and cost/benefit evaluations are finding increasing application at the U.S. Nuclear Regulatory Commission (USNRC), Office of Nuclear Reactor Regulation. An early utilization of these techniques was reported for the Systematic Evaluation Program (Reference 1). More recently, probabilistic risk assessment has been applied to the areas of reactor licensing, backfit evaluations, assessment of plant technical specifications, and evaluation of startup test programs.

The objective of this paper is to present some recent examples of regulatory activities which have involved application of PSA methodology. Difficulties and limitations in applying the techniques to actual cases will be discussed. In reactor licensing, the GESSAR-II Final Design Approval (FDA) will be discussed. In the areas of backfit evaluations and startup tests, a staff assessment of the risk benefit potential for remote shutdown panel tests on a large PWR will be presented. Other examples of PSA applications such as in the assessment of Technical Specification changes will also be mentioned briefly.

Standard Design Reviews

A major use of Probabilistic Risk Assessment methodologies has been in the FDA review for the GESSAR-II standard plant design. This review entailed applications of the USNRC's Severe Accident Policy (Reference 2) which was under development during the GESSAR FDA review. Among other requirements, this policy requires that applications for new custom or standard plants provide, Completion of a probabilistic risk assessment (PRA) and consideration of the severe accident vulnerabilities that the PRA exposes, along with the insights that it may add to the assurance that there is no undue risk to public health and safety. Additionally, prior to approval, the USNRC must demonstrate, Completion of the staff review of the design with a conclusion of safety acceptability using an approach that stresses deterministic engineering analyses and judgment complemented by PRA.

The above process was unique in that it comprised the first instance where probabilistic treatment of severe accidents was an explicit element of the USNRC licensing safety review procedure.

During the course of this review, the USNRC staff and Brookhaven National Laboratory subjected the General Electric GESSAR-II PRA to a detailed assessment. One major goal of this assessment was to develop a clear understanding of the design's risk profile, along with knowledge of corresponding strengths and weaknesses. Both internal and limited external events were within the scope of this study. Significant difficulties were encountered in the treatment of external events for a standardized design which was not yet sited. Yet these could not be excluded from review due to their potentially significant contribution to the total risk profile for the design.

Deterministic assessments and engineering judgment were applied to compile an extensive listing of various plant design improvements. Insights gained from the PRA along with other engineering input were utilized to develop a reduced list of potential design modifications which could result in a safety enhancement. Both preventive and mitigative features were considered within the scope of this work. The staff and its contractors performed a more detailed cost/benefit analysis for this limited list of potential design improvements. They investigated the benefits of the improvements both individually and in various combinations. The analyses used the modified core-melt frequencies developed from the PRA review. Consequence estimates were developed using the staff's upper range source term estimate which was based upon interim improved source term methodology then underway.

For various proposed design modifications, the staff and its contractors estimated the impact of modifications on the frequency of accident classes and on release categories. Revised total core-melt and risk estimates were obtained based on estimates on the impact of the proposed modification upon accident frequency or event progression.

The impact of the various proposed design modifications was determined separately for internal events and seismically initiated events. Major modifications considered included such items as: Ultimate Plant Protection System (UPPS), seismic upgrades, dedicated DC battery chargers, and improved hydrogen control. UPPS, a plant improvement proposed by General Electric, is a simple manually initiated system designed to provide core cooling, primary system depressurization, and containment heat removal without reliance on normal or emergency AC/DC power systems. A summary of staff findings is presented in Tables 1 and 2 (Reference 3). These data were utilized to develop cost/benefit impacts for various modification schemes. Along with other engineering criteria, this information was utilized to arrive at conclusions regarding the most effective modifications to, and the safety acceptability of the final design.

The staff concluded the following design modifications to the GESSAR-II design were necessary to satisfy the staff concerns related to severe-accident considerations for future designs:

o   seismic upgrade to UPPS
o   dedicated power supply to hydrogen ignitor system
o   10-hour station batteries
o   ability to power a DC battery charger from ignitor power supply

Without these changes, the staff estimates the annual public risk from the GESSAR-II design to be approximately 600 person-rems per year. With the changes, the staff estimates a resulting public risk of approximately 240

Cause of core melt	Base case	UPPS	UPPS and seismic upgrade	UPPS and DC charger
Internal event	3.8(-5)*	8.2(-6)	8.2(-6)	5.7(-6)
Seismic event	6.7(-5)	5.9(-5)	4.6(-5)	4.6(-5)
Total	1.1(-4)	6.7(-5)**	5.4(-5)	5.2(-5)

*3.8(-5) = 3.8 x 10^{-5}
** Core-melt estimate includes large contribution from relay chatter. Resolution of this issue could reduce core-melt contribution to approximately $2x10^{-5}$.

Table 1   Core-melt frequency probabilities (per year) for GESSAR-II base case and with design modifications.

Risk	Base Case	UPPS	UPPS seismic	UPPS & igniters	UPPS & perfect hydrogen control	UPPS & seismic upgrade & perfect hydrogen control	UPPS & seismic upgrade with igniters
Internal event risk	130	30	30	30	20	20	30
Seismic risk	630	560	440	260	140	130	210
Total	760	590	470	290	160	150	240

Tabel 2   Estimated accidental releases to the public (person-rems per year) for GESSAR-II base case and with modifications.

person-rems per year. The staff found this to be a worthwhile risk reduction. However, it is acknowledged that these risk estimates inherently include large uncertainties.

Backfit Evaluations-Test Program Planning

In addition to the above case, PRA techniques are being utilized for such actions as backfit evaluation, Technical Specification changes, and test program planning; as well as in support of licensee and vendor submittals. In many cases no plant specific PRA is available, therefore increasing the complexity of a regulatory decision. The GESSAR severe accident assessment above typifies a project which comprises application of a detailed design specific PRA. Some projects allow a less rigorous approach.

One interesting application of PRA techniques involved a plant (large PWR) request to forgo complete functional testing of a second unit's remote shutdown panel. This request was based upon a successful test of the lead unit's remote panel, and argued that this original test demonstrated the design's acceptability.

The staff considered what support existed for the backfit requirement of a unit specific test of the shutdown panel. This issue was subjected to a risk assessment to determine whether the test requirement was cost beneficial. Due to a number of considerations, it was quite difficult to arrive at meaningful cost/benefit estimates of this action. These considerations include the lack of a plant specific PRA, and insufficient information on the impact of restricted testing on the remote shutdown panel reliability. However, sufficient information was available to infer reasonable risk insights into the potential impact of inadequate shutdown panel testing.

Since no plant specific PRA was available, the staff applied a surrogate PRA approach and utilized the Millstone 3 PRA. This study was useful since it modeled in some detail the function of the remote shutdown panel in responding to situations where control room function would be lost. While the Millstone 3 NSSS is of Westinghouse design rather than the study plant's CE NSSS, this did not pose serious problems for our study. Accident scenarios requiring use of the remote shutdown panel are those involving fire damage to the control room, cabling, or instrument areas. Reactor fluid system design and response has little impact on accidents involving such fires. Of more relevance would be the plant's containment response to a core damage event following a fire which impacts plant control ability. Both Millstone and the study plant utilize large dry containments which would be expected to perform roughly the same for a core damage event of this kind.

Since an equivalent fire risk assessment was not available for the study plant, we also utilized the Millstone probabilistic assessment fire analysis for developing our insights. This study indicated that fire sequences were the only accidents requiring remote shutdown panel function. These were identified in the Millstone PRA as TE sequences, and involved fire in the control room, instrument rack room, and cable spreading room. After review of both the utility PRA and Livermore National Laboratory evaluation, the staff concluded that the frequency of these TE sequences would be approximately (3E-6) per reactor year. No mechanical failure modes of the remote shutdown panel were factored into this sequence quantification. Rather, only human failure to actuate the panel were considered. The staff estimated human failures of this nature to be (2E-2) per demand.

Assuming that fire initiated core melt sequence frequency for the study plant was approximately equivalent to that calculated for Millstone 3, our cost/benefit assessment requires a determination of likely remote shutdown panel failure due to causes other than human error. The study plant did not plan to conduct full functional tests of these shutdown panels due to similarity to the Unit 1 panel, which was tested. Engineering judgment would indicate that the lack of complete functional tests would result in some increased system unreliability, perhaps on the order of a few percent. This could be due to installation, calibration, or other system integration errors which could not be discovered without a full function test.

To supplement our engineering judgment estimates in this area, the staff also performed a very brief inspection of the test history in industry for remote shutdown panels. Since required by Regulatory Guide 1.68, approximately 33 units have performed shutdown tests from outside the control room. At least one of these tests, the June 27, 1986 test at Catawba 2, identified serious failures of shutdown panel capability. Due to problems with the remote panel installation, control of the reactor was actually lost and rapid depressurization of the reactor ensued. The plant was recovered when control was returned to the control room. If this had been an actual emergency event requiring function of the remote shutdown panel, it is doubtful that successful plant recovery would have occurred.

Based on the above failure, we would calculate a point estimate of approximately 3 percent for panel failure, due from nonhuman sources. Requantification of the "TE" fire sequences including this failure mode would yield an incremental core melt frequency of approximately (5E-6) per reactor year. Based upon our assumptions presented here, this value represents the core melt reduction worth of remote shutdown panel tests. Both our engineering judgment and limited data review have indicated that mechanical panel failures without testing is at least equal to the assumed panel failure rates due to human error.

To arrive at our cost/benefit conclusions, the accident consequences must be considered. The Millstone 3 PRA found the TE fire sequences resulted in core melt followed by late overpressure containment failure. Similar behavior would be expected by the study plant's large dry containment. This failure mode was identified as "M7" in the Millstone PRA. The conditional mean consequences at the Millstone site for such a release was estimated to be (2E+7) man-rem. The core inventory is similar for the two reactors, however, population density and distribution is quite different. Utilizing calculations from "Estimates of the Financial Consequences of Nuclear Power Reactor Accidents," NUREG/CR-2723, it was possible to estimate that differences in site characteristics would result in approximately a factor of 6 reduction in population dose. This would mean that a similar late overpressure M7 release at the study plant would result in conditional consequences of approximately (4.5E+6) man-rem.

Utilizing our incremental core melt value of 5×10^{-6} per reactor year, we find an expected risk increase of approximately 20 man-rem per year, or 800 man-rem per unit over the 40 year lifetime of the plant.

Cost to the licensee for performing remote shutdown panel tests were assumed to be negligible in that the licensee could perform this test during a power ascension stage of their power ascension test program currently underway, at their next extended shutdown, or refueling outage. The cost of implementation should include test planning, performance, data collection and post test analysis. We estimated that at most two man weeks of engineering support would be required along with 30 man hours of operational support to perform the test. Upper estimates of the test costs would, therefore, be under $20,000 per unit. Utilizing our previously calculated risk reduction worth from the tests of 800 man-rem per unit, we found a cost benefit of $25 per man-rem. Further calculations to include averted onsite risk and other financial considerations were unnecessary in the NRC's judgement, since the conduct of testing was cost effective based solely on the public risk results.

Our simplified study did show a potential increased public risk, due to lack of remote shutdown panel testing, of approximately 800 man-rem per unit over the life of the plant. Assuming that effective testing would eliminate the postulated failure mode (as did occur at Catawba), this public risk can be reduced at a cost of $25 per man-rem and would appear to be a very beneficial action. These conclusions were based upon the above stated assumptions that the fire sequence analysis for the study plant would be somewhat similar to that assembled for Millstone 3. This is not an unreasonable assumption in light of other recent PRAs which show external events such as fire to be an important element in plant risk studies. Based upon the above findings, the U.S. NRC required testing of the study plant's remote shutdown panel.

Summary

The above two examples present extremes in the application of Probabilistic Safety Assessment methodology to regulatory decision making at the U.S. NRC. While the GESSAR Standard Plant Review involved the rigorous application of a plant specific PRA to investigate the benefit of numerous design improvements, the shutdown panel case involved a quite coarse analysis relying on surrogate PRAs to provide some general cost/benefit guidance. Both applications are appropriate and useful in the proper situation. The coarser, simplified approaches continue to be useful in conducting screening evaluations and in establishing trends. In the shutdown panel case, the overwhelming favorable cost/benefit results suggested that more sophisticated techniques would not in themselves be cost/beneficial. In all cases, uncertainties and limitations of the analyses must be clearly understood and considered.

Both rigorous and the more general application of PSA tools continue at the U.S. NRC as an aid to our regulatory decision making. Currently, detailed reliability evaluations have been provided by all four U.S. reactor vendors to support changes in the test intervals of safety related components in the reactor protection system or safety features actuation system. It is expected that PSA/PRA tools will play an increasingly large role in the U.S. NRC's regulatory programs.

References

1.   Application of Probabilistic Risk Assessment Techniques as a Decision
        Tool in the U.S. Nuclear Regulatory Commission's Systematic Evaluation
        Program, M. Rubin, B. Atefi, D. W. Gallagher, R. Liner, Fifth Inter-
        national Meeting on Thermal Reactor Safety, September 1984.

2.   Policy Statement on Severe Reactor Accidents Regarding Future Designs
        and Existing Plants, U.S. Nuclear Regulatory Commission, Federal
        Register, Vol. 50, No. 153, August 8, 1985.

3.   Safety Evaluation Report related to the FDA of the GESSAR-II BWR/6
        Nuclear Island Design, NUREG-0979, Supplement 4, U.S. Nuclear
        Regulatory Commission, July 1985.

RELIABILITY DESIGN OF A CRITICAL FACILITY: AN APPLICATION OF PRA METHODS

Antonio Souza Vieira Neto,
(Instituto de Pesquisas Energéticas e Nucleares, São Paulo, Brasil)
Wagner de Souza Borges,
(Universidade de São Paulo, São Paulo, Brasil)

Abstract

Although a general agreement concerning the enforcement of reliability (probabilistic) design criteria for nuclear utilities is yet to be achieved, PRA methodology can still be used successfully as a project design and review tool, aimed at improving system's prospective performance or minimizing expected accident consequences. In this paper, the potential of such an application of PRA methods is examined in the special case of a critical facility design project currently being developed in Brazil.

1 Introduction

One of the main nuclear engineering research and development projects in Brazil is the design and construction of a critical facility, to be used in experimental neutronic studies.

Despite the low power levels of operation that characterize these facilities, reliability and safety were of particular concern in this project, even in its conceptual design phase, when no precise results were available with respect to the final facility states due to the propagation of accident initiators. Consequently there was a strong motivation to evaluate, as early as that, the reliability characteristics of safety systems and the frequency of occurrence of potentially hazardous accident scenarios, by means of PRA methods. The major objective was to try to integrate the reliability and safety assessment activities with those of design development in order to maintain potential hazards under statistical control.

With this objective in mind the facility's shutdown systems preliminary designs were submited to a reliability analysis to evaluate the failure to scram probability. A goal of 1.0 E-05 for this failure probability was set at this stage, based on performance characteristics of similar conventional shutdown systems of commercial nuclear power plants in operation. This reliability assessment led to improvements on the shutdown systems designs and is detailed to the possible extent in section 3.

Following, with these improvements fed into the project, the frequencies of occurence of potentially hazardous accident scenarios were evaluated to compare them with the generally accepted 1.0 E-07 / year safety goal. This safety assessment is detailed in section 4.

Fault and event tree methodologies were the basic tools used in these studies. The basic assumptions made were the following:

- Maintenance activities are always performed with the facility in shutdown condition;
- The facility will be operating 8 hours / day, 5 days / week, with a total a mission time of 1920 hours for one year of operation.

The WASH-1400 [1] data base was taken as reference in the quantification of the basic events in the fault tree models, exept for the "rod fails to insert" event in which case data was obtained from [2].

2 The Shutdown Systems

The following shutdown systems will be of interest throughout this paper:

- **Rod Insertion Mechanism (RIM)** - this system, when actuated, deenergizes the control/safety rods magnets, shutting the facility down if at least two of the four rods are inserted in the facility core;
- **Moderator Discharge System (MDS)** - this system, when actuated, produces the opening of two valves, to let flow out the water (coolant / moderator) from the facility tank, shutting the facility down if at least one of the valves operates satisfactorily.

Both of these systems are automatically actuated by the protection system which, in its original form, consisted of six protection channels (two period channels and four power channels). The RIM is actuated on first abnormal period and power levels, and the MDS on second abnormal period and power levels. A push button manual atuaction of these systems is also provided. Furthermore, since valves in MDS are air operated and actuated by a solenoid valve, support systems failures such as loss of electric power or loss of air pressure, are safe in the sense that they actuate RIM or MDS. Figure 2-1 shows the integrated shutdown systems functional block diagram, where I1 and I2 represent the RIM and MDS interlock circuit, respectively, and the Ci's (i = 1, 2, ..., 6) represent the protection channels.

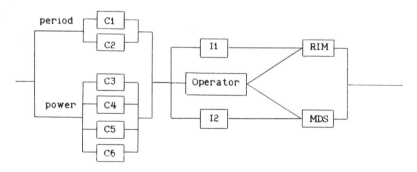

Figure 2-1 Funcional Block Diagram

3 Reliability Analysis of the Shutdown Systems

The reliability analysis of the facility's shutdown systems concentrated on evaluating the probability of the failure to scram event, given a continuous reactivity insertion at the rate of 5 ¢/s. At that stage in design development no precise information was available concerning the maximum reactivity insertion rate and the 5 ¢/s figure was suggested by the specialists as a reference.

Figure 3-1 shows the power curves corresponding to the cases in which this insertion rate starts when the operating power equals 0.001 W, 1 W, 50 W and 100 W. A detailed exam of these curves, taking into account the fact that facility shutdown occurs one second after RIM actuation and eight seconds after MDS actuation, leads to the following conclusion: if reactivity insertion starts when the operating power lies betweem ≈ 0 W and 1 W (50 W and 100 W), only the period (power) channels will be able to produce facility shutdown before power reaches excessively high levels.

For this reason, three accident conditions were considered, corresponding to pre reactivity insertion operating power ranges of 0 W ∟—— 1 W (condition AC1); 1 W ∟—— 50 W (condition AC2) and 50 W ∟—— 100 W (condition AC3). Under each of these conditions credit was given only to those protection channels that could produce facility shutdown before an excessive power increase. It is also worth noting that the facility's power operanting range is 0 W to 100 W.

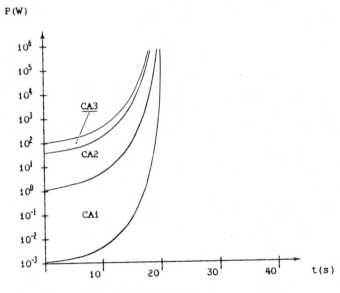

Figure 3-1 Power Curves

3.1 Failure to Scram Fault Tree

The fault tree from which the results of this study were obtained, was constructed from preliminary design documentation. The model covers not only RIM and MDS hardware, but also the protection channels and interlock circuits hardware. Constructive details of this fault tree are presented in [3].

3.2 Fault Tree Quantification

A first quantification of the fault tree was run in the most unfavourable case, which is that of unrepairable basic events. The results obtained showed that only under condition AC1 the reliability goal of 1.0 E-05

719

for the failure to scram probability was not attained. In this case failures
in protection channels contributed with 95 % of total top event probability.
It is worth noticing that no credit was given to MDS in this case, since an
expectation existed towards the fact that power could possibly reach
excecively high levels within the time necessary for MDS to shut the facility
down.

From this point on, the analysis concentrated on accident condition
AC1 and examined the joint effect of alternative protection channels network
configurations and periodic testing strategies, on top event probability. More
precisely, successive runs for fault trees quantification were made
corresponding to combinations of two and three period channel alternatives for
the protection system with one of the four periodic testing strategies of
table 3.2-1. The main results obtained are shown in table 3.2-2.

Basic Events	Periodic Testing Strategies			
	A	B	C	D
Failure of channel to operate	8 h	8 h	8 h	8 h
Shift in channel calibration	480 h	320 h	160 h	80 h
Short to power (RIM interlock)	1920 h	1920 h	1920 h	1920 h
Short to power (other)	8 h	8 h	8 h	8 h

Table 3.2-1 Periodic Testing Strategies

The the results of table 3.2-2, indicated that better performance
was possible provided that the protection channels network contained three
period channels instead of two, and that maintenance procedures satisfied the
requirements of periodic testing strategies A, B, C or D.

It can also be noted from table 3.2-2 that further improvement on
the failure to scram probability will depend predominantly on circuitry
improvements.

4 Accident Scenarios Evaluation

In this session, the improved 3 period and 3 power channels version
of the protection system is considered under maintenance strategy B and the
following two categories of initiating events are examined: reactivity
insertions and power distribution anomalies; and radioactive release from a
system or component [3]. Of foremost importance in each of these categories
are:

IE1: uncontroled rod withdrawal at the speed of 1 mm/s (corresponding to
the true project continuous reactivity insertion rate of 1.8 ¢/s) and

IE2: experimental apparatus drop (corresponding to an instantaneous
reactivity insertion of 66 ¢), respectively.

STRA-TEGIES	NC*	Shift in Channels Calibrat.	Short to Power in 3 of 4 Magn.	Short to Power in Interlocks	Failure to Insert 3 of Scram Rods	TOTAL
Unrep.	2	5, 7 E-03	ϵ^*	3, 1 E-04	ϵ	6, 0 E-03
	3	3, 9 E-04	ϵ	3, 1 E-04	ϵ	7, 0 E-04
A	2	3, 8 E-04	ϵ	1, 3 E-06	ϵ	3, 8 E-04
	3	7, 5 E-06	ϵ	1, 3 E-06	ϵ	8, 8 E-06
B	2	1, 7 E-04	ϵ	1, 3 E-06	ϵ	1, 7 E-04
	3	2, 2 E-06	ϵ	1, 3 E-06	ϵ	3, 5 E-06
C	2	4, 3 E-05	ϵ	1, 3 E-06	ϵ	4, 4 E-05
	3	2, 8 E-07	ϵ	1, 3 E-06	ϵ	1, 6 E-06
D	2	1, 1 E-05	ϵ	1, 3 E-06	ϵ	1, 4 E-05
	3	3, 6 E-08	ϵ	1, 3 E-06	ϵ	1, 3 E-06

Table 3.2-2 Unavailability Contributions

*Note: NC = number of period channels and $\epsilon \leq 1, 0$ E-10.

4.1 Event Trees

The event trees heading were chosen in such a way that no basic event is common to the fault tree development of two or more of them. Furthermore, in order to have the accident propagation cronology better represented, an option was made to repeat system functions in the event trees headings.

Figures 4.1-1 and 4.1-2 are the event tree models for the initiating events IE1 and IE2, respectively, where PoC and PeC denote the power and period protection channel network, respectively, and the Vi's (i = 1, 2) denote the valves of MDS.

Each of these models contains three accident scenarios which depict an undesirable final condition with power level crossing the 1000 W threshold. No further quantification or qualification of the final conditions corresponding to the accident scenarios was possible at the time this study was being developed.

4.2 Annual Frequency of the Accident Scenarios

The last column of figures 4.1-1 and 4.1-2 contains the annual frequencies of each accident scenario resulting from the propagation of the initiating events IE1 and IE2, described earlier in the session, divided by their annual frequencies F1 and F2, respectively. Observe that whenever an undesirable or hazardous final condition could possibly arise, an annual frequency below the generally acceptable 1.0 E-07 safety bound is obtained, provided F1 and F2 do not exceed 1,0 E-05 / year.

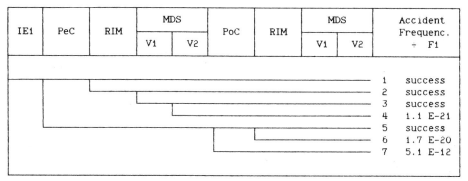

Figure 4.1-1   IE1 Event Tree

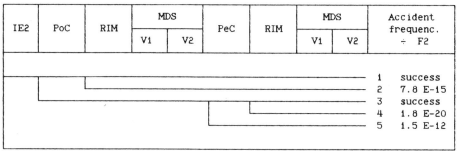

Figure 4.1-2   IE2 Event Tree

5 Final Remarks

One last comment concerns common-cause failure contributions. Since the analysis was conducted during the early stages of project development, concern with respect to common cause contributions where qualitative in nature. More precisely common-cause contributors where identified to allow the application of suitable preventive design criteria.

The application of other analysis techniques such as the Beta-factor method and other Markovian alternatives, was left to second stage in development when more detailed documentation become available.

6 References

[1]   U.S. NUCLEAR REGULATORY COMMISSION. Reactor safety study: an assessment of accident risks in U.S. commercial nuclear power plants. Washington, DC. 1975. (NUREG-0480).

[2]   U.S. NUCLEAR REGULATORY COMMISSION. Antecipated Transients without scram for light water reactors. Washington, DC. 1978. (NUREG-0480).

[3]   COMISSAO NACIONAL DE ENERGIA NUCLEAR. Final safety analysis report: critical facility - IPEN-CNEN/SP. São Paulo, Brazil. To be published in 1987.

RECENT AND PROSPECTIVE USES OF PROBABILISTIC SAFETY ASSESSMENT AS AN AID TO NUCLEAR POWER PLANT MANAGEMENT

N J Holloway
Safety & Reliability
Directorate
U K Atomic Energy Authority
Wigshaw Lane, Culcheth
Warrington WA3 4NE, UK.

J Caisley
OECD Nuclear Energy
Agency
38, Boulevard Suchet
75016 Paris, France

M V Bonaca.
Northeast Utilities
PO Box 270
Hartford
Connecticut, USA

(All authors are members of Task 7 of Principal Working Group 5 of NEA/CSNI)

Abstract

Although the techniques of PSA were originally developed for the assessment of 'bottom line' risks to the public, there has been an increasing realization, in recent years, of their potential in general safety and reliability management

A CSNI task force on 'PSA as an aid to NPP management' has been collecting information about such applications in a variety of OECD countries. These applications of PSA based safety management can now be found in the conceptual design process, detailed design and construction, normal plant operation, and the evaluation of life extension for aged plants. Information has been collected exemplifying applications to each of the above stages of plant life. Although no one plant has exemplified all stages of application in sequence, it is now possible to look forward to such integrated approaches for some plants currently under design and construction.

1. Introduction

1.1 The plant management perspective on PSA

The plant management perspective on PSA, exemplified in this paper by that of Northeast Utilities (USA), is now substantially different from the original perspectives which led to the WASH-1400 PRA [1] and related subsequent studies. WASH-1400 was motivated primarily by the desire to quantify the overall risks of accidents at US NPPs, because the absolute magnitudes of these risks were unknown and decisions concerning their acceptability lacked essential information. The detailed reasoning behind the calculation of accident sequences and associated risks were a means to the primary end of quantitative risk assessment.

In contrast, the plant management perspective is that the 'process' of WASH-1400 - the detailed analysis of how accidents might happen - is the primary 'product' of PSA, while the quantification of risks is secondary. The accident analysis provides the essential understanding of the plant operations which is the key to PSA based safety management, while the numerical results play a secondary role, in such matters as prioritization of issues and comparisons with risk guidelines. This perspective is entirely in accordance with that of the Lewis Report [2], in which the virtues of the accident sequence analysis structure were extolled while the probabilistic quantification was significantly qualified on the grounds of uncertainties and lack of data.

An obvious consequence of the plant management perspective on PSA is that level 1 analysis has priority over levels 2 and 3. Plants run in level 1 states all the time whereas there have been only two examples (TMI-2 and Chernobyl) of plants in states covered by levels 2 and 3 analysis. Furthermore, the systems (including containment systems) whose states dominate the plant behaviour in level 1, are more clearly amenable to management by the operators than are some of the important phenomena and offsite events in levels 2 and 3. Thus,'PSA as an aid to NPP management' refers primarily to level 1 analysis rather than to the 3 level process which constitutes complete probabilistic risk assessment (PRA).

1.2 The effects of the management perspective on PSA organization

In the early days of PSA, most of the technical capability required for the process resided with the major vendors and consultant firms, and their pioneering studies such as WASH-1400, the Zion and Indian Point PSSs [3,4], and the German Risk Study [5] provided the basis on which many other organizations may build their own analyses.

However, plants are managed and operated by utilities, and the most effective use of PSA techniques in plant management requires a first hand capability rather than a second hand one. Thus, an increasing number of utilities are establishing their own organizations and capabilities in PSA, so that they can gain a first hand understanding of their plants' likely behaviour in accident conditions to accompany the detailed understanding of systems and normal operations which is usually the operating organization's privilege alone.

The CSNI task force has observed a number of situations in which utilities have planned and created their own PSA capabilities, so that they can perform a study unassisted if necessary. Examples include :

Northeast Utilities	-	Connecticut Yankee PSS
Ontario Hydro	-	Darlington PS Evaluation
EdF	-	PWR 1300MWe (Paluel) PSA

and there are other cases of utilities which have either set up their own capability or are in the process of so doing.

The Northeast Utilities PSA organization, which serves as the lead example for the CSNI task force and for this paper, is illustrated in Fig. 1. This organization first performed the Millstone 3 PSS in conjunction with Westinghouse, and in so doing acquired the necessary technology to perform further studies in house. Complete in-house studies on the older Connecticut Yankee and Millstone 1 plants have now been performed.

The Northeast organization illustrates a number of features which appear to be conducive to the effective operation of PSA in plant management, although we do not intend to suggest that these are the only effective options. Firstly, the boundaries of the PSA team and their responsibilities are well defined. This enables the PSA experts tointeract closely and also enables the utility management to identify the costs and results associated with the PSA efforts. Secondly, and most importantly, the PSA team has many working level and management level links with the station operators and station engineers. This fosters a mutual understanding and a speedy communication of information in response to operational or regulatory issues as they arise. The success of the links with the stations has encouraged the PSA team to forge similar links with engineering design teams within the utility, so that design and PSA based evaluation can be run in parallel rather than sequentially, to exploit the PSA based management insights which are valuable in the design process.

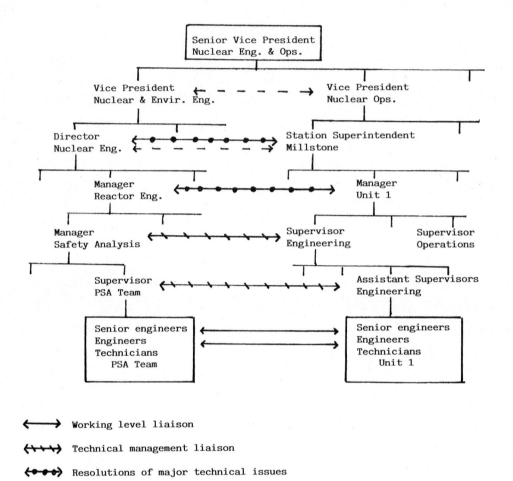

```
┌──────────────────────┐
│ Senior Vice President │
│ Nuclear Eng. & Ops.   │
└──────────────────────┘
```

Vice President   ◄─ ─ ─ ─ ─►   Vice President
Nuclear & Envir. Eng.   Nuclear Ops.

Director   ◄─●─●─●─●─●─►   Station Superintendent
Nuclear Eng.   ◄─ ─ ─ ─ ─ ─►   Millstone

Manager   ◄─●─●─●─●─●─●─►   Manager
Reactor Eng.   Unit 1

Manager   ◄─v─v─v─v─v─►   Supervisor   Supervisor
Safety Analysis   Engineering   Operations

Supervisor   ◄─v─v─v─v─v─v─►   Assistant Supervisors
PSA Team   Engineering

┌──────────────────┐   ┌──────────────────┐
│ Senior engineers │ ◄──────────────►   │ Senior engineers │
│ Engineers   │   │ Engineers   │
│ Technicians   │ ◄──────────────►   │ Technicians   │
│   PSA Team   │   │   Unit 1   │
└──────────────────┘   └──────────────────┘
```

◄─────►   Working level liaison

◄─v─v─►   Technical management liaison

◄─●─●─►   Resolutions of major technical issues

◄─ ─ ─►   Policy liaison and resolution


Key Features :   Horizontal links at all levels
                 PSA team well defined
                 'Ultimate' resolutions still within 'Nuclear' executive levels
                 Staff exchanges between Engineering and Stations/Units


Figure 1.   :   Northeast Utilities Organization relevant to PSA for Millstone 1
                (Organization for other NU plants PSA is similar)
```

2. Selected Examples from PSA Based Safety Management

2.1 Conceptual design management - the UK utilities' use of PSA based design

During the development of the later Advanced Gas-Cooled Reactors at Heysham and Torness, and the development of the Sizewell B PWR design, the UK electric utilities (CEGB and SSEB) have used PSA based guidelines [6]. A principal guideline amongst these is :

> The total frequency of all accidents leading to uncontrolled releases should be less than 10^{-6} per reactor year.

This guideline, and the related guideline of 10^{-7} uncontrolled releases per year per fault sequence, is used from the earliest design conceptualization to determine such matters as the requirements for redundancy and diversity of protection systems. A consequence of the application of the guideline has been the requirement to provide two diverse fast acting shutdown systems for both the AGR and PWR plants and to provide a capability in the Sizewell B PWR for survival of complete loss of offsite and onsite AC power.

The AGR fault analyses, which have been used to justify the designs against the PSA based guidelines, are now being incorporated into a PSA-based 'Essential Systems Status Monitor'[7] at the Heysham 2 AGR. As this plant starts operating, the status monitor will be used in 'managing' the essential system reliability to ensure that the operating plant conforms with the PSA-based design intent.

The UK Atomic Energy Authority, in its roles as operator and regulator of prototype NPPs, has been using PSA-based safety guidelines, based on permissible frequencies and magnitudes of releases, to design and manage plants. These guidelines are also applied to the conduct of experiments in prototype NPPs.

2.2 Detailed design management - Ontario Hydro's Darlington evaluation

The application of PSA to CANDU design evaluation began with the CANDU vendor (AECL) performing individual system reliability evaluations and developed into the studies known as 'Safety Design Matrices' [8].

Following from these early analyses, Ontario Hydro established its own PSA team to perform the Darlington Probabilistic Safety Evaluation (DPSE) [9] for its 4 x 850MWe CANDU plants at Darlington. This study is a major detailed level 1 analysis of plants during the last stages of detailed design and construction.

Although the DPSE has been performed at a fairly late stage of design, it has identified quite a large number (85 at the time of Ref 9) of beneficial design changes, which have been implemented by the plant engineers and designers. The detail of the DPSE has enabled design improvements to be identified at very low levels in system fault trees, where relatively small design details can have major impacts on system dependencies and interactions. The in-house organization, origins and motivation of the DPSE were thought by the PSA team to promote a more inquiring attitude to plant safety design than might have been the case had the study been performed only to demonstrate an overall numerical result. It is also interesting to note that most of the design changes arising from the DPSE were indicated by the fault analysis without recourse to the numerical quantification of probabilities

It is quite clear that the DPSE will continue life in a safety management role for plant operation when the Darlington station is in its operating phase.

2.3 Operating plant management - Northeast Utilities' Millstone 1 PSS and the USNRC Integrated Safety Assessment Programme (ISAP)

The Northeast Utilities Millstone 1 PSS, performed in-house following the PSA technology transfer from Westinghouse (in the Millstone 3 PSS performance), is now used in two distinct, but related, management activities.

The first is the utility's own management of safety for the Millstone 1 BWR, following the lines already discussed in section 1.2, and following on from one of the original motivating incidents - multiple system failures during Hurricane Belle in 1976. The second, more recent activity, is the use of the PSS as the basis for safety discussion and resolution between the utility and the USNRC.

This second activity, in which the utility puts up the initial stake of a PSA already performed, is a logical regulatory development from the utility's use of PSA in managing its own affairs. The initial purpose of ISAP was the evaluation of backfitting priorities in the NRC-mandated backfit programme and it has been used for that purpose. However, the exposure of the utility's technical safety management process to the regulator has the much more general benefit of enabling the regulator to observe the detailed insights available to the utility and the competence of the utility to manage the technical safety of its plants.

2.4 Aging plant and backfit re-evaluation - NOK's Beznau studies

The 2 x 350 MWe PWRs at NPP Beznau have been run at high availability by Nordostschweizerische Kraftwerke AG (NOK) since 1969/71. However, the Swiss regulations require that older plants be upgraded to meet the substantially more demanding safety requirements of modern times, and as a result, an add-on bunkered safety system has been under consideration in the last few years [10].

The original bunkered system design, known as NANO (Nachrusten Notstandsystem/ Notstromversorgung) was evaluated as very expensive, and with a very long (9yr) prospective construction time. The cost-effectiveness of such a system was far from apparent to the utility. Thus, in search of a viable alternative safety upgrade, NOK initiated a PSA-based evaluation of the plant as it was, and of possible PSA-based modifications. Since this was the first NOK PSA, consultants (from PLG and Westinghouse) played a leading part in its performance, under the utility's direction. The results displayed some interesting features.

One of the backfit options which received a favourable evaluation was the installation of an additional single train system (denoted 'Re-Re') and the modification of various existing procedures and plant items to enhance its effectiveness. This was found to be cheaper and safer than the original 2-train NANO proposal, although falling short of the effectiveness of a 2-train NANO plus the minor modifications. It is interesting to note that neither the single train system, nor the collection of minor modifications, would normally have been recommended without the benefit of the PSA-based insights. The single train system would not have met the single failure criterion and would thus not have been considered, and the minor improvements would not have affected the deterministic safety considerations. However, in a PSA basis, a single train which is capable of operation is quite valid for risk reduction, as are many minor modifications which have no significance in traditional deterministic safety analysis. Thus the Beznau case illustrates an output of PSA-based evaluation which is different in kind from the outputs of traditional deterministic safety evaluations alone, and which generates options often inaccessible to the traditional evaluation methods.

3. Conclusions

3.1 Current status of PSA-based management

The CSNI task force survey of current applications of PSA-based management in OECD utilities has found several positive examples. In these examples, utilities have made a substantial commitment in establishing their own PSA capabilities and have reaped even more substantial rewards as a result of their enhanced understanding of their plant and the benefits which derive therefrom. These benefits include more effective analysis of plant engineering and operations, creation of an effective basis for regulatory interfaces, and avoidance of both unnecessary risks and unnecessary expenditures. These benefits derive primarily from the utilities' commitment and organization in the PSA performance rather than from the merits of any particular PSA methodologies.

3.2 Prospective integrated applications to whole plant life cycles

Although no one plant has yet benefitted from PSA application throughout its life cycle, it is now apparent that such an integrated application is feasible for some plants currently under design or construction. The examples from the Darlington station and the recent UK AGRs illustrate the transition between applications during detailed design and construction and applications to operation and the prospects for Sizewell B and other recent LWR designs suggest that applications from design concept onwards will soon be manifested as far as the operating phase. This integrated use is a natural progression from the current status, in which applications to the various life cycle stages are apparent in plants of different ages.

3.3 Prospects for PSA-based regulation of safety management

Some recent developments, notably the implementation of the Integrated Safety Assessment Programme in the USA and the implementation of PSA-based design safety guidelines in the UK, raise the prospect of an effective PSA-based regulation method.

The use of PSA as a plant management tool, which emphasises the structural rather than the numerical probabilistic aspects of accident development, can provide the regulator with the following insights :

> The detailed plant and system knowledge of the utility/operators.
> A view of the competence of the utility to understand its plants.
> A flexible scheme for inspecting safety management options.
> A numerical evaluation where necessary.

The use of a plant specific PSA as a basis for the interface between utility and regulator can allow the regulator to see, and judge, how the utility is managing its own safety affairs. The use of such a scheme, in which the utility takes the lead in PSA-based management and the regulator observes the process in the detail which PSA provides, may become one of the most effective ways in which regulators can ensure that utilities fulfil their obligations to operate their plants safely.

Acknowledgements

The authors wish to acknowledge the members of CSNI Task Force 7 of the CSNI Principal Working Group 5, who are participating in a task of which this paper is an interim report. The other task force members are :

R I Barrett (USNRC), H-P Balfanz (TuV West Germany), J I Calvo (CSN Spain), S Chakraborty (Nuclear Inspectorate Switzerland), M Cullingford (IAEA), P Gumley (AECL Canada), P M Herttrich (BMUNR West Germany), B E Horne (CEGB UK), J-M Lanore (IPSN France), B T F Liwaang (SKI Sweden), T Tobioka & K Abe (JAERI Japan), R Virolainen (STUK Finland),

References

1. The Reactor Safety Study, WASH-1400, N Rasmusson et al, Oct 1975.
2. Risk assessment review group report to the US Nuclear Regulatory Commission, NUREG/CR-0400, H W Lewis et al, Sept 1978.
3. Zion probabilistic safety study, Commonwealth Edison Company of Chicago, Sept 1981.
4. Indian Point probabilistic safety study, Power Authority of the state of New York & Consolidated Edison Company of New York Inc., 1982.
5. Deutsche Risikostudie Kernkraftwerke (German Risk Study), Verlag TuV Rheinland, 1979.
6. Design safety criteria for CEGB nuclear power stations, Central Electricity Generating Board UK, March 1982.
7. The use of PSA techniques in a CEGB power station operational environment, B E Horne, 1986 (**).
8. Revision of Gentilly 2 Safety Design Matrix studies, R Comeau et al, 1986 (**).
9. Application of PSA to the safety design verification of Darlington Nuclear Generating Station, V M Raina, 1986 (**).
10. Risk-benefit evaluation of backfit options at nuclear power plant Beznau, S Sahgal & A Torri, 1986 (**).

(**) Papers at the CSNI workshop on 'PSA as an aid to NPP management', Brighton, UK, May 1986 (Proceedings - CSNI report No 125).

USE OF PSA METHODS FOR IMPROVING OPERATIONAL SAFETY OF VVER TYPE NUCLEAR UNITS

Előd Holló, Lajos Vöröss
(Institute for Electric Power Research, Budapest, Hungary)

Abstract

The approach to safety of VVER-type nuclear units has been based on conventional deterministic technique and on well-proved defense-in-depth principle. Currently probabilistic safety assessment of nuclear units of this type under construction and operation in Hungary was initiated to improve their operational safety. The article summarizes results gained from small LOCA event sequence quantification carried out presently and gives a state-of--the-art survey of methods used for the analysis.

1. PSA-activity in Hungary

Research and development works in Hungarian institutions have been carried out for eight years. At the early stage, methodological development and code adaptation with some examples for gaining experiences have been done, while practical use of fault tree/event tree method has been under work since 1983.

A comprehensive feasibility study summarized aims of the reliability and safety analysis on the probabilistic bases. Level-1. PSA was considered as the main important tool for answering some questions, as follows:

- what are the core melt frequencies of our nuclear units for event sequencies initiated by LOCA's and transients,
- what are the importance of the safety related systems and components from the point of view of their contributions to the potential risk,
- which parts - if any - of the operational, maintenance and testing procedures should be changed to improve the operational safety of the plant.

The Hungarian PSA-activity has always been in very close connection with international cooperation, expecially with the PSA-program of IAEA.

In 1985 Hungary joined to the IAEA's Interregional Project on PSA.

Hungary hosts the biennial workshops on "Advances in Reliability Analysis and PSA". The first meeting was organized in 1985 and the second one is to be organized in October 1987, with case study presentation of the CMEA - countries participants and Peer-revierers from countries where PSA - experiences and experts are available. PC-based safety information tools and expert systems is to be demonstrated, as well.

In the CMEA, with participation of all member countries operating VVER-type reactors, a coordinated activity is being initiated in the field of PSA. Exchange of information is being planned regularly on specialist meetings.

Present status of Hungarian PSA - activity is as follows:

- event sequences initiated with large and small break LOCA have been analysed,

- reliability data bank in Paks NPP is being established,

- some case studies for prediction of safety related system reliability have been carried out (e.g. diesel-generator,ECCS),

- testing and maintenance practice of the main condenser cooling system have been investigated,

- software development for personnel computer (PC) systems is going on with aim of improving data handling, sensitivity analysis, uncertainties, etc.

From these results, small break LOCA event sequence analysis and ECCS test frequency optimisation is being reported in this paper. This work was carried out in the frame of a national coordinated research program on nuclear safety initiated in 1986. Within this R/D program strong emphasis has been devoted to PSA of Hungarian nuclear units, specially after Chernobil accident. With the coordination of VEIKI, several institutions /ERŐTERV engineering company, PAKS NPP, etc./ are involved in the PSA program.

2 Small LOCA Event Sequence Analysis

2.1 Event Sequence Description

The type of top events of concern for the present study are core meltdown and radioactivity release within the hermetic rooms initiated by small LOCA event. The simplified sequence of succesful functional interactions of safety systems can be summarized as follow (Fig.1.):

- initiating event (D=25 mm LOCA) occurs before annual refuelling,

- control logic shuts-down the reactor (SDR) and starts-up the emergency diesel generators (SUD), the unit is switched off from the external power network. After diesel start-up (DG) the high pressure emergency core cooling system is operated in injection mode taking borated water from its vessel (ECCSI),

- within 5-6 min the hydroaccumulators flood the reactor (HA), as well as the hermetic rooms spray system is operated in injection mode (HRSSI),

- after 0,5-1,5 hours the vessels of HRSS and ECCS systems become empty and the control logics (CLSS,CLCC) switch their pumps over to sump suction. From this time both systems operate in recirculation mode (HRSSR, ECCSR),

- the nuclear unit is supposed to be connected back to the external network within one day.

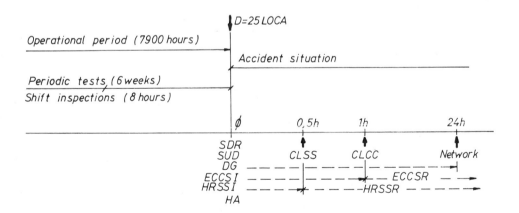

Figure 1: Simplified Sequence of Interactions

2.2. Survey of Analysis Methodology

Event tree construction

Both functional and systemic event trees are constructed to determine interrelations of small LOCA initiating event and related
plant safety system failures. "Small event tree, large fault tree"
concept was choosen, i.e. within level-I analysis 4 front-line
nodes are incorporated within the event tree.
Dependencies involved are as follows:

- if RSS fails, core melt occurs,
- if ECCSI fails, ECCSR fails, too, and core melt occurs,
- if HRSSI fails, HRSSR and radioactivity removal within hermetic
  rooms fail, too /beyond Level-I analysis/,
- actuation of redundant trains is dependent on operators.

Fault tree construction

Fault trees of front-line and support systems are constructed with
modular structure. Each system is functionally split into technological, electrical, and control sub-systems, their joint fault
tree was constructed by using the CAT methodology. Joint fault
trees are setup for stand-by and long-term operational periods. As
a summary, the small LOCA event tree involves about 25 fault trees,
each incorporates 10-20 component failures.

Modelling limitations

For human interaction failures two-level task-oriented models are
applied. On event tree level manual malfunctions during accident
identification, evaluation, and decision making are considered,
failures of interactions are modelled within system fault trees.
Only "error of ommission" failure mode is involved.

For common cause failures simple β-factor models are used. No
external effects (fire, earthquake) are considered. Only common inherent failures of redundant equipments of the same type as well
as multiple manual failures of test and maintenance are involved.

As very limited operational failure statistics exist for VVER-type
reactors, generic failure data from PRA-PSA procedure guides were
used.

2.3 Results of Quantification

For quantification of event sequences PREP/KITT codes were used.

Occurence frequency of small LOCA (of D=25 mm) is estimated as
1×10^{-3}/y. Probabilities of redundant safety system failures are
given in Table 1/a. Frequency of core melt final event due to
small LOCA is estimated as $6,56 \times 10^{-6}$/y. As for quantification generic data were used, the absolut values presented can only be
used as general orientation for expectable ranges of exact quantities.

Importance of safety systems within influencing event sequences due
to small LOCA are characterized by "risk reduction worth" parameters
introduced by Fussel-Vesely. RRW values for basic front-line systems
and for sub-systems of ECCSR are given in Table 1/b. Numerical values illustrate highest importance of support /intermediate and se-
fety/ cooling systems in influencing core melt frequency.

System Identifier	Failure Redundancy	Failure Probability $[1/y]$
RSS	multiple	$1,74 \times 10^{-5}$
ECCSI	$3 \rightarrow 3$	$2,28 \times 10^{-3}$
ECCSR	$3 \rightarrow 3$	$4,27 \times 10^{-3}$

Table 1/a: Failure Probability of Front-Line Systems

System Identifier	RRW_{abs}	RRW_{rel} $[\%]$
RSS	1,002	0,3
ECCSI	1,52	34,7
ECCSR	2,85	65 (!)
for ECCSR: diesel system	1,03	3,2
intermediate cooling system	1,5	33,3
safety cooling system	2,04	51,2(!)
energency core cooling system	1,02	1,7

Table 1/b: RRW Values for small LOCA

3. ECCS Test Frequency Optimisation

Within small LOCA analysis sensitivity study of high pressure
emergency core cooling system test frequency was carried out. The
study was extended to the main cooling circuit (ECCS), as well as
to its support systems, i.e. to diesel unit (DG), to control/in-
strumentation (CI), to intermediate (ICC) and safety (SCC) cooling
circuits. Only stand-by and start-up operational modes were analyzed, 11 month stand-by period was considered. For quantification
the FRANTIC code was used.

Numerical results gained for one train are summarized on Fig.2.
/in practice the optimal test frequency is independent of the
order of redundancy/.

Numerical data consider 1 month residual heat removal period.

Two main issues can be deduced:

- the failure probability of one comlex ECCS train slighthy changes due to different test frequencies. The range of changes is $6 \times 10^{-2} \rightarrow 1 \times 10^{-1}/y$ related to $1 \rightarrow 6$ weeks test periods,
- the ECCS failure probability is mostly sensitive to the diesel unit test frequency. Therefore an introduction of a separated test procedure for the diesel units is recommended.

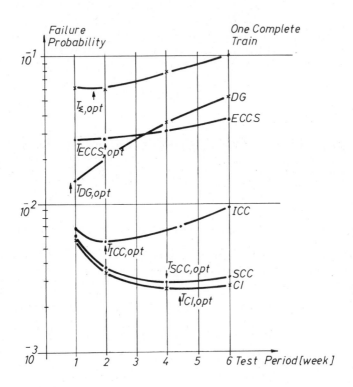

Figure 2: Results of ECCS Test Frequency Sensitivity Study

HIPRIM: A LIMITED-SCOPE LIVING PRA FOR THE EDWIN I. HATCH
NUCLEAR PLANT

Anees A. Farruk,[1] and John W. Stetkar[2]
[1--Southern Company Services, Inc., Birmingham, Alabama, USA]
[2--Pickard, Lowe and Garrick, Inc., Newport Beach, California, USA]

Abstract

The Hatch Integrated Plant Risk Model (HIPRIM) is a state-of-the-art,
limited-scope, "living" probabilistic risk assessment (PRA) for the Edwin I.
Hatch Nuclear Plant, Units 1 and 2. The HIPRIM models were developed jointly by
Southern Company Services, Inc. (SCS), and Pickard, Lowe and Garrick, Inc.
(PLG), in 1985. An example HIPRIM application analyzes the risk sensitivity
from proposed changes to the allowed outage times (AOT) and surveillance test
intervals (STI) for seven safety-related systems covered by the plant technical
specifications.

1 Background

The primary motivation for this project was the desire for an integrated
risk-based model of the plant that could be used to support internal utility
decision making. The objectives delineated at the beginning of the project
provided a focus for the HIPRIM study that was somewhat different from previous
limited-scope PRAs.

The basic scope of HIPRIM was defined as a Level 1 risk study that would focus
on core damage event sequences initiated from internal plant conditions.
"External" events were not included although the models could not preclude their
addition at a later date. The most important objectives affecting the focus and
level of detail in the plant response and system models were the desire to use
HIPRIM to evaluate proposed component and system modifications, design change
requests, changes to surveillance and maintenance procedures, and to provide a
risk-based foundation for changes to the plant technical specifications.
Another important goal for the study was to develop the HIPRIM models in an
interactive computer-based format that would allow rapid analysis turnaround
time.

2 The Hatch Risk Model

An important decision made early during the project was to strike an appropriate
balance between the "breadth" and "depth" of the HIPRIM models. Previous
limited-scope studies have taken a relatively broad modeling perspective to
identify, most importantly, the general level of risk from a plant. This broad
perspective generally does not provide adequate detail in the plant and systems
models for answering the types of questions required by the HIPRIM objectives.

The "breadth" of the HIPRIM models was limited by excluding the effects from
"external" initiating events, by grouping the "internal" initiating events into
functional categories, and by modeling only a few limited operator recovery
actions. These limitations allowed expansion of the depth of detail for

explicitly modeling a larger number of causes for system failures and for developing detailed models of intersystem dependencies that are equivalent to those normally found only in completed full-scope studies.

Figure 1 shows the basic framework of the HIPRIM models. The four initiating event categories were selected to encompass plant and systems response. The categories are "general transients" (e.g., turbine trip, reactor scram, loss of feedwater, etc.), loss of offsite power, small break loss of coolant accident (LOCA), and large break LOCA. Plant response to scram failures (i.e., ATWS) was modeled explicitly for each of these event categories.

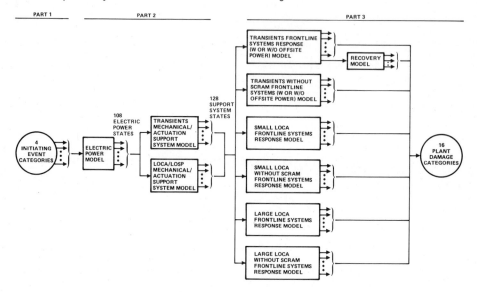

Figure 1: HIPRIM Plant Model

Detailed models of all plant support systems were based on a comprehensive set of plant dependency matrices. The electric power event trees include models for the plant switchyard, 4,160V AC buses and diesel generators (one of which is shared between the two units), 600V AC buses, 125V DC buses, and portions of the 120V vital AC instrument power system. The mechanical/actuation system event trees model response of the analog transmitter trip system, reactor protection system, plant service water, control room HVAC system, reactor building closed cooling water, plant instrument air, and drywell pneumatic systems.

The frontline event trees include models for 14 plant systems that control reactor vessel inventory and core heat removal after each of the initiating events. The 16 plant damage states include important information about the timing and pressure at which core damage occurs, the availability of water for debris bed cooling, and the availability of containment protection and isolation systems for the interface with a Level 2 containment model.

The event trees and all system models were modularized in the RISKMAN® modeling format (References 1 and 2) to facilitate ease of model construction and understanding of the results. Event sequences leading to core damage are displayed in order of their importance along with the major contributing systems or subsystems for each. Each system and subsystem model is developed in a cause table format that displays the contributions to system unavailability from independent hardware failure, dependent (common cause) failures, testing, maintenance, inadvertent human errors, and other causes identified by each analyst. This two-tiered framework facilitates detailed investigation of many system-level changes without requiring reevaluation of the full plant model. Evaluation of more extensive changes that may require requantification of the entire risk model is made more efficient by the modularized nature of the event trees.

3 Technical Specification Study

The purpose of this study was to investigate the effect on core damage frequency from extending technical specification AOTs and STIs for the residual heat removal system (RHR), the RHR service water system (RHRSW), the core spray system, the high pressure coolant injection system (HPCI), the reactor core isolation cooling system (RCIC), the diesel generators, and the main steam isolation valves (MSIVs). It should be recognized that, at the present time, HIPRIM results are preliminary and the core damage frequency values are being refined to include various recovery actions.

Briefly, the methodology involved: (1) creating a risk model suitable for repeated calculations, (2) estimating the base case core damage frequency, (3) changing the parameter of interest, and (4) requantifying the core damage frequency and comparing the results with the base value.

3.1 Simplified Model for Sensitivity Analysis

The simplified HIPRIM model that could be quickly requantified uses the top 90% of contributors to core damage. This is a good approximation, considering that the top 90% includes about 160 separate sequences, and the largest sequence that is neglected contributes only 0.05% to core damage.

The simplified model is a good approximation for the change in core damage frequency only if the perturbations are small. If a change is made to an AOT or an STI that causes the core damage frequency to double, the impact of the neglected 10% of contributors is uncertain. This model also cannot be used to study changes in the contribution to core damage from rare sequences like the large LOCA since these sequences tend to be in the neglected 10%.

3.2 AOT Sensitivity Analysis Methodology

Because the AOT and testing requirements on two-train systems are more complicated than for single-train systems, the equations used to estimate unavailability for these two cases are developed separately.

For a single component or system, the unavailability due to maintenance is given by the equation

$$U_m = \lambda \times MTTR$$

where λ is the maintenance frequency calculated from the number of times the component or system has been taken out for unscheduled maintenance over a period of time. U_m and MTTR are unavailability due to maintenance and mean time to repair, respectively. Tables 1 and 2 provide the values for λ and MTTR.

Category		Mean Frequency (events/hour)
Type 1:	Standby Equipment, Tested Monthly	8.42×10^{-5}
Type 2:	Normally Operating Component, Low Failure Rate	1.26×10^{-4}
Type 3:	Components Requiring Frequency Maintenance	2.19×10^{-4}
Type 4:	Components Requiring Infrequent Maintenance	2.75×10^{-5}

Table 1: HIPRIM Maintenance Frequency Categories

Category		MTTR (hours)
Type A:	Short Duration Events	5.6
Type B:	72-Hour Inoperability Time Limit	20.9
Type C:	7-Day Inoperability Time Limit	40.4
Type D:	No Inoperability Time Limit	116.4
Type E:	14-Day Inoperability Time Limit	95.8
Type F:	24-Hour Inoperability Time Limit	10.8

Table 2: HIPRIM Mean Time To Repair Categories

If a system has two parallel, redundant components, there may exist one AOT for one component out of service and a more stringent AOT for both components or the entire system out of service. Thus, a different MTTR is applicable when the second AOT is in effect. Also, when one component is down, it is common for the redundant component to be tested frequently, leading to a higher probability that the remaining component will be taken out for maintenance. Thus, a different λ is applicable when the first AOT is in effect.

If it is assumed that the primary contributor to the second train becoming unavailable is a test-caused demand failure, then the unavailability of a two-train system can be stated as

$$Um = (\lambda \times MTTR) \times (Tf \times Qd \times MTTR') \times 2$$

where

    Qd   = demand failure rate for one train.
    MTTR' = mean time to repair one train when two trains are down.
    Tf   = test frequency when one train is down.

When a system is taken out of service, it can be left out of service for the entire technical specification AOT. Realistically, the system is usually returned to service sometime prior to the lapse of the AOT. The two options available for this analysis are to assume that the MTTR is the same length as the AOT or to estimate a realistic MTTR from plant data. These approaches will be referred to as the conservative and realistic approaches, respectively.

In the conservative approach, all AOTs of interest are modeled by assuming the MTTR is the AOT. When this model is quantified, a new conservatively high core damage frequency results. This new value is used as the base case for sensitivity runs using the conservative approach. Sensitivity runs are then made by changing one AOT at a time and requantifying the model. The conservative method predicts an artificially high increase in risk for a given AOT increase. This is especially true if the system already has a long AOT.

The realistic approach yields signficantly lower increases in core damage frequency for a given increase in AOT. The drawback to this approach is estimating how an increase in AOT will increase the MTTR in the absence of actual data. This problem is handled by assuming that the controlling factor in determining MTTR is the AOT. For example, to evaluate changing the diesel generator AOT from 3 to 7 days, the diesel MTTR would change from 21 to 40 hours, as given in Table 2. This approach is an approximation, but it is not unreasonable considering generic plant experience.

3.3 STI Sensitivity Analysis Methodology

The probability that a component is unavailable can be modeled as the sum of its maintenance unavailability and the likelihood that the component fails to function on demand. This relationship is expressed as

$$Q_s = U_m + Q_d$$

This equation has been expanded in Reference 3 (Equation 3-1), to include the surveillance test interval as a variable:

$$Q_s = f_s T_s + f_d T_d/T + (1-F)Q_d + FQ_d$$

The four terms in this equation have the following meanings:

$f_s T_s$ = maintenance unavailability due to standby-related failures.

$f_d T_d/T$ = maintenance unavailability due to test-caused demand failures.

$(1-F)Q_d$ = demand failure probability attributable to standby failures $(1/2\lambda_s T)$.

FQ_d = demand failure probability attributable to shock-related failure (q_d).

where

f_s = maintenance frequency, standby-stress related.

f_d = maintenance frequency, demand-stress related.

λ_s = standby failure rate.

F = fraction of demand failures caused by demand-stress or shock-related stress.

Q_d = on-demand unavailability.

Q_s = unavailability.

Td = mean time to repair for demand failures.

Ts = mean time to repair for standby failures.

T = test interval.

qd = unavailability, demand-stress related.

In this study, standby failure rates are extracted from the demand failure rate by using the variable F. To realistically estimate the effects of changing test intervals, it is necessary to realistically estimate F. When trying to extend the test interval, it is conservative to assume that all observed demand failures are due to standby failures, and estimate F to be 0. For diesel generators, at least one data analysis has been done to separate standby-related failures from shock-related failures. From Reference 3, F was estimated to be 0.3 to 0.4 for diesel generators (see Table 3). In this study for diesel generators, 0.4 was used as a realistic value for F. For all other components, in the absence of any data, F was roughly estimated to be 0.5. For this study, one set of sensitivity runs was made using the conservative estimate of 0 for F, and a second set of runs was made using a best estimate for F.

Source of Data	Standby-Related Failures	Shock-Related Failures	Total	Calculated Value of F
Reference 3, Appendix A.2				
Diesel Generator A	9	4	13	0.3
Diesel Generator B	9	5	14	0.4

Note: These data include only catastrophic failures.

Table 3: Diesel Generator Reference Data for F

3.4 Results

3.4.1 AOT Sensitivity Calculations

The results are summarized graphically in Figures 2 and 3 for the conservative and realistic approaches, which show the sensitivity of core damage for each AOT. The core damage frequency is shown to be most sensitive to changes in the AOT for a single loop of RHR. The next most critical AOTs are for one RHR pump, HPCI, RCIC and, then, one diesel generator. AOTs for diesel generator 1B, one MSIV, one core spray pump, and the RHRSW system had very little effect on core damage frequency in either the conservative or realistic cases.

The conservative method predicts a signficantly higher absolute and percentage change in core damage frequency than the realistic method. Both of these differences are due to the fact that assuming a piece of equipment will be out of service for its entire AOT every time it is taken out for maintenance causes the maintenance contribution to system unavailability to be signficantly inflated.

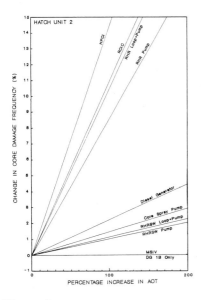

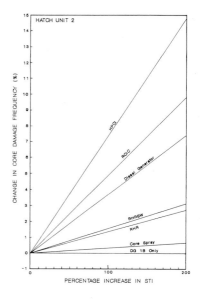

Figure 2: AOT Study Results: Core
Damage Sensitivity to Changes in
Equipment Allowed Outage Times Based
on Conservative Methodology

Figure 4: STI Study Results: Core
Damage Sensitivity to Changes in
Surveillance Test Intervals for
Limiting Case (F=0)

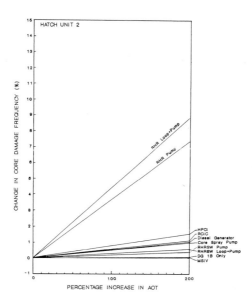

Figure 3: AOT Study Results: Core Damage Sensitivity to Changes in Equipment
Allowed Outage Times Based on Realistic Methodology

3.4.2 STI Sensitivity Calculations

The results are summarized graphically in Figures 4, 5, and 6. Briefly, the most sensitive STI was the HPCI test interval, followed by RCIC and the diesel generators. The least sensitive STIs were diesel generator 1B only and the core spray system.

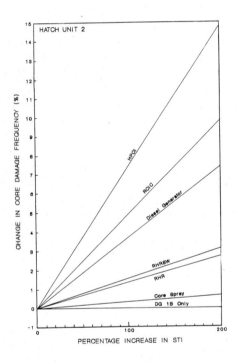

Figure 5: STI Study Results: Core Damage Sensitivity to Changes in Surveillance Test Intervals for Best Estimate of F

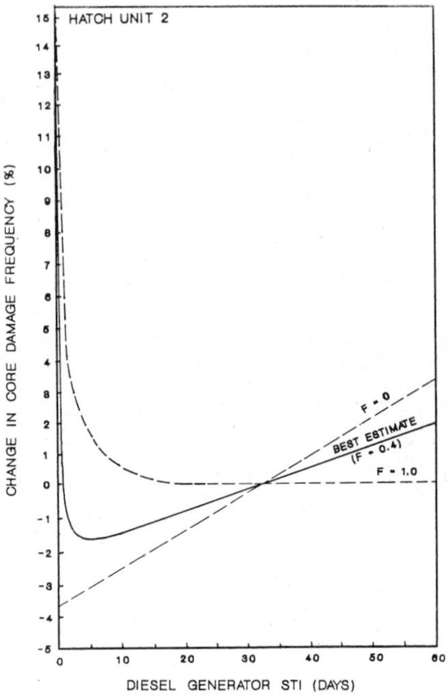

Figure 6: STI Study Results: Core Damage Sensitivity to Diesel Generator Surveillance Test Interval

4   References

1.   Kaplan, S., and S. Arueti, "The RISKMAN Concept for Quantitative Risk Mangement", presented at the Society for Risk Analysis 1986 Annual Meeting, Boston, Massachusetts, November 9-12, 1986.

2.   Arueti, S., F. R. Hubbard, and S. Kaplan, "From Risk Assessment to Risk Management", presented at the 1986 ASME Winter Annual Meeting, Anaheim, California, December 7-12, 1986.

3.   DeMoss, G., and P. Appignani, "Procedures for Evaluating Technical Specifications (PETS), Data Analysis of DG Failures for Separating Standby Stress and Demand Stress Failure Modes: Preliminary Report," August 1985.

THE LASALLE PROBABILISTIC SAFETY ANALYSIS

L. G. Frederick, H. L. Massin, G. R. Crane
[General Electric Company, San Jose, CA USA; Commonwealth Edison Company, Chicago, IL, USA; George R. Crane, Consultant, Springville,, UT, USA]

Abstract

A probabilistic safety analysis has been performed for LaSalle County Station, a twin-unit General Electric BWR5 Mark II nuclear power plant operated by Commonwealth Edison Company of Chicago, Illinois, U.S.A. A primary objective of this PSA is to provide Commonwealth Edison engineers with a useful and useable tool for making design decisions, performing technical specification optimization, evaluating proposed regulatory changes to equipment and procedures, and as an aid in operator training. Other objectives are to identify the hypothetical accident sequences that would contribute to core damage frequency, and to provide assurance that the total expected frequency of core-damaging accidents is below 10^{-4} per reactor-year in response to suggested goals.

1. Introduction

A probabilistic safety analysis has been performed for LaSalle County Station, a twin-unit General Electric BWR5 Mark II nuclear power plant operated by Commonwealth Edison Company of Chicago, Illinois, U.S.A. A primary objective of this PSA is to provide Commonwealth Edison engineers with a useful and useable tool for making design decisions, performing technical specification optimization, evaluating proposed regulatory changes to equipment and procedures, and as an aid in operator training. Other objectives are to identify the hypothetical accident sequences that would contribute to core damage frequency, and to provide assurance that the total expected frequency of core-damaging accidents is below 10^{-4} per reactor-year in response to suggested goals.

To meet the first objective, the analysis was performed entirely on a personal computer using methods and software developed specifically to provide the user with the most flexibility and ease in performing sensitivity analyses and in evaluating alternate design configurations. The methodology uses fault trees and event trees constructed to correspond to the existing (as-built) plant configuration. The software provides automatic production of fault tree diagrams with AUTOCAD software (Reference 1) and a plotter directly from outputs of the computer analysis. Event trees are initially constructed using a standard LOTUS 1-2-3 macro (Reference 2) and are then printed on a plotter using AUTOCAD software. The entire procedure is integrated with a management software package developed by General Electric Company.

This activity was initiated in mid-1985 and resulted in a Phase I report issued in February, 1986 (Reference 3). This report provided the fault tree analyses for reactivity control and core cooling and preliminary analyses of decay heat removal and station blackout. A Phase II activity was initiated in November, 1986 and resulted in a Phase II report issued in January, 1987 (Reference 4). The Phase II analysis provided additional fault trees, accident sequence analyses, and the computer programs. A Phase III activity, scheduled for late 1987, will add containment and consequence analyses and provide guidelines for use of the model.

2. Methodology

The LaSalle probabilistic safety analysis was performed using PRA techniques and methodology (fault trees and event trees) to provide an estimate of core damage frequency. A diagram of the procedure used is shown on Figure 1. Basic system fault tree models were constructed based on the existing plant configuration, and then quantified at the component level based on reliability data. Event trees

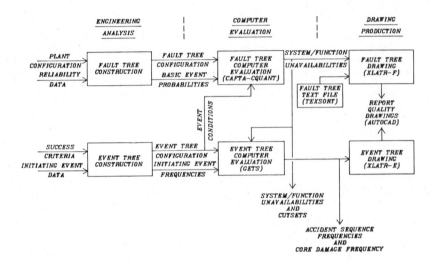

Figure 1: LaSalle Safety Evaluation Process

were constructed for the accident initiating events of interest including transient events, loss-of-coolant accidents and loss of offsite power. Realistic success criteria were used to establish event timing, and the necessary equipment and actions required to perform the primary safety functions.

Following construction of the basic fault trees and event trees, the remainder of the process is performed on a personal computer using several computer programs. It is desirable to have a model that will provide rapid and visual indications of the effects of input changes on different levels of assembly as well as the effect on individual accident sequences. To provide this feature, it was decided to construct and analyze fault trees for each complete safety function of interest, with all support system and front-line system interdependencies included in the fault tree of the function. The fault trees can be easily reevaluated for varying conditions and combinations of input values, producing corresponding cutsets and unavailabilities at any desired gate level. The primary safety functions modeled in the analysis are reactivity control, pressure control, core temperature control, containment control and reactor coolant inventory maintenance after a containment failure.

The system and function fault tree analyses are performed using a set of PC-based computer programs called CAFTA-CQUANT (Reference 5) developed by the Electric Power Research Institute (EPRI). The CAFTA program provides the mechanism for constructing and editing the fault tree. The CQUANT program computes the value of the top gate and all intermediate gates of the tree, and provides corresponding cutsets.

The reactivity control function fault tree includes subfunction or system gates and subtrees for the reactor protection system (RPS), the alternate rod insertion system (ARI) the recirculation pump trip function (RPT), the reactor water level control function, and the standby liquid control system (SLC). The top of the LaSalle reactivity control fault tree is shown on Figure 2. Support systems, intersystem dependencies, operator errors, common-cause failures, and maintenance unavailability are modeled in the fault tree.

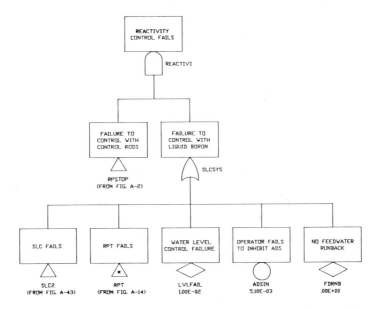

Figure 2: Example of a Function Fault Tree (Top Level)

The core temperature control fault tree includes the subfunctions for feedwater, high pressure core spray, control rod drive water, reactor core isolation cooling, reactor depressurization, low pressure core spray, condensate, and low pressure coolant injection. All support systems and system interdependencies are included in the tree.

The containment control fault tree includes the subfunctions for shutdown cooling, suppression pool cooling, main condenser, steam condensing, containment sprays and containment venting. All support systems are also included in the tree.

A coolant inventory control fault tree is used to evaluate the probability that
core cooling could be lost as a consequence of rupture of containment due to
failure of heat removal and failure to vent the containment. The coolant inventory control fault tree includes the possibility of water or steam destroying ECCS
instrumentation capability and the possibility of repressurization of the reactor
due to loss of control of relief valves caused by high containment pressure.

Event trees were constructed and used to identify, trace, and evaluate different
sequences. The LaSalle accident sequence event trees are very simple since the
primary safety functions are modeled completely in the fault trees. One or more
event trees are constructed for each accident initiating event group. The event
tree for the turbine trip initiating event group is shown on Figure 3. The event
trees are evaluated using a computer code called GETS (Reference 6) developed by

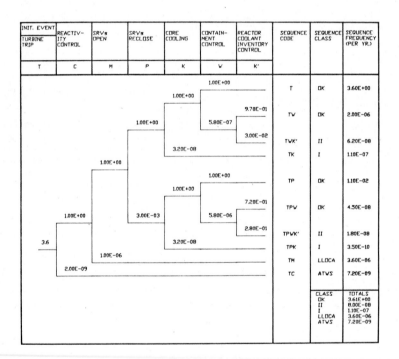

Figure 3:   Event Tree for Turbine Trip Transients

General Electric Company. Each branch of an event tree has a conditional
probability of failing based on all events preceding that branch. The safety
function fault trees are evaluated for the specific conditions related to each
branch of each event tree to provide the appropriate value for that branch. The

product of the branch values along any path through the event tree represents the expected frequency for that sequence of events. Core-damaging accident sequences are grouped into classes depending on whether core damage occurs prior to or following containment failure.

Failure of safety-relief valves to open is treated as a loss-of-coolant accident and transferred as an input to the appropriate loss-of-coolant event tree. Because of the multiple and diverse methods of reactivity control at LaSalle, failure of reactivity control (ATWS) has a very low probability and is a negligible contributor to core damage frequency.

Individual accident sequences are evaluated as to the relative contribution to core damage frequency and whether the cutsets included in the sequences have any significant dominating contributors. The individual sequence frequencies from all event trees are summed to provide the total core damage frequency estimate.

It was also desirable to have a means for automatically producing graphic fault trees and event trees for reports and visual display. This is accomplished by several computer codes, XLATR-F and TEXSORT for fault trees, and XLATR-E for event trees; together with AUTOCAD for driving a plotter. This software was used to draw all fault trees and event trees in the Phase II LaSalle PSA report. Figures 2 and 3 in this paper were drawn using these programs.

3. Results of the Analysis

The total calculated core damage frequency at LaSalle County Station is less than 1.0E-6 per unit-year, a factor of more than 100 below the goal. This provides assurance to Commonwealth Edison that their risk of operating LaSalle is extremely low and the probability of any severe accident that would result in core damage is extremely low. Because of the extremely low value of expected core damage frequency, it is reasonable to infer that any risk to the public is also very low. This will be verified in the Phase III analysis.

There are no "dominant" accident sequences contributing to the total calculated core damage frequency at LaSalle. About 45% of the total core damage frequency is from accident sequences initiated by trips (scrams) where turbine bypass is available. Less than 15% of the total is from sequences initiated by loss of offsite power due to the high reliability of the power grid (Reference 7) and the multiplicity of LaSalle's connections to the grid. About 61% of the core damage frequency is from sequences resulting in loss of core cooling with the containment intact, and 39% of the total from sequences where reactor coolant inventory is lost following hypothetical breach of containment.

4. Conclusion

The three primary objectives of the PSA have been met:

1. The expected core damage frequency is far below 10^{-4} per reactor year,

2. All significant accident sequences and cutsets have been identified, and

3. Commonwealth Edison has a simple and flexible tool for evaluating the effects of plant modifications, technical specification changes, and regulatory directives.

In summary, the LaSalle PSA has produced a personal computer based model designed for future utility applications, including identification and implementation of plant technical specification improvements, support of day-to-day operational decisions affecting plant safety, and resolution of regulatory issues.

4. References

1. "AUTOCAD Drafting Package User Guide," April 9, 1985, Autodesk, Inc.

2. "1-2-3 Reference Manual," (Release 2), (Undated), Lotus Development Corporation.

3. "LaSalle County Station Probabilistic Safety Analysis," (Phase I), NEDO-31085, February, 1986, General Electric Company.

4. "LaSalle County Station Probabilistic Safety Analysis - Phase II," NEDO-(Later), January, 1987, General Electric Company.

5. "CAFTA Manual," (Draft Version), January 15, 1987, Electric Power Research Institute.

6. "General Electric Tree Software (GETS) Users Manual," January, 1987, General Electric Company.

7. "Predicting Transmission Outage for System Reliability Evaulations," EPRI-EL-3880, Vol. 1 (May, 1985) and Vol. 2 (October, 1986).

APPLICATION OF SEABROOK STATION PSA IN EVALUATION OF CORE MELT, EMERGENCY
PLANNING STRATEGIES AND DECISION MAKING

James H. Moody, Jr.
[New Hampshire Yankee, P. O. Box 300, Seabrook, NH 03874 USA]
Karl N. Fleming
[Pickard, Lowe and Garrick, Inc., 2260 University Drive, Newport Beach,
CA 92660 USA]

The Seabrook Station PSA is being used to provide technical input to
enhance Seabrook's risk management techniques for decision making. The
PSA is a fullscope level 3 study completed in December 1983 (Reference 1)
and updated in 1985 (Reference 2). Phase I applications of the PSA have
been focused on addressing regulatory criterion required to satisfy the
full power operating license. This includes emergency planning and related accident management considerations. Phase II applications include
the review of proposed plant modifications and regulatory requirements to
examine their effect on the PSA to ensure corporate management's commitment
to minimizing risk.

Phase I Application - Operating License

There is only one issue that needs to be resolved before a full power
license can be granted to Seabrook Station: The approval of an emergency
plan for immediate offsite protective actions in the event of a radiological
emergency. The Owners of Seabrook Station, who had fully implemented
their responsibilities according to the normal emergency planning process
set forth in existing guidelines and regulations (References 3 and 4),
found that process blocked by the Governor of Massachusetts. He refused
to submit to the Federal Government emergency plans for communities in
his state that are within the 10-mile radius plume exposure pathway
emergency planning zone (EPZ), which was generically established for all
plants in Reference 4. Seabrook Station is in the state of New Hampshire,
about 2 miles from the Massachusetts border. The existing full-scope
level Probabilistic Safety Assessment (PSA) model was used and updated
(References 2 and 5) to help resolve this emergency planning issue for
Seabrook Station. It is an important example of the use of PRA technology
to help resolve licensing and emergency planning issues.

The application of PSA technology to emergency planning at Seabrook
Station has provided many new insights about the effectiveness of evacuation and sheltering as a means of reducing risk levels. It also provides a potential means to enhance the process by which emergency plans
are developed. In addition, enhanced models were developed to provide
a more realistic perspective of the importance of a number of risk
factors long held to be important in the determination of reactor accident
risk levels. The following conclusions were reached for Seabrook Station,
a four-loop Westinghouse Pressurized Water Reactor (PWR) plant with a
large dry containment.

1. The definition of accident sequences that are important for emergency
   planning is plant specific and must include a full consideration of
   dependent events, such as external events, in-plant hazards, and
   internal events. Previous attempts to define generic sequences for
   this type of plant were not adequate for Seabrook Station. A full-
   scope, plant-specific, and level 3 PRA is needed for this purpose.
   A generic PRA or a generic list of sequences will not suffice.

2. It has long been recognized that source terms have an important
   impact on risk level determination and in the selection of appropriate protective action strategies. However, if WASH-1400 methodology (Reference 6) is used as a basis, it has been determined in
   References 2 and 5 that, in the case of Seabrook Station, the
   effectiveness of the containment in the prevention of large-scale
   early releases is every bit as important, if not more important,
   than the magnitude of source terms. Even without any credit for
   new source terms, a shortened EPZ distance of 1 to 2 miles was
   justified for Seabrook Station because of the strength of the
   containment.

3. The risk significance of the interfacing system Loss of Coolant
   Accident (LOCA) class of accident sequences is much less than
   previously thought. This is because of a number of conservatisms that were identified and removed in the most recent PSA
   update for Seabrook Station. These include the usual V-sequence
   assumptions that overpressurization of the Residual Heat Removal
   (RHR) system always leads to piping rupture, containment bypass,
   and core melt and has no potential for operator intervention. A
   more realistic treatment of these assumptions has led to a much
   lower level of risk contribution at Seabrook Station.

4. The criteria used in NUREG-0396 to set the EPZ distance at 10-miles
   were found to be quite satisfactory in relation to other criteria
   that were used to evaluate emergency planning options at Seabrook
   Station. The NUREG-0396 criteria were found to support the same
   approximate EPZ distance as the WASH-1400 risk curves, NRC safety
   goals, and spatial distribution of risk criteria. What has
   changed is not the criteria but the plant-specific PSA information
   compared to these criteria in the case of Seabrook Station.

5. Although there are large uncertainties in the estimation of risk
   levels, conclusions about the need for evacuation out to various
   distances can be, and have been, shown to be robust even in light
   of these uncertainties. This was the opinion of a distinguished
   peer review group that reviewed the PSA of emergency planning at
   Seabrook.

Some key results of the emergency planning study for Seabrook Station
are presented in Figures 1, 2, and 3. In Figure 1, dose versus distance
curves developed specifically for Seabrook Station are compared against

The corresponding results from Reference 4, which provided a key basis for the current generic EPZ distance of 10 miles. These results support an EPZ distance for Seabrook Station of 1 mile or less even when WASH-1400 source term methodology is used. In Figure 2, the same conclusion is reached in terms of the NRC safety goal for individual risk. In Figure 3, it is shown that a 2-mile evacuation zone for Seabrook Station yields an early health risk curve well inside the WASH-1400 results, which assumed a 25-mile evacuation, again using old source term technology. The effectiveness of the containment was the most important factor in justifying a shortened evacuation distance for Seabrook Station.

A number of detailed followup studies have resulted from the U.S. Nuclear Regulatory Commission's (NRC) review of the Seabrook Station PSAs. They include the following:

1. Detailed plant specific evaluations of induced steam generator tube ruptures and direct containment heating as potential early containment failure sequences. These are considered potentially important because of the low frequency of early release at Seabrook Station.

2. Detailed plant specific evaluation of risk from shutdown events (Modes 4, 5, and 6). No restrictions on Equipment Hatches in Mode 5 is considered another potential low frequency release path.

3. Plant specific evaluation of spent fuel storage risk.

Although these studies have not significantly changed the conclusions in Figures 1, 2, and 3, these studies, the original PSA, and other studies have been used to identify potential safety improvements to the plant. Some of these include the following:

1. Improved operator training to diagnose and recover from an interfacing LOCA.

2. Procedures and plant improvements to reduce the risk from potential induced steam generator tube failure and direct containment heating.

3. Independent heat removal capability (includes additional ac power capability, independent charging pump for reactor coolant pump seal protection, and additional emergency feed capability).

4. Independent means of injecting water to the containment and filtered vented containment concepts.

5. Containment leakage monitoring to ensure no pre-existing openings.

FIGURE 1

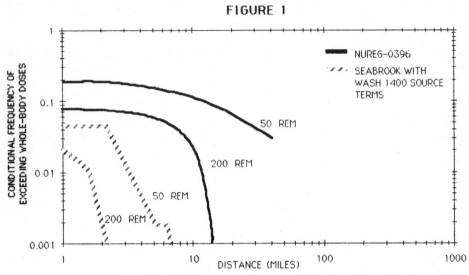

**WHOLE-BODY DOSES (NO IMMEDIATE PROTECTIVE ACTIONS)
SEABROOK STATION VS. NUREG-0396**

FIGURE 2

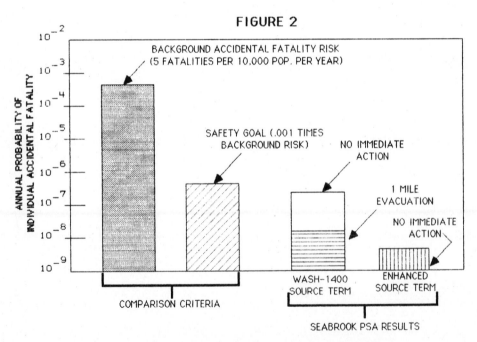

**SEABROOK STATION SENSITIVITY RESULTS
USING DIFFERENT SOURCE TERM METHODOLOGIES**

FIGURE 3

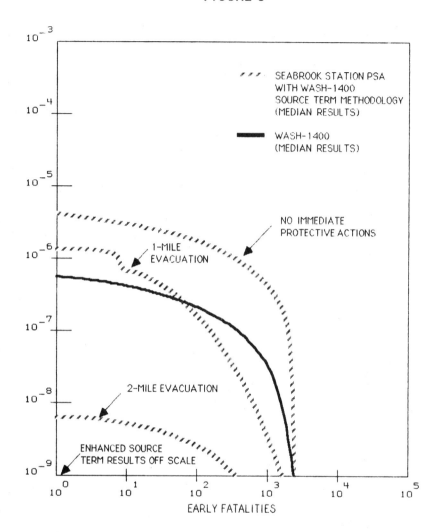

MEDIAN RISK OF EARLY FATALITIES AT SEABROOK STATION
FOR DIFFERENT EMERGENCY PLANNING OPTIONS
AND SOURCE TERM METHODOLOGIES

Phase II Application – Plant Operations

A spectrum of risks including public, financial, and plant economics
should be considered in decision making. Consideration of these risks
is consistent with corporate policy, goals, and objectives. The PSA model
is being computerized to make it more interactive and easier to use.
The PSA will be used in the change review process to provide risk input
to decisions and support the safety evaluation process. It will be used
to evaluate regulatory issues/concerns/requirements and support implementation of the backfit rule. Insights from the PSA are used to establish reliability and performance monitoring programs for safety and risk important
systems and equipment. Insights are also used to provide feedback and interaction with procedures and training.

Acknowledgement:

The authors acknowledge the contributions of Joseph M. Vargas and Kenneth
L. Kiper of NHY, Alfred Torri and Keith Woodard of PLG, and William C.
Doskocil of YAEC.

References:

1. Pickard, Lowe and Garrick, Inc., "Seabrook Station Probabilistic
    Safety Assessment", prepared for Public Service Company of New
    Hampshire and Yankee Atomic Electric Company, PLG-0300,
    December 1983.

2. K.N. Fleming, A. Torri, K. Woodard, and R.K. Deremer, "Seabrook
    Station Risk Management and Emergency Planning Study", prepared
    for New Hampshire Yankee Division, Public Service Company of
    New Hampshire, PLG-0432, December 1983.

3. Federal Emergency Management Agency, "Criteria for Preparation
    and Evaluation of Radiological Emergency Response Plans and
    Preparedness in Support of Nuclear Power Plants", NUREG-0654,
    January 1980.

4. Collins, H.E., et al., "Planning basis for the Development of
    State and Local Government Radiological Emergency Response Plans
    in Support of Light Water Nuclear Power Plants", Environmental
    Protection Agency, prepared for Nuclear Regulatory Commission,
    NUREG-0396.

5. K.N. Fleming, "Seabrook Station Emergency Planning Sensitivity
    Study", prepared for New Hampshire Yankee Division, Public Service
    Company of New Hampshire, PLG-0465, April 1986.

6. U.S. Nuclear Regulatory Commission, "Reactor Safety Study: An
    Assessment of Accident Risks in U.S. Commercial Nuclear Power
    Plants", WASH-1400, NUREG-75/014, October 1975.

OPTIMIZATION OF DETERMINISTIC BASED DESIGN OF THE PWR 1000 MW BY AID OF PSA

A. Feigel, H. Fabian
(Kraftwerk Union AG, 8520 Erlangen, Germany)

PSA was used to optimize the deterministic based design of the PWR 1000 MW. For this three reference accidents which are known to be the covering onse from previous valuations were investigated in detail. On basis of these accidents the integral core damage frequency has been estimated to be about 2 E-5/a. This result reflects a sufficient safety level and thus the quality of the requirement which has to be used for the design. Neverthless the influence of some plant modifications was estimated in addition. It shows that especially the consideration of a modul with a diverse power generator results in a more balanced design on an increased safety level.

The PWR 1000 MW plant is to be seen as a development within the standardized KWU PWR line which takes into account the positiv operational experience. Thus this plant shows the typical KWU features as e.g.

- Full pressure steel containment enclosed by an concrete shield building, see fig. 1.

- Safety system redundancy (3x100 %) according to loop configuration (3 loops), see fig. 2

- Spatial separation of independent redundant trains

- Automatization: no manual actions within the first time interval after accident onset (up to ten hours, depending on the accident sequence)

The design is based on the requirements from the deterministic orientated licensing procedure.
In parallel PSA was used to optimize the design of the PWR 1000 MW. For this reference accident sequences which are known to be the covering ones from previous system valuations of a KWU PWR e.g. in the German Licensing were investigated in detail:

- LOCA-Small
- Emergency Power Mode (EPM)
- Loss of Feedwater Supply

with the objective to demonstrate

- Balance of system design
- Safety level of the plant.

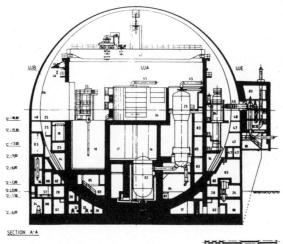

Fig. 1: Reactor Building
PWR 1000

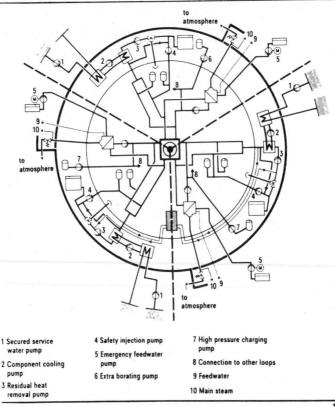

1 Secured service water pump	4 Safety injection pump	7 High pressure charging pump
2 Component cooling pump	5 Emergency feedwater pump	8 Connection to other loops
3 Residual heat removal pump	6 Extra borating pump	9 Feedwater
		10 Main steam

Fig. 2: Emergency Core Cooling System
PWR 1000

In case of LOCA-Small the systems unavailabilities from secondary
and primary residual heat removal systems are in the same order
of magnitde and thus balanced. For the EPM the system unavilability
is dominated by the power supply due to the restrictive valuation
of common mode failure for diesel generator as postulated in the
German licensing. Due to this fact the EPM is the most significant
contributer to the 'core damage frequency' (CDF). It should be mentioned however that on a realistic base the time intervall which
is available until dryout of steam generators is about 1 h. Due
to this and an additional time which is characterized by heat up
of the closed intact primary circuit there is sufficient time to
restart or to recover failed diesel generators by operator actions.
Thus the time duration of at least 1 h and the possibilities for
actions in this time would have to be evaluated in a realistic PRA
thus reducing the contribution to CDF from EPM. Furthermore is the
duration of more than 1 h for a failure in the external supply
much more unlikely than the assumed occurrance frequency. The loss
of feedwater supply which is characterized by a relatively large
occurrence frequency demands the same systems as the EPM but with
available power supply. It shows that in spite of the high occurrence frequency systems unavailability is low enough so that loss
of feedwater supply is not dominating sequence.

On basis of this three reference accident sequences the integral
CDF has been estimated to be about 2 E-5/a. In the frame of the
conservative valuation this value has to be interpreted as frequency
of exceeding the design basis requirements. The possibility of recovery of failed systems with respect to the time sufficient for
operator actions to prevent severe core damage (accident management)
has not been taken into account as indicated above.

This result reflects a sufficient safety level and thus the quality
of the requirement which has to be used for the design. The result
shows even more the influence of assumptions of the calculation
and so the possibilities to improve the results by more realistic
procedures.

Nevertheless the influence of plant modifications was discussed.
The first is that with respect to possible weeknesses in external
grid or due to extreme failure postulates in power supply a modu-
lus with a diverse power generation was developed in addition. The
second is that due to operational advantages a second startup and
shutdown pump was introduced.
The inclusion of these modifications showed that on PRA base the
influence of a second startup and shutdown pump is not reflected
in the PRA values and had no important influence on 'CDF'.The consideration of a diverse power generation - wether gas turbine or smaller, diverse diesel generator powering startup and shutdown pump -
had an influence with respect to balance of the plant design and
an increase of safety level which can be estimated to be less than
1 E-5/a for 'CDF' (see fig. 3).

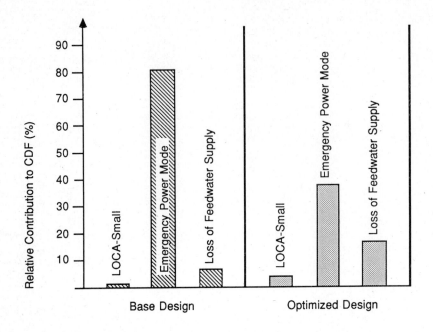

FIG.3: COMPARISON OF RELATIVE CONTRIBUTION OF REFERENCE ACCIDENT
SEQUENCES TO CORE DAMAGE FREQUENCY (CDF) OF BASE/OPTIMIZED
DESIGN.
PWR 1000 MW